Modern High-end Valve Amplifiers

based on toroidal output transformers

Ir. Menno van der Veen

Modern High-end Valve Amplifiers

based on toroidal output transformers

Elektor Electronics (Publishing)
Dorchester, England

Elektor Electronics (Publishing)
P.O. Box 1414
Dorchester
England DT2 8YH

British Library Cataloguing in Publication Data

A catalogue record for this book is available from the British Library.

ISBN 0-905705-63-7

Distribution within Europe: Segment bv (sales@elektor-electronics.co.uk)
Distribution outside Europe: Ir. buro Vanderveen (fax: 31 (0)38 453 3178)

Cover design: T. Gulikers, Segment bv
Translation: Phillip Mantica
                     Hans Pelleboer
                     Menno van der Veen
Editing and layout: Kenneth Cox Technical Translations

First published in the United Kingdom 1999

Printed in the Netherlands by Wilco, Amersfoort

Contents

7　Output Transformer Low-Frequency Tuning

8　Special Output Coupling Techniques

9　Single-Ended Toroidal Output Transformers

10 Building a Push-Pull Valve Amplifier: the Phase Splitter

11 Building a Push-Pull Valve Amplifier: from 10 to 100 Watts

12 Building a Push-Pull Valve Amplifier: the Power Supply

13 Building a Push-Pull Amplifier: Construction Hints

14 Valve Amplifiers using a Printed Circuit Board

15 Practical Aspects of Overall Negative Feedback

19 Experiments with the Specialist Series of Output Transformers

20 The VDV-6AS7 (The Maurits)

Appendix

About the author

Ir. Menno van der Veen (born 1949) built his first valve amplifier when he was twelve years old, and this technology has captivated his imagination ever since. He studied Engineering Physics at the Rijks Universiteit Groningen in the Netherlands, where he graduated in the discipline of semiconductor electronics.

Until 1991 he combined teaching physics to budding secondary-school teachers at the Hogeschool Windesheim with a second vocation as an audio engineer at the Papenstraat Theatre in Zwolle. There he learned the difficult skills needed to tune and/or tame both wonderful public address systems and excellent artists.

As a reviewer of high-end audio equipment, he has written more than 360 articles for a variety of

Photo: Mollink Zwolle

Dutch audio magazines. His articles deal with high-end consumer equipment and professional gear for the recording studio, research into state-of-the-art electronic and acoustic measuring equipment, studies of interinks and loudspeaker cables, the effects of feedback in amplifiers and the characteristics of output transformers for valve amplifiers. He has also published a number of his own valve amplifier designs. The guiding theme in his articles is the set of related questions 'Do we measure what we hear?' and 'Do we hear what we measure?' Portions of his research have also been published in books, lab reports and preprints of the Audio Engineering Society.

Music is the golden thread that binds all his audio activities together, and he plays his guitars with zest. He also makes recordings – both analogue and digital – for DCDC, the Dutch Compact Disk Company.

In 1986 he founded Ir. buro Vanderveen, dedicated to research and consultation related to new technologies for applications in the audio engineering field. Research related to EMC and CE, such as generating a clean mains supply, is one of the special interests. The main activity of this enterprise is designing valve amplifiers, loud-speakers and special toroidal transformers.

Ir. van der Veen is a member of the Audio Engineering Society and the Netherlands Acoustical Society.

Introduction

This book deals with valve power amplifiers for the amplification of audio signals. It is based on a vast body of knowledge that has been gathered by numerous excellent researchers over the centuries. The new element added by this book is the toroidal output transformer, which has been developed over the last fifteen years by me and my company. Among the remarkable properties of this transformer are its unusually wide frequency response and its low level of linear and nonlinear distortion. In this book I explain the whys and wherefores of toroidal transformers, starting at an introductory level in Chapters 2, 3 and 4 and culminating in a complete mathematical description in Chapters 5 through 9. The latter chapters also shed light on the interactions between the transformer, the valves and the loudspeaker. Chapters 10 through 15 present a comprehensive set of easy-to-build, high-end valve amplifiers, with output powers ranging from 10 to 100 watts. They are based on a general concept that is easy to grasp and that is illustrated by circuit diagrams. The construction details are also highlighted. The following chapters, 16 through 20, discuss special valve amplifiers that are not built according to the general concept of the previous chapters, but which represent alternative strategies for achieving exemplary audio reproduction. And first but not least, Chapter 1 explains why the valve amplifier still stands its ground in our solid-state digital era.

This book is intended for both hobbyists and those who want to gain insight into the complex issues involved with transformers and valve amplifiers in audio signal chains. It is therefore a textbook as well as a do-it-yourself guide.

Many people have contributed to the completion of this book. Those that deserve special mention are Derk Rouwhorst of Amplimo bv, Howard and Brian Gladstone of Plitron Manufacturing Inc (Canada) and the translators Rainer zur Linde, Phillip Mantica and Hans Pelleboer. I have received much support from Maurits van't Hof and Rinus Boone, as well as from the audio associations Audio Club Nunspeet, Audio Forum and Audio Vereniging Midden Nederland. The Audio Engineering Society deserves my gratitude, as well as the editors and collaborators of the audio magazines that I have written for. They have brought me in contact with audio designers all over the world, who have taught me much. Gerrit Dam, among them, has made remarkable contributions to the round-up phase of this book. Thanks also go to my initiator into valve amplifiers, Mr Leezenberg, who got me glowing for valves as a youngster. Those who built the foundation on which I could work – my wife Karen, my daughters Monique and Nienke, as well as my parents – were forever willing to double as an enthusiastic audience with exclamations such as 'How beautiful!' or 'This one sounds totally different!' whenever I demonstrated a new product. This book is dedicated to them.

March 23rd, 1998
Zwolle, the Netherlands
Ir. Menno van der Veen
Ir. buro Vanderveen

1

Why Valve Amplifiers?

This is a book about valve amplifiers for high-fidelity sound reproduction. Why are valve amplifiers still around? And what is so special about them in the first place — are transistor amplifiers not just as good? These are the central questions in this introductory chapter. We briefly explain the theory of operation of vacuum valves – characteristics and all – and discuss the basic configuration of a valve amplifier. Valve amplifiers utilize output transformers, for reasons that are explained in the following sections. There are various types of output transformers; in this book we consistently employ the toroidal type, for reasons that will also become clear. A selected list of available literature regarding valves and amplifiers concludes this chapter.

1.1 | What's special about valve amplifiers?

In 1906 Lee de Forest invented the audion, the first radio valve capable of amplification. This led to the development of the triode by Idzerda a few years later. The early radio valve consisted of an evacuated, blown glass envelope containing three elements: a glowing metal wire (the cathode), a metal grid and a metal plate to capture the electrons (the anode). These three elements explain the name 'triode'. Somehow, this contraption was able to amplify alternating currents, a priceless property in those pioneering years of rapid long-distance communication — think of the famous experiments of Marconi, for example. Radio waves were produced back then by high-frequency generators – huge behemoths resembling power generators – and received via long-wire antennas. As these signals were exceedingly weak, extra amplification at the receiving end was a godsend. During the First World War, the radio valve rapidly developed into a professional and reliable amplification device, and it steadily matured to its full stature in the following years, up until the 1970s. By then, the most sophisticated vacuum devices imaginable were being produced industrially under tight quality control, and they found applications everywhere.

The 1970s saw a watershed in the electronics industry. The transistor, invented some twenty years earlier, started to penetrate all areas of design. This small piece of semiconducting material was able to amplify much more efficiently than a radio valve. The market was flooded with cheap and cool-running transistor amplifiers, and as a result the radio valve quickly receded into the background. There were cries of "transistor amplifiers sound awful!", but market pressure was enough to squash these opinions until they became a mere murmur. The valve amplifier was out of fashion, and that was that.

You might think the death of the valve amplifier was a quirk of history, unique and never to be repeated, but that is not the case. Today, in the nineties, the same thing is happening again; this time the victim is the vinyl LP record. After being developed for more than a century, it has matured into an extremely high-quality medium. The CD made its debut in 1983, causing the LP to be quickly discarded. There were a few vociferous eccentrics who stayed loyal to the LP, proclaiming that the vinyl record was a much better medium, but those voices were shouted down by the roaring chorus of CD marketers.

It cannot be denied that audio engineering as a whole has been enriched by new impulses originating from transistor and digital technologies, which have yielded astonishingly good results. But the murmurs in the background, coming from those who constantly resisted these developments and refused to change their opinions, finally began to be heard. A number of people took their grimy old valve amplifiers out of the attic, cleaned them off, fitted them with a new set of valves – still available today! – replaced capacitors and tweaked wires, plugs, cables and what have you. When these old boxes were switched on, many people suddenly realized to their surprise that their old valve gear sounded a lot better than their ultra-modern transistor amplifiers. The sound was much more pleasant – warm, mild and more natural to listen to – and allowed for effortless enjoyment of the music, in contrast to the cold tones of transistors. Many people had experiences like this, which were convincing enough to cause them to reconsider valves as a viable alternative — and that held true for manufacturers as well. Nowadays, respected hi-fi journals regularly publish articles on high-quality valve amplifiers. These devices are not as cheap as they used to be. Their prices have increased to roughly ten times their original levels, and valve amplifiers are now seen as exceptionally high-value products.

Remarkably, exactly the same thing is happening in the LP versus CD debate. Only fifteen years after the introduction of the CD, music enthusiasts are starting to rediscover the long-playing record. The sound of an LP is more natural, warmer and livelier than the super-clean and tight CD sound. It does not really matter what is said about signal-to-noise ratios or distortion levels – which are definitely worse for both valve amplifiers and LPs – the subjective choice is always in favour of these devices. This movement has grown so strong in recent years that even the enormous marketing machinery behind CD sales has not been able to stop it. The lower noise and distortion levels of the CD do not impress us any more. This has led to a re-evaluation of CDs and the recording techniques used to produce them. The assertion that 'digital is simply better than analogue' has lost its power. Today's researchers have a big problem to solve — why does analogue sound better than digital? This question is not addressed any further here, but our era is experiencing a new turning point, in which the problem of what the human ear finds pleasing needs to be addressed.

On the basis of a simple example, I will now explain why valve amplifiers are so drastically different from transistor amplifiers. Let us forget about the analog-versus-digital debate for a moment, and concentrate on the amplification of analog signals. The biggest difference between valves and transistors is their distortion behavior. If we compare amplifier specifications, the distortion produced by a valve amplifier at full power will be in range of a few percent, while transistor amplifiers distort less than a tenth or even hundredth of a percent in a comparable situation. These figures corroborate the marketing claims that transistors are much 'cleaner' than valves. But is that really true? Out of consideration for our neighbours, we do not always listen to music at full power and deafening volume levels. In fact, the typical music program has a low level, with occasional high-power peaks; the average power level is not more than a few watts. Now the good thing about valve amplifiers is that the lower the volume, the lower the distortion. For transistor amplifiers the opposite is true; the distortion increases as the output power is reduced, with the exception of very high-end and well-conceived designs, in which this effect is virtually undetectable. Generally speaking, valve amplifiers handle small signals with utmost care, while transistor amplifiers are much more 'rough-and-tumble'. The first generation of transistor amplifiers, in particular, excelled at generating sizable amounts of distortion at low output levels (mainly crossover distortion). For many, this was a reason to dub transistor amplifiers 'hard' and 'cold'. Surprisingly, this difference in distortion behaviour is comparable to the difference between LPs and CDs. This example illustrates the fact that distortion measurements at maximum power output say very little about the listening pleasure experienced in the living room, although they are naturally interesting to the researcher. Their distinctively different distortion behaviour is only one example of the differences between transistors and valves.

A second example is the amount of feedback used in valve and transistor amplifiers. A valve amplifier is intrinsically 'straight through', as long as some basic requirements are met. It compares its input and output signals only loosely, refraining from excessive correction (which is the hallmark of feedback). A transistor amplifier, on the other hand, cannot even maintain its operating point without strong feedback. There are additional differences between the two, but these examples should be sufficient.

Naturally, differing characteristics result in differing sound reproduction. The subjective appreciation of the results is the main consideration, of course, and this is invariably higher for valve amplifiers than for their solid-state counterparts. Fundamental research into these observations is being carried out at this very moment, and scientific answers are slowly beginning to trickle in. Regardless of whether there is a solid explanation, the bottom line is that valve amplifiers score exceptionally high with music lovers.

These 'enigmatic' valve amplifiers are the subject of this book. Based on historic research and engineering lore, a bridge can be built to the modern technology available today. When these factors – the old and the new – are joined in harmony, the valve amplifier will soar to previously unattained heights. This book sheds light from many angles on that modern yet old-fashioned device, the valve amplifier for high-fidelity sound reproduction.

1.2 | How do valves work?

Figure 1.1 is a schematic representation of an amplifier valve. In the centre of the evacuated glass bulb is the cathode, a small metal sleeve enclosing a heated filament. Not all valves are constructed this way; some have only a naked filament without the surrounding sleeve. The cathode is usually plated with various metals to ensure that sufficient numbers of electrons leave its surface when it is moderately heated. This property has to remain stable over a prolonged length of time. One of the inherent problems with valves is 'cathode poisoning', which is the formation of chemical compounds by reactions between trace gases and the cathode metal. This seriously reduces the electron emission. A pure tungsten cathode can easily withstand the detrimental effects of trace gases left in the vacuum. This is why tungsten is used in high power valves[1]. It is also used in combination with thorium, which improves the electron flow from the cathode, but thorium is unfortunately extremely prone to cathode poisoning. Barium is another useful additive in combination with tungsten, but it suffers from the same disadvantage as thorium — fast poisoning. The technique usually employed today is to apply a very thin plating of barium or calcium oxide (10 to 100 microns thick) to the cathode. It is imperative that this type of cathode is operated at the correct temperature. Poisoning occurs quickly if the filament voltage is too low, while too high a voltage may significantly reduce the valve's life expectancy. It is therefore essential to stick to the manufacturer's recommended filament voltage. The valves employed in this book all require a filament voltage of 6.3 V_{eff}, which should be strictly adhered to for the reasons just given.

Heating the cathode K causes electrons to be emitted. Due to the loss of electrons, which are negative, the cathode becomes polarized with a small net positive charge. As this posi-

▼ **Figure 1.1** *Schematic representation of a triode valve.*

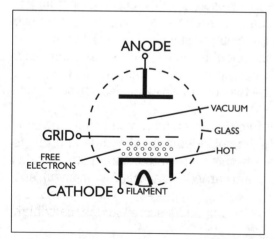

tive charge tends to pull the electrons back, an equilibrium ensues in which the net emission equals the net return of electrons to the cathode. A 'charge cloud' thus surrounds the cathode, and it will remain stable unless it is disturbed by external forces.

A short distance away from the cathode is the metal grid G, to which a voltage can be applied. If the grid is given a negative potential (relative to the cathode), the electron cloud will be pushed back towards the cathode. The smaller the negative voltage on the grid, the more the cloud can expand, and vice versa. Should the grid become positive relative to the cathode, the electrons will accelerate straight towards the grid and be captured there. This effect produces a grid current. None of the amplifier circuits in this book use a positive grid voltage, so the potential effects of grid current can be ignored. The main task of the grid is to repel the electron cloud.

In addition to the cathode and grid, there is also a metal plate in the amplifier valve. This plate – the anode – is not heated and therefore produces no free electrons. A voltage can be applied to the anode to make it positive relative to the cathode; this positive charge attracts the free electron cloud towards the anode. The more positive the anode, the stronger the attraction. However, the grid is in the path of the electrons and is much closer to the cathode and its electron cloud than is the anode. That is why a small negative voltage on the grid can easily compensate for the pull from the positive anode. Evidently, when the repelling force from the grid decreases – that is, the voltage on the grid becomes less negative – the attraction of the positive anode will overcome the repulsion by the grid.

This is actually the most important characteristic of the amplifier valve. By making the grid voltage more or less negative, we can control the flow of free electrons to the anode. For a schematic representation of this process, see Figure 1.2.

How this regulation actually works can be explained by applying what are known as the characteristics of an amplifier valve. Figure 1.3 shows a simple circuit that can be used to measure these characteristics. An adjustable voltage is applied between the grid and the cathode, making the grid negative relative to the cathode. This volt-

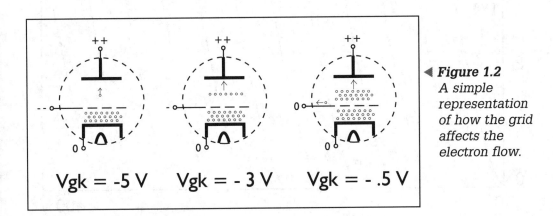

◀ Figure 1.2
A simple representation of how the grid affects the electron flow.

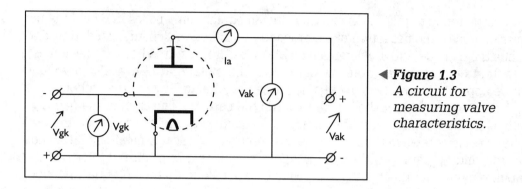

◀ **Figure 1.3**
A circuit for
measuring valve
characteristics.

age (V_{gk}) is measured by a voltmeter. Another adjustable voltage (V_{ak}) is applied between the anode and the cathode, with the anode positive relative to the cathode; this too is measured with a voltmeter. The flow of electrons emitted by the grid and cathode towards the anode (I_a) can be measured with an ammeter.

Measuring the valve characteristics goes as follows: the grid voltage is initially set to 0 V and the voltage between the cathode and anode is slowly increased. The anode current I_a is measured for a number of successive values of V_{ak}. These data points can then be plotted as a graph. This produces the leftmost curve in Figure 1.4.

▼ **Figure 1.4** *A sample set of valve characteristics for the ECC88.*

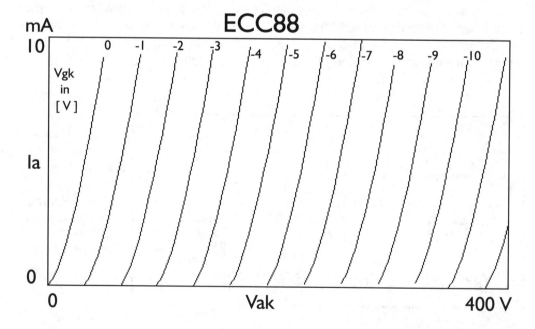

Next, the grid voltage is reduced to –1 V and the measurements are repeated; once again the voltage between the cathode and the anode is increased from 0 V while I_a is measured for each value of V_{ak}. This generates the second curve from the left in Figure 1.4. Notice that each curve is labeled with its respective grid voltage V_{gk}. If we perform the same measurements for many different values of V_{gk} and plot the data, then a bundle of curves – the valve characteristics – can be seen in their entirety.

These valve characteristics are the designer's tools *par excellence*. With them we can determine exactly how much a valve will amplify and what the best settings are for minimum distortion and maximum AC output voltage. All this is discussed later; for now it is important to gain an initial understanding of what a valve can do.

Remarkably enough, it is easier to explain how valves amplify by using a circuit diagram than by making use of their characteristics. Figure 1.5 shows an elementary amplifier stage, consisting of a triode, a high-voltage power supply and an anode resistor R_a. The power supply provides 200 V and the anode resistor has a value of 100 kΩ. Three situations are depicted in Figure 5, in which the grid voltages are –3 V, –2 V and –1 V respectively, yielding corresponding anode currents of 0.25 mA, 0.5 mA and 0.75 mA. Due to the fact that this current passes through the anode resistor R_a, the actual anode voltage becomes (200 – 0.25 × 100) = 175 V, (200 – 0.5 × 100) = 150 V and (200 – 0.75 × 100) = 125 V, respectively.

It can be seen that while the grid voltage has changed from –3 V to –1 V (a difference of 2 V), the corresponding anode voltage has changed from 175 V to 125 V (a difference of 50 V). Thus, a 2 V AC change on the grid appears as a 50 V AC change on the anode. Evidently, this circuit does indeed amplify; the factor is 50 ÷ 2 = 25 times. This is the essence of how valves amplify; small alternating voltages can be converted into large alternating voltages. An audio amplifier works in exactly the same way.

▼ **Figure 1.5** *How a triode amplifies.*

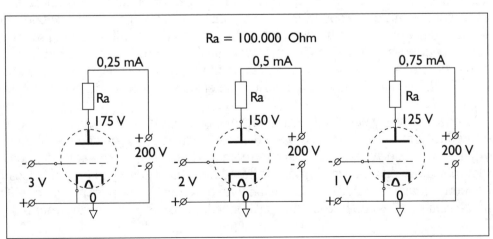

The tiny voltages produced by a turntable cartridge or CD player are amplified to levels that can stimulate speaker cones into motion, causing the audible vibrations in the air that we call sound. Because the grid is very close to the cathode, its voltage can be used to control the electron stream through the valve; the variation of this current causes amplification.

Is this all there is to be said about valve amplifiers, so that we can merrily start to design our own now? No! We first need more insight and knowhow. These can be gained from the books in the reference list at the end of the chapter. Reference 1 is suitable for people with a good understanding of mathematics. It is exhaustive, contains all sorts of useful information and is written by a veteran of valve technology. I had the pleasure of attending classes taught by this author (quite a few years ago!). References 2–4 are a series of books that start on a much more general basis and contain many do-it-yourself examples, so that you can learn how to build an amplifier yourself through practical experience. The method is similar to that used in this book: teaching by example using finished designs that can be copied as is. Reference 5 contains an excellent account of the historical development of the technology. This book is unfortunately only available in French at the moment, but I understand that an English version is on its way. Reference 6 is a graduate-level university textbook, difficult yet exhaustive. References 7, 8 and 9 present general background information. Reference 8 also gives some useful explanations and theory.

1.3 | What types of valves are there?

We do not need large valves to amplify small currents and voltages, since their electrodes can be small. As the current increases, the stream of electrons becomes so substantial that both the cathode and the anode need large surface areas. The cathode has to be large in order to emit the necessary electrons. Since the electrons are accelerated by the positive anode voltage, high-speed collisions occur which cause the anode to heat up. This can not be allowed, since if the anode is too hot it will re-emit electrons that move against the regular flow. The anode must therefore be large enough to dissipate its heat through radiation, staying relatively cool in the process. Understandably, power valves are large to accommodate these sizable electrodes: the envelope of a preamplifier valve measures on average about 1.5 by 3 centimeters, while a power valve's dimensions can be 4 by 12 centimeters or even larger.

As power valves were developed, it became apparent that more than one grid was required to control the current flow. The electron cloud at the cathode is influenced by the high anode voltages, and this retrograde effect reduces the amplification. In order to counter this, a second grid was introduced, the screen grid (*G2*). It is located between *G1* and the anode, and is usually held at a constant positive voltage. The charge cloud now mainly 'sees' the constant voltage on the screen, and very little of

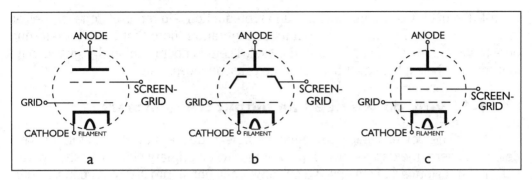

▲ Figure 1.6 *Various types of valves:*
(a) tetrode with screen grid, (b) beam-power tetrode, (c) pentode.

the varying voltage on the anode. This kind of valve is called a tetrode; its construction is shown in Figure 1.6a.

However, the velocity of the electrons arriving at the anode is still high enough to cause secondary electrons to be knocked loose from the anode metal, and this also has a detrimental effect on the amplification, as described above. Two solutions have been found for this problem. The first is the 'beam-power' tetrode, which focuses the electron flow in laminar sheets, thereby allowing the locations where the electrons impact the anode to be closely controlled. Through the clever addition of a set of steering plates along the sides of the beam, re-emission can be prevented. This type of construction is often seen in valves of American origin.

The second solution introduces a third grid, the suppressor grid (G3), which is a widely-spaced grid located close to the anode. The voltage on this grid is low as a rule, often being close to the cathode potential. If an electron is foolish enough to bounce off the anode, it will be immediately repulsed by the suppressor grid and returned to the anode before it can disturb the electric field in the valve. This type of valve is called a pentode, because it contains five active elements. This is the valve of choice in most of the designs found in this book. Not surprisingly, it originated in Europe.

Naturally, the characteristics of the valve will be influenced by these three grids. Triodes, for example, have steep curves, while tetrodes and pentodes show nearly horizontal slopes. This behaviour directly influences the 'auditory image' of the valve amplifier. Triodes produce less distortion and have higher damping factors, as a rule. Tetrodes and pentodes yield higher output power – often twice the power of a comparable triode – at the price of higher distortion and reduced damping. The latter is heard as a rounder, less well-defined bass response. Heated discussions always arise regarding the pros and cons of triode versus pentode/tetrode amplifiers. In the light of the above, it is understandable that amplifiers using different types of valves sound different, and the listener's preferences form yet an additional factor. As a small remark, the quality of an amplifier's sound reproduction – in terms of 'tone' as well as 'space' – can often be deduced from its configuration (note that I am not referring here to distortion specifications and the like). There is no 'magic' in this, just behaviour that can be explained with predictable consequences.

1.4 | Why do we need an output transformer?

The power valves are usually connected to a output transformer. This device converts the dangerously high voltages at its primary side to safely low values, and transforms the small valve currents (milliamps) into sizable secondary currents (several amperes) that can drive modern loudspeakers. The output transformer is the cardinal subject of this book, as can clearly be seen in the following chapters. It is a difficult part to design, and it must have special properties that require meticulous construction. The bulk of the research done at Ir. buro Vanderveen is dedicated to the optimization of output transformers. This has led to the development of a special configuration, the toroidal transformer. The reasons why these toroidal transformers are so well suited for use as output transformers are dealt with in detail in the rest of this book. For the moment, it is enough to say that the toroidal construction guarantees high power efficiency due to its small internal losses, and that it combines a small stray magnetic field with a remarkably wide frequency response.

1.5 | How is a valve amplifier constructed?

On the basis of what has been explained in the previous sections, it is possible to grasp the general outline of a valve amplifier. Figure 1.7 shows a somewhat simplified circuit diagram of a balanced or 'push-pull' amplifier. It consists of four valves. The first of these, B_{1a}, is the preamplifier, which amplifies the input signal to a level high enough to be further processed by the rest of the circuit. The second valve, B_{1b}. has two outputs. This deserves some explanation: the power valves in a balanced configuration need to be driven by antiphase voltages. When the voltage on the grid of the first valve increases, the voltage on the grid of the second valve must decrease by the same amount, and vice versa. Providing these proportional yet inverted voltages is the function of valve B_{1b}. An entire chapter is dedicated to this function of this 'phase inverter' stage. The outputs of valve B_{1b} go to the driver valves B_{2a} and B_{2b}, which amplify both voltage and current, delivering strong signals to the actual power valves B_3 and B_4. These in turn provide output power to the transformer, which converts high voltages and small currents into low voltages and large currents suitable for driving the loudspeaker. The power supply is missing from this diagram; it provides the operating voltages, here labeled V_0, V_2 and V_3, which are 400 V, 350 V and 200 V, respectively. The general signal flow in the diagram of a balanced amplifier is thus: preamplification, phase inversion, more preamplification, power amplification, output transformation and then, finally, the loudspeaker.

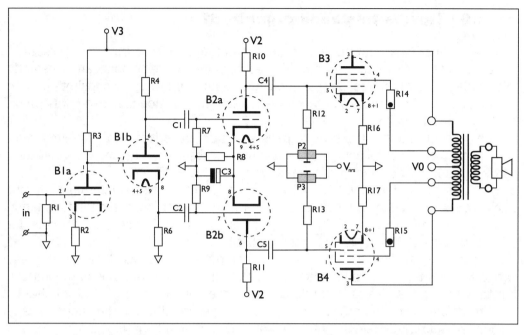

▲ *Figure 1.7* *Simplified circuit diagram of a balanced valve amplifier.*

The configuration of a single-ended triode amplifier is somewhat different. Power amplification is performed by a single power triode, followed by an output trans-former (note that this transformer has totally different properties than a balanced transformer). The necessary preamplification is provided by one or more preamplifier valves. Figure 1.8 shows the general configuration of a triode amplifier.

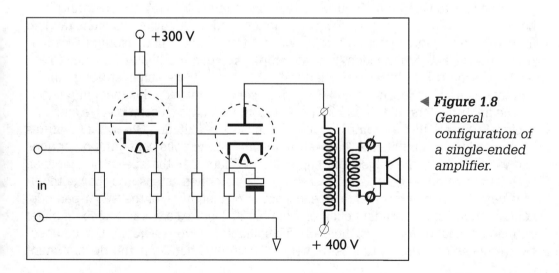

◀ *Figure 1.8*
General configuration of a single-ended amplifier.

1.6 | How is this book organized?

This book contains much new material, resulting from many years of research and development by Ir. buro Vanderveen. New developments are constantly taking place, for which reason this book can be no more than a 'snapshot', a mere introduction to the activities of recent years. Its organization is based on a certain method, which deserves some explanation.

The present chapter, Chapter 1, gives a general introduction to the whys and wherefores of valve amplifiers. It explains what makes them different and what their role is in our rapidly changing electronics world.

Chapters 2, 3 and 4 provide detailed discussions of the issues relating to output transformers. As already mentioned, modern toroidal transformers are the foundation of this book. They are remarkably different from standard EI-core transformers, for reasons that are clearly explained in these chapters.

Chapters 5, 6 and 7 do not shy away from complex calculations. Some readers may find these chapters a bit too theoretical for their liking. They are indeed theoretical, but they provide the basis for understanding the construction of state-of-the-art transformers and amplifier technology, which makes good use of the capabilities of modern computers. These chapters are not obligatory reading; they can be skipped by those readers who just want to build amplifiers. However, readers who want to gain an in-depth understanding of current issues and the theoretical considerations that underlie them will find all the knowhow they need in these chapters.

Chapters 8 and 9 present new theoretical models for the calculation and construction of 'specialist' amplifiers and single-ended amplifiers. The new 'super pentode' and 'super triode' configurations are introduced here, as well as detailed calculations for single-ended amplifiers. The new high-end range of output transformers forms a showcase for the state-of-the-art design capabilities of Ir.buro Vanderveen.

Moving on to Chapters 10 through 15, it's time to warm up your soldering iron, because here you will find practical construction guides for power amplifiers ranging from 10 to 100 watts, featuring toroidal output transformers in a leading role. Engineering savvy and construction hints are amply provided in Chapter 13, while Chapter 14 presents a PCB-based amplifier design. As a rule, valve amplifier design incorporates some sort of feedback, and Chapter 15 shows how to do this the right way.

The final chapters, 16 through 20, present somewhat more esoteric valve amplifier designs. Chapter 16, for example, discusses the UL40-S kit, and Chapter 17 features an unusual guitar amplifier. A 100 watt amplifier with various configuration options and variable bias is the subject of Chapter 18. In Chapter 19 the 'specialist' amplifier, with its matching range of 'specialist' output transformers, steps into the spotlight. This amplifier design represents an excellent implementation of the 'super-pentode' configuration. The concluding chapter, Chapter 20, features a 7 watt stereo amplifier with an unusual power valve, the 6AS7. This chapter is written from a DIY perspective: there is not a single measurement to be found here, but the development process and the necessary fine tuning are fully described, so that we virtually build the amplifier along with the constructor.

The final pages of this book deal with obtaining 'difficult' parts, such as valves and transformers. There you can find the physical addresses and Internet locations of a number of suppliers.

1.7 | Where can I learn more?

The following references are recommended for further reading and self-study on the subjects of valves and valve amplifiers.

1 Dr. H. de Waard, *Electronica*, fourth edition 1966. W. de Haan, Hilversum.
   (theoretical; a very good textbook from the University of Groningen; in Dutch)
2 R. zur Linde, *Build your Own Audio Valve Amplifiers*. Elektor, ISBN 0-905705-39-4.
   (theoretical and practical; also available in Dutch and German)
3 ——, *Audio- en Gitaarschakelingen met buizen, voor een zo goed als nieuw geluid*. Elektuur, ISBN 90-70160-78-.
   (theoretical and practical; in Dutch, also available in German)
4 ——, *Audio en HiFi-buizen, gegevens – karakteristieken – schema's*. Elektuur, ISBN 90-5381-076-5.
   (valve information and characteristics; in Dutch)
5 Jean Hiraga, *Initiation aux Amplis a Tubes*. Eyrolles. 61, bld Saint Germain; 75240 Paris Cedex 05.
   (historical developments, sample designs, plenty of attention to SE; in French)
6 John D. Ryder, Ph.D, *Engineering Electronics*. McGraw-Hill, 1957.
   (theoretical; very detailed, wide-ranging, high quality)
7 Gerald F. J. Tyne, *Saga of the vacuum tube*. ISBN 0-672-21470-9.
   (the historical development of the radio valve; in English)
8 Morgan Jones, *Valve Amplifiers*. ISBN 0-7506-2337-3.
   (theoretical and fundamental; sample amplifiers)
9 Gerald Weber, *A desktop reference of hip vintage guitar amps*. ISBN 0-7935-6368-2.
   (historical and modern developments in professional guitar amplifiers)

2

• • • | • • • • •

Output Transformer
Specifications

In this chapter, we focus our attention on the specifications of output transformers.

Specification sheets for five new, standard-model toroidal output transformers are located at the end of this chapter. These present the most important characteristics and factors for each transformer, with three graphs depicting the frequency, phase and differential phase responses. The significance and use of these data are explained in this chapter.

On the first page of each transformer specification sheet you will see a list of certain characteristic values, including the turns ratio a, the primary inductance L_p, the primary leakage inductance L_{sp}, the effective internal capacitance of the primary winding C_{ip}, the total resistance of the primary winding R_{ip} and the total resistance of the secondary winding R_{is}. Quite remarkably, these five quantities are almost all that is needed to describe the properties of the transformer.

2.1 | The transformer turns ratio *a*

The turns ratio a is the ratio of the number of turns on the secondary winding to the number of turns on primary winding:

$$a = \frac{N_s}{N_p} \quad \text{or} \quad \frac{1}{a} = a^{-1} = \frac{N_p}{N_s} \tag{1-1}$$

In valve amplifiers, the winding with the most turns (N_p) is always connected to the anodes of the output valves, while N_s is connected to the loudspeaker. Figure 2.1 shows the circuit diagram of a standard push-pull valve amplifier. The number of primary turns N_p is always significantly larger than N_s. This means that the high voltage present at the anodes of the output valves is *reduced* by the transformer before it is applied to the loudspeaker connections.

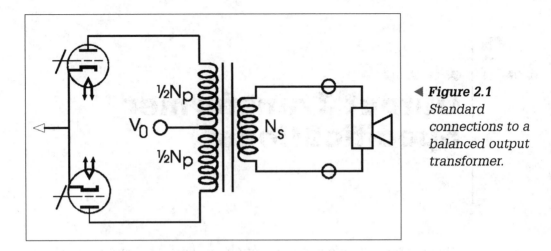

◀ **Figure 2.1**
Standard connections to a balanced output transformer.

For example, suppose that the effective voltage across N_s is 18.7 V. This means that a 5 Ω speaker will produce 70 W. Taking the VDV3070 as an example, a is 23.5. The effective voltage across the ends of the primary winding is then (23.5 × 18.7) = 440 V.

This is our first indication that valve amplifiers use high voltages. Each output valve has to provide only half of the primary voltage needed (in opposite phase because the valves are in a push-pull circuit). This means that each output valve produces an effective alternating voltage of 220 V.

2.2 | Class A and Class AB operation

If each output valve operates in class A (the valve is always conducting), then the anode of each output valve will have a maximum voltage of (220 × 2 × 1.414) = 622 V peak to peak. This implies that the supply voltage V_0 (connected to the middle of the primary winding) must be at least 622 V. It is common to use a supply voltage of only approximately 400 V. This means that the amplifier no longer operates in class A at the maximum output power level. At the maximum positive or negative output voltage, one of the valves is non-conducting, so the other valve completely controls the transformer (this is called class AB_1). See Figure 2.2.

You should realize that changing from class A to class AB changes the damping of the output transformer as well. In class A both output valves work all the time (high damping), while in class AB voltage peaks always switch one of the valves off (low damping). Some people with 'golden ears' can hear the damping transitions, and they find class A better than class AB. There is much more that can be said about this, but that is outside the scope of this chapter.

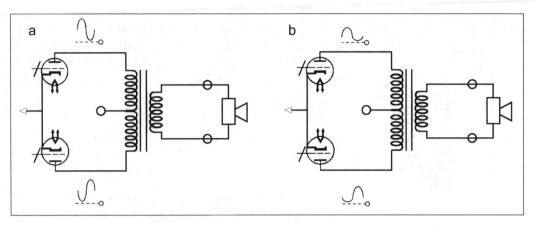

▲ **Figure 2.2** *Operating modes: (a) class A, (b) Class AB.*

2.3 | The relationship between the primary and secondary impedances

The output valves cannot directly deliver large currents. They can deliver currents of a only few hundred milliamperes, which is not enough to drive speakers. We thus have arrived at the second task of the output transformer, which is to convert the speaker impedance (which we consistently take to have an average value of 5 Ω) to the primary winding impedance and vice versa. Taking the VDV3070p as an example again, we find the impedance between the ends of the primary winding to be:

$$Z_{aa} = \frac{N_p^2}{N_s^2} \cdot Z_L = 23 \cdot 5^2 = 2761 \ \Omega \qquad\qquad [1\text{-}2]$$

The transformer's part number (VDV3070) reflects this value. The first digit (3) indicates the primary impedance, rounded to the nearest thousand ohms. The next three digits refer to the maximum power that the transformer can deliver at low frequencies without saturating. The value in this case is 70 W.

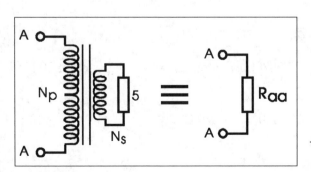

◀ *Figure 2.3*
Impedance transformation.

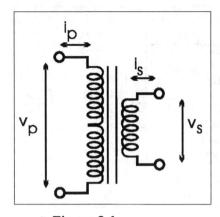

▲ *Figure 2.4*
Transformation
of alternating currents
and voltages.

Now we can easily calculate how much current the output valves have to provide. The total alternating voltage is 440 V and the total impedance is 2761 Ω, so the current is given by the formula:

$$i_p = \frac{440\text{ V}}{2761\text{ Ω}} = 0.159\text{ A} \qquad [2\text{-}3]$$

This calculation shows that the output valves must deliver a current of about 150 mA to produce an output of 70 W in a 5 Ω speaker.

To summarize: using the turns ratio *a*, we can calculate the relationships between the currents, the impedances and the voltages on the primary and secondary sides of the transformer.

2.4 | The primary winding inductance L_p

The second specific transformer characteristic is the primary winding inductance L_p. This quantity is determined by the size of the core, the number of primary turns and the degree of magnetisation (the relative magnetic permeability) of the core. The degree of magnetisation depends on the alternating voltage on the primary winding, so the measuring conditions must always be stated when L_p is specified. The standard voltage used for making measurements is 240 V (effective) at 60 Hz on the primary winding. The current that flows through the primary winding is measured, and the value of L_p can then be calculated. If the measurement were repeated using only 20 V, for example, the measured value of L_p would be lower.

The primary inductance is primarily important for handling low frequencies. The following condition must be satisfied if the transformer is to handle low frequencies easily:

$$2\pi f L_p \gg Z_p \quad (\text{where } \pi = 3.14\ldots) \qquad [2\text{-}4]$$

For example, L_p = 490 H for the VDV3070p transformer. At a frequency of 20 Hz, Formula 2-4 yields:

$$2 \cdot 3.14 \cdot 20 \cdot 490 = 61{,}575\text{ Ω} \qquad [2\text{-}5]$$

This is significantly larger than Z_{aa}, which is 2761 Ω (see Formula 2-2). It is clear in this example that Formula 2-4 is satisfied for large alternating voltages (such as an effective voltage of 240 V). The difference between 2761 Ω and 61575 Ω is so large that Formula 2-4 will still be satisfied even with lower alternating voltages (such as 20 V between the anodes of the output valves), even though L_p will considerably smaller under these conditions.

To summarize: a sufficiently large value of L_p is necessary to allow low frequency voltages to be faithfully converted from the primary to the secondary side of the transformer.

2.5 | The primary winding leakage inductance L_{sp}

The quantity that we are now going to discuss is very important for the faithful transformation of high frequencies. Ideally, each turn of the primary winding should completely 'see' each turn of the secondary winding. This means that the magnetic field lines of each primary turn should completely enclose each secondary turn (and vice versa). Unfortunately, this is not always the case. High frequencies are especially likely to cause problems, because at high frequencies parts of the primary and secondary windings (and their inductances) must be considered to be inactive. The inactive parts behave like series coils, which may cause undesirable problems at high frequencies.

Officially, we speak in terms of a coupling factor k between the primary and secondary windings. Ideally, this factor should be equal to 1. In practice, however, it will be found to lie between 0.9 and 0.9999999. Even though these values are very close to 1, they still mean that some parts of the transformer windings are inactive. We thus should take into account the inductance L_{sp} of the inactive series winding.

$$L_{sp} = (1 - k^2) L_p \qquad [2\text{-}6]$$

Depending on the theoretical approach, the factor k is sometimes used in place of k^2. For this model, the implications of this are not relevant.

What this all means is that at high frequencies we must take into account an extra (useless) series winding on the primary side with a self-inductance

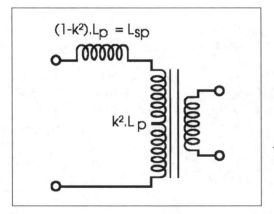

◀ *Figure 2.5*
The primary leakage inductance L_{sp}.
The secondary winding can be
similarly modeled.

L_{sp}. This 'extra' winding represents an impedance in series with the output valves. A portion of the high frequency energy is lost in the series winding, and therefore does not reach the transformer or the loudspeakers. Here we have an outstanding example of the good properties of toroidal-core designs for which the coupling factor has been made as high as possible during the design stage. Toroidal-core transformers excel in this aspect. In addition, special winding techniques and construction methods are used to achieve highest possible coupling factor.

For example: L_{sp} is 0.003 H for the VDV3070p. If we calculate the impedance loss in the series winding at an arbitrary frequency of 80 kHz, we find:

$$Z_{Lsp} = 2\pi f L_{sp} \qquad [2\text{-}7]$$

$$2 \cdot 3.14 \cdot 80{,}000 \cdot 0.003 = 1507 \ \Omega \qquad [2\text{-}8]$$

It is clear from this calculation that Z_{Lsp} will approach the level of Z_p (2761 Ω) for frequencies above 80 kHz. As long as Z_{Lsp} is smaller then Z_{aa}, most of the output voltage of the power valves will reach the primary of the transformer. At some high frequency Z_{Lsp} will be nearly equal to Z_{aa}. When this occurs, only half of the output voltage reaches the transformer. (This is the first indication of the existence of the so-called –6 dB frequency). Now it becomes clear why we compare the values of Z_{Lsp} and Z_{aa}. It follows that this particular transformer will have few problems with frequencies up to 80 kHz.

The same calculation can be performed for the other transformers. Table 2.1 shows the results at 80 kHz.

The above calculations are sufficiently indicative but not complete, because the internal capacitance of the primary winding must also be taken into account, as well as the internal plate resistances of the power valves that drive the transformer. It should be evident by now that careful design of the toroidal core, careful construction and the use of modern computer software all contribute to achieving a frequency range that is unusually large for valve amplifiers.

Type	L_{sp} (H)	Z_{Lsp} (Ω)	Z_{aa} (Ω)
VDV1080	0.001	503	1232 ~ 1k
VDV2100	0.002	1005	1885 ~ 2k
VDV3070p	0.003	1507	2761 ~ 3k
VDV6040p	0.004	2011	5878 ~ 6k
VDV8020	0.009	4523	8000 ~ 8k

◀ **Table 2.1**
Z_{Lsp} and Z_{aa} at 80 kHz for several types of toroidal transformers.

2.6 ┃ The primary winding internal capacitance C_{ip}

The primary winding internal capacitance is another annoying factor that can also influence the frequency range of an output transformer. Because the turns of the primary winding are close to each other, there is some capacitance between adjacent conductors of each transformer winding. In a transformer there are numerous such capacitances. What is important in this case is the *effective* internal capacitance of the primary winding. This is represented by C_{ip}.

This capacitance cannot be measured directly with a normal capacitance meter, for two reasons. Firstly, a normal capacitance meter uses a voltage at a certain frequency (such as 10 kHz) to make the measurement. At such frequencies, the influence of L_{sp} or a nearby metal casing can be large enough to invalidate the measurement. Secondly, this capacitance cannot be directly measured because we are in fact only measuring a single conductor (the primary winding). A procedure has been developed to deal with these difficulties and arrive at an unambiguous value for C_{ip}.

Figure 2.6 shows how we can visualise C_{ip} in a transformer; L_{sp} is shown as well. At high frequencies, relatively more current flows through a capacitance. This is annoying in our case, because the impedance then decreases and less current flows through the windings of the transformer. If we look at Figure 2.6, we can see that if the impedance of C_{ip} becomes low the current i_{HF} bypasses the transformer, which is an undesirable effect.

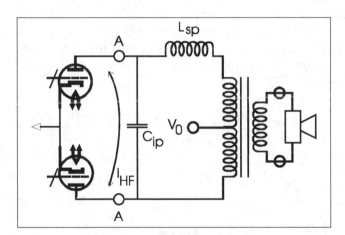

◀ *Figure 2.6*
Equivalent circuit with C_{ip} and L_{sp}. The arrow labeled i_{HF} indicates how the alternating current bypasses the transformer at high frequencies.

If we perform the same calculation as for L_{sp}, we find that the impedance of the capacitance C_{ip} at a frequency f is given by Formula 2-9:

$$Z_{Cip} = \frac{1}{2\pi f C_{ip}}$$ [2-9]

Type	C_{ip} (pF)	Z_{Cip} (Ω)	Z_{aa} (Ω)
VDV1080	593	3354	1239 ~ 1k
VDV2100	585	3401	1885 ~ 2k
VDV3070p	558	3565	2756 ~ 3k
VDV6040p	613	3245	5878 ~ 6k
VDV8020	240	7958	8000 ~ 8k

◀ **Table 2.2**
Z_{Cip} and Z_{aa} at 80 kHz
for several types of
toroidal transformers.

Once again, we can compare the value of Z_{aa} to the impedance of C_{ip} at 80 kHz. This comparison is only indicative, because the internal plate resistance of the output valves and Z_L should be included as well, but that relationship is explained later. The results are listed in Table 2.2.

Clearly, just as for L_{sp}, the size of C_{ip} is such that the values of Z_{Cip} and Z_{aa} are close. This implies that both C_{ip} and L_{sp} have been minimized in order to maximize the frequency range over which the transformer can work faithfully.

2.7 | The winding resistances R_{ip} and R_{is}

As soon as we wind copper wire (for example) around a core, we have to consider not only the inductances and capacitances created but also the resistance of the wire used. This means that the thickest wire possible is used in our designs, in order to minimize the resistance and consequent power loss. For example, if the secondary winding has a resistance of 0.17 Ω, the power loss in the transformer's secondary winding is given by Formula 2-10:

$$\text{Loss factor} = \frac{Z_s}{R_{is} + Z_s} = \frac{5}{0.17 + 5} = 0.03 \qquad [2\text{-}10]$$

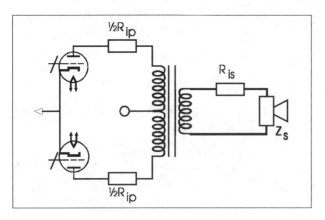

◀ **Figure 2.7**
The winding resistances
R_{ip} and R_{is} of the output
transformer.

In other words, there is a power loss of 3%, which is insignificant.

The power loss in the primary can be calculated in the same way, as shown in Formula 2.11. Calculations show that this loss is also negligible.

$$\text{Primary loss} = \frac{R_{ip}}{R_{ip} + R_{aa}} \cdot 100\% \qquad\qquad [2\text{-}11]$$

To summarize, the resistive power losses in the windings can be minimized by using optimum wire thicknesses. There are also losses due to hysteresis and eddy currents in the core, which can be considered to be negligible. Toroidal transformers thus have very high efficencies, which approach 100%.

2.8 | Summary and conclusions

Using a few simple calculations, we have shown that only five specific quantities are needed to satisfactorily predict essential transformers properties. The factor L_p, in particular, plays an important role at low frequencies. The turns ratio a is important because it enables the output valves and the loudspeaker impedances (which are relatively low) to be optimally coupled. The values of L_{sp} and C_{ip} have been minimized, so that their effects are only noticeable at frequencies much higher than 80 kHz. This means that this type of toroidal output transformer can reproduce very high audio frequencies without the use of negative feedback. Finally, we have shown that the internal power losses due to R_{ip} and R_{is} are negligibly small.

Model: Amplimo VDV1080

T^{-1}	=	15.742	$[N_p/N_s]$
L_p	=	360	H
L_{sp}	=	0.001	H
C_{ip}	=	5.93×10^{-10}	F
R_{ip}	=	37.8	Ω
R_{is}	=	0.16	Ω

Test conditions:

Z_L	=	5	Ω
f_{3b}	=	1.707×10^5	Hz
R_{ib}	=	390	Ω
DF	=	2.424	

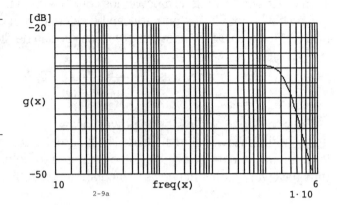

Complex response

R	=	real part
I	=	imaginary part
T	=	vector sum (R + I)

T	=	upper curve
R	=	middle curve
I	=	lower curve

Q	=	relative phase,
		V_{out} to V_{in}

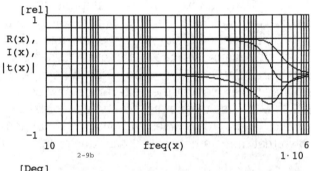

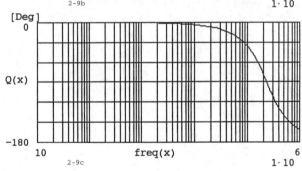

f_{3b} = −3 dB frequency with ideal valve drive (tolerance ± 15%)
G(x)= transfer function assuming purely resistive source and load impedances
L_p = primary inductance (200 V, 50 Hz) valves = 8 x EL34, triode mode
L_{sp} = primary leakage inductance R_{ib} = plate resistance per primary half
C_{ip} = effective primary capicitance R_{ls} = loundseaker impedance
R_{ip} = primary winding resistance   DF = damping factor, no feedback
R_{is} = secondary winding resistance R_{aa} = $(Np/Ns)^2 \cdot R_{ls}$

Calculated by Ir. buro Vanderveen, 30-10-1993   © Ir. buro Vanderveen

Model: Amplimo VDV2100

T^{-1} = 19.417　　$[N_p/N_s]$
L_p = 560　　　　H
L_{sp} = 0.002　　　H
C_{ip} = 6.39×10^{-10}　F
R_{ip} = 104　　　　Ω
R_{is} = 0.18　　　Ω

Test conditions:

Z_L = 5　　　　　Ω
f_{3b} = 1.296×10^5　Hz
R_{ib} = 2×10^3　　Ω
DF = 0.735

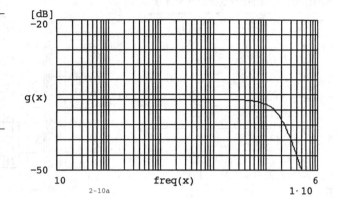

Complex response

R = real part
I = imaginary part
T = vector sum (R + I)

T = upper curve
R = middle curve
I = lower curve

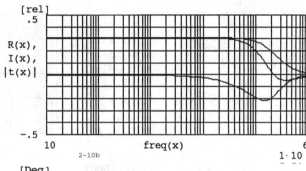

Q = relative phase,
　　V_{out} to V_{in}

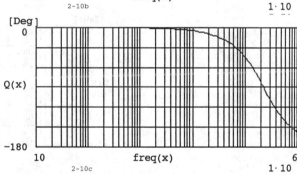

f_{3b} = –3 dB frequency with ideal valve drive (tolerance ± 15%)
G(x) = transfer function assuming purely resistive source and load impedances
L_p = primary inductance (200 V, 50 Hz)　valves = 4 x EL34, ultralinear mode
L_{sp} = primary leakage inductance　　　R_{ib} = plate resistance per primary half
C_{ip} = effective primary capicitance　　R_{ls} = loundseaker impedance
R_{ip} = primary winding resistance　　　DF = damping factor, no feedback
R_{is} = secondary winding resistance　　R_{aa} = $(Np/Ns)^2 \cdot R_{ls}$

Calculated by Ir. buro Vanderveen, 30-10-1993　　© Ir. buro Vanderveen

Model: Amplimo VDV3070

T^{-1}	=	23.478	$[N_p/N_s]$
L_p	=	490	H
L_{sp}	=	0.003	H
C_{ip}	=	4.95×10^{-10}	F
R_{ip}	=	173.7	Ω
R_{is}	=	0.168	Ω

Test conditions:

Z_L	=	5	Ω
f_{3b}	=	1.336×10^5	Hz
R_{ib}	=	2×10^3	Ω
DF	=	1.057	

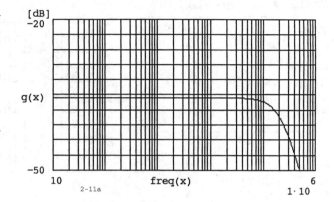

g(x)

2-11a

freq(x)

Complex response

R = real part
I = imaginary part
T = vector sum (R + I)

T = upper curve
R = middle curve
I = lower curve

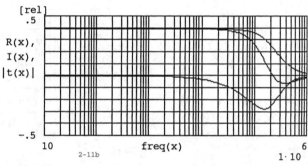

R(x),
I(x),
|t(x)|

2-11b

freq(x)

Q = relative phase,
V_{out} to V_{in}

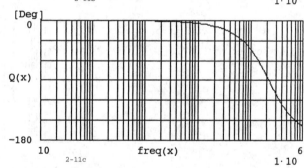

Q(x)

2-11c

freq(x)

f_{3b} = −3 dB frequency with ideal valve drive (tolerance ± 15%)
G(x) = transfer function assuming purely resistive source and load impedances
L_p = primary inductance (200 V, 50 Hz)   valves = 4 x EL34, ultralinear mode
L_{sp} = primary leakage inductance R_{ib} = plate resistance per primary half
C_{ip} = effective primary capicitance R_{ls} = loundseaker impedance
R_{ip} = primary winding resistance   DF = damping factor, no feedback
R_{is} = secondary winding resistance R_{aa} = $(Np/Ns)^2 \cdot R_{ls}$

Calculated by Ir. buro Vanderveen, 30-10-1993   © Ir. buro Vanderveen

Model: Amplimo VDV6040

T^{-1} = 34.286 $[N_p/N_s]$
L_p = 535   H
L_{sp} = 0.004   H
C_{ip} = 5.18 x 10^{-10} F
R_{ip} = 68.1   Ω
R_{is} = 0.158   Ω

Test conditions:
Z_L = 5   Ω
f_{3b} = 7.699 x 10^4 Hz
R_{ib} = 4.3 x 10^3 Ω
DF = 1.085

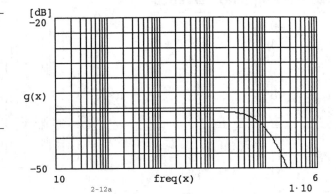

Complex response

R = real part
I = imaginary part
T = vector sum (R + I)

T = upper curve
R = middle curve
I = lower curve

Q = relative phase,
     V_{out} to V_{in}

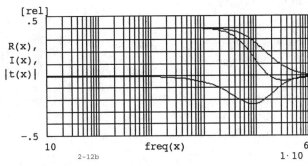

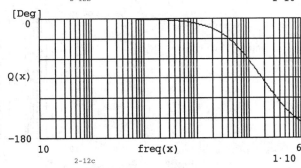

f_{3b} = –3 dB frequency with ideal valve drive (tolerance ± 15%)
G(x) = transfer function assuming purely resistive source and load impedances
L_p = primary inductance (200 V, 50 Hz)   valves = 2 x EL34, ultralinear mode
L_{sp} = primary leakage inductance R_{ib} = plate resistance per primary half
C_{ip} = effective primary capicitance R_{ls} = loundseaker impedance
R_{ip} = primary winding resistance   DF = damping factor, no feedback
R_{is} = secondary winding resistance R_{aa} = $(N_p/N_s)^2 \cdot R_{ls}$

Calculated by Ir. buro Vanderveen, 21-6-1993   © Ir. buro Vanderveen

Model: Amplimo VDV8020

T^{-1}	=	40	$[N_p/N_s]$
L_p	=	544	H
L_{sp}	=	0.009	H
C_{ip}	=	2.4×10^{-10}	F
R_{ip}	=	155.4	Ω
R_{is}	=	0.152	Ω

Test conditions:

Z_L	=	5	Ω
f_{3b}	=	9.691×10^4	Hz
R_{ib}	=	8×10^3	Ω
DF	=	0.792	

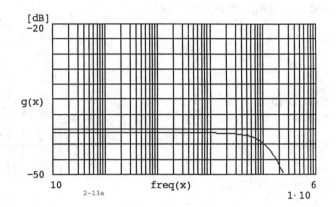

[dB]
-20
g(x)
-50
10   freq(x)   6
2-13a $1 \cdot 10$

Complex response

R = real part
I = imaginary part
T = vector sum (R + I)

T = upper curve
R = middle curve
I = lower curve

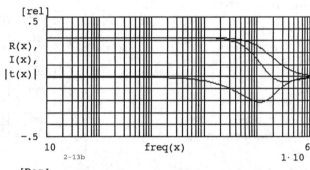

[rel]
.5
R(x),
I(x),
|t(x)|
-.5
10   freq(x)   6
2-13b $1 \cdot 10$

Q = relative phase,
V_{out} to V_{in}

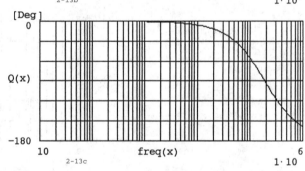

[Deg]
0
Q(x)
-180
10   freq(x)   6
2-13c $1 \cdot 10$

f_{3b} = –3 dB frequency with ideal valve drive (tolerance ± 15%)
G(x) = transfer function assuming purely resistive source and load impedances
L_p = primary inductance (200 V, 50 Hz)   valves = 2 x EL34, ultralinear mode
L_{sp} = primary leakage inductance R_{ib} = plate resistance per primary half
C_{ip} = effective primary capicitance R_{ls} = loundseaker impedance
R_{ip} = primary winding resistance   DF = damping factor, no feedback
R_{is} = secondary winding resistance R_{aa} = $(Np/Ns)^2 \cdot R_{ls}$

Calculated by Ir. buro Vanderveen, 30-10-1993   © Ir. buro Vanderveen

3

The Output Transformer, Valves and Loudspeaker

As noted in the previous chapter, the best results are obtained when the output transformer, the power valves and the loudspeaker are matched to each other. The necessary adaptations are discussed in this chapter. We also look at output transformer power calculations, as well as how to calculate the damping factor for the amplifier as a whole in the absence of negative feedback.

The quantities needed to describe the coupling between the transformer and the output valves are located on the first page of the transformer specification sheet. The first is the impedance of the loudspeaker, Z_L. The second quantity, R_g (= $2\,r_p$), supplies us with information about the internal resistance of the power valves. The final quantity is of course a, the turns ratio of the transformer.

With optimum matching, the -3 dB bandwidth bounded by f_{-3L} and f_{-3H} can be extended.

3.1 | Loudspeaker impedance

Most output transformers have a number of secondary taps to provide the best possible connections for different types of loudspeakers. In the past, these extra connections were necessary because there was a wide range of loudspeaker impedances. Values of 800, 16, 8 and 4 ohms were common. Nowadays the situation has stabilized somewhat, and speakers generally have impedances of 8 or 4 ohms.

We all know that speaker impedances are not constant but can vary enormously. Examining several common speakers shows that their impedances range from a minimum of 3 ohms to a maximum of as much as 40 to 50 ohms, being especially high at the crossover frequency for the woofer and the midrange unit. The impedance also increases significantly at the crossover frequency for the midrange unit and the tweeter.

It is useless to hope that the output transformer will work optimally over such wide ranges of impedances and frequencies. A much better solution is to provide the

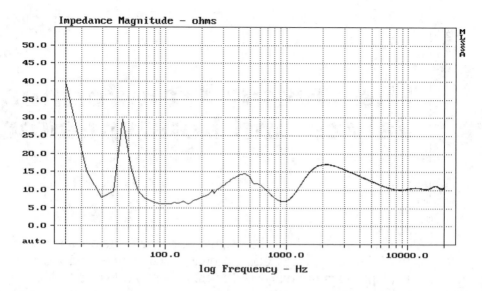

▲ *Figure 3.1* *Impedance curve of a typical electrodynamic loudspeaker.*

valve amplifier with an output impedance that remains constant throughout the entire audio band.

Aside from this, we also have to consider the power transfer from the amplifier to the loudspeaker. This depends on the transformer turns ratio, the plate resistance of the output valves and the loudspeaker impedance. Extensive listening tests and measurements have shown that a single secondary impedance that accommodates most loudspeakers is the best solution in most cases. From these results, an impedance of 5 Ω seems to be the optimum value. Therefore, all the standard toroidal transformers are designed for a secondary impedance of 5 Ω.

Table 3.1 and Figure 3.2 show an example of the measured output power for a VDV6040p driven by two EL34 valves in the ultralinear configuration. The loudspeaker impedance Z_L varies in these measurements from 2 to 8 ohms.

These measurements demonstrate that the output power varies less than 30% for values of Z_L ranging from 3 to 8 ohms. Formula 3-1 converts this into decibels:

$$\Delta dB = 10 \log_{10} \left[\frac{100 - 30}{100} \right] = -1.5 \text{ dB} \qquad [3\text{-}1]$$

This difference is so small that extra secondary taps are not justified, particularly since they would also impair the high frequency response of the transformer.

However, it may be that your loudspeakers have an impedance of 2 Ω. This can easily be accommodated by using the formulas from the last chapter to calculate new specifications for the transformer. For example, if maximum power output must

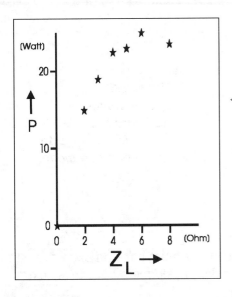

◀ **Figure 3.2**
*Output power
versus Z_L
(VDV6040pp
with two
EL34 valves,
ultralinear).*

▼ **Table 3.1**
*Measured values of
output power versus Z_L.*

Z_L	Output power
0 Ω	0 W
2 Ω	15 W
3 Ω	19.3 W
4 Ω	22.4 W
5 Ω	23.3 W
6 Ω	24.8 W
8 Ω	23.8 W

be delivered using 2 Ω loudspeakers and the optimum primary impedance (see further on) Z_{aa} is 2000 Ω, the impedance ratio is:

$$\frac{Z_{aa}}{Z_L} = \frac{N_p^2}{N_s^2} = \frac{2000}{2} = 1000 \qquad [3\text{-}2]$$

This yields $N_p{:}N_s = 31.6$. The transformer model that best fits this value is the VDV6040pp.

If necessary, this calculation can be performed with other transformers to find the best possible match between a non-standard nominal speaker impedance and the valve impedance.

Our experience has shown that a secondary impedance of 5 Ω is more than satisfactory for 99% of all speakers.

3.2 | Triodes, pentodes and the ultralinear mode

Output valves obviously come in different sizes and types. One type is the triode, consisting of a cathode K, a control grid G and an anode A. There are also tetrodes, which have a second grid called the screen grid. Pentode valves contain yet another grid that is usually connected directly to the cathode.

In this chapter we employ pentodes, since a pentode can function as an ultralinear valve or a triode by making appropriate connections between the screen grid and the various taps of the output transformer. The three most important modes are illustrated in Figure 3.3.

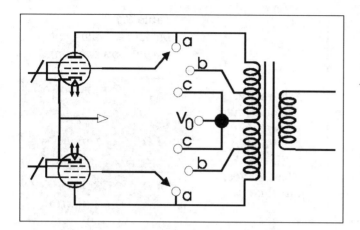

◀ *Figure 3.3*
Output valves
configured in
a) triode, b) ultralinear
and c) pentode mode.

It's clear from the figure that the output transformer must have an extra tap on each half of its primary winding. All VDV/PAT toroidal transformers have these extra taps and may be used in all three modes.

The taps are usually at the 40% position on each half of the winding. Some publications specify a value of 30%. This aspect of our design has been extensively researched, resulting in a standard value of 40% for the first four transformers described in Chapter 1. The fifth transformer (type VDV8020) is an exception, since it has the taps at 33%. This is because this transformer is optimized for applications using EL84 power valves.

Now, what consequences do these different modes have for the output valves? At least one relates to the maximum power. An efficiency of 50% can be achieved with a pentode. In ultralinear mode up to 40% can be reached, depending on the position of the tap on the winding. The lowest efficiency is only 25%, in the triode mode.

For example, suppose that we have a valve with V_{ak} = 380 V between the anode and the cathode and a quiescent current of I_a = 60 mA. This means that the energy dissipation is 380 · 0.06 = 23 W. In a push-pull amplifier there are two output valves, so the total dissipation is 46 W. If we connect the valves in pentode mode, 50% of the 46 W (= 23 W) can be passed on to the speakers (in class A). In ultralinear mode approximately 20 W goes to the speakers, while the triode mode delivers only 12 W. The actual maximum power that we measure will usually be higher than these values, because the amplifier gradually changes from class A to class AB operation.

3.3 | The effect of r_p

The output power varies for the different modes due to the different screen connections and the differences in the effective internal resistances of the output valves. The following experiment illustrates this.

We connected two identical output valves in a push-pull circuit, using each of the three modes described above. The damping factor (see further on) was used to mea-

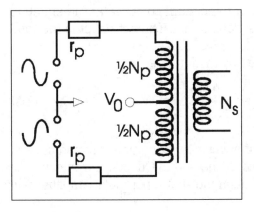

sure r_p for each valve. In the pentode mode r_p was 25 kΩ for each valve, in the ultralinear mode it was approximately 5 kΩ and in the triode mode it was 1.6 kΩ. Experts will recognize that the EL34 was used for these tests. The loads and valve operating points were calculated to maintain class A operation.

From these measurements, it is clear that the value of r_p depends on the mode used. The lowest value of r_p is obtained in the triode mode.

These results allow us to extend our model. A push-pull amplifier circuit can be modeled by replacing each output valve by a voltage source with a series output resistance r_p, as illustrated in Figure 3.4.

▲ **Figure 3.4**
A simple equivalent circuit
for output valves
and transformers.

This equivalent circuit is extremely simplified, since many other factors must be considered at both high and low frequencies. Still, the diagram indicates where we should expect problems when connecting transformers to output valves. The factors C_{ip} and L_{sp} of the transformer, as well as r_p, all affect high frequencies. The factors Z_{aa}, r_p, Z_L and L_p affect low frequencies.

3.4 | Calculating the damping factor

At midrange frequencies (such as 1 kHz) the influences of L_p, L_{sp} and C_{ip} are negligible, which means we can obtain a good indication of the damping factor of the valve amplifier (without overall negative feedback) at these frequencies.

This can be done as follows: on the primary side of the transformer we see 2 r_p (or 2 R_{ib}) plus the internal wiring resistance of the primary winding R_{ip}. The transformer converts these resistances to the secondary side of the transformer. The secondary

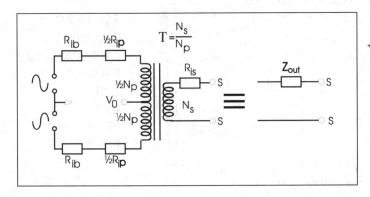

◄ **Figure 3.5**
The equivalent
output resistance Z_{out}
depends on the valve
source resistance and
the transformer
winding resistances.

winding resistance R_{is} also has to be taken into account to arrive at the effective resistance as seen at the speaker side of the transformer. The net result is the total secondary resistance, which we label Z_{out}.

The value of the damping factor DF is given by the formula:

$$DF = \frac{Z_L}{Z_{out}} = \frac{8}{Z_{out}}$$ [3-3]

The calculated damping factor for a specific valve configuration is stated in each of the transformer specification sheets located at the end of Chapter 2. You can thus get an advance impression of the amount of damping that a particular amplifier will exercise on the loudspeaker.

Note that we have assumed here that the loudspeaker impedance is 8 Ω. Most manufacturers use this as a standard value. In our case, we could have used our standard output impedance of 5 Ω. Generally, you should replace the value '8' in Formula 3-3 with the actual value of the load impedance that you are working with. To conclude: as long as the standard impedance of the loudspeaker is not stated, the damping factor is not defined.

Opinions about the influence of the damping factor on sound quality are strongly divided. One view is that a high damping factor is essential for correct bass reproduction. Another is that a high damping factor is by definition tied to a high level of overall negative feedback, which results in reduced spatial definition.

We have performed a few simple experiments in the frequency domain to examine the influence of the damping factor on the sound character of an amplifier and loudspeaker. Using a normal dynamic loudspeaker, we measured the frequency response acoustically in an anechoic environment using the MLSSA system. The amplifier was configured with the following damping factors: 100, 8, 4, 2 and 1 (referred to the standard load impedance of 8 Ω). To give a clear impression of the results, we have mathematically straightened the frequency response for DF = 100. In Figure 3.6 you can easily see how the frequency response changes as the damping factor decreases.

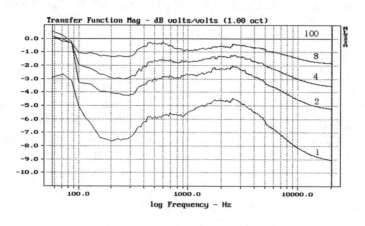

◀ **Figure 3.6**
The influence of the damping factor on the frequency response of an 'average' loudspeaker.

What can we conclude from this experiment? The middle and high frequencies become relatively weak as the damping factor decreases. We can see that the low frequencies will thus be louder than the middle and high frequencies. This effect clearly indicates why some valve amplifiers sound dull, and also why some valve amplifiers sound fine with one set of speakers and mediocre with others.

Since the coupling (the damping factor) between the valve amplifier and the speaker has such a strong effect on the frequency response, the damping factor that can be expected without feedback is always stated on the transformer specification sheet.

An 'optimum' value for the damping factor is given in many older publications. This value usually ranges between 10 and 15. Such values imply feedback (for valve amplifiers), which is considered a disadvantage by many. Slight deviations in the bass are more acceptable to most listeners than the problems caused by feedback, such as loss of spatial resolution and a gritty sound quality. However, a discussion of all the advantages and disadvantages of overall negative feedback is outside the scope of this chapter.

3.5 | The −3 dB high frequency limit

In the preceding paragraphs we have hinted at the reasons why a valve amplifier stops working at high frequencies. We have already stated that toroidal core transformers exhibit no problems at all up to very high frequencies. An indicative examination of the influence of the valves and their configurations on the frequency range is now in order.

This is based on the sample circuit mentioned above, which employs EL34s in three different configurations. We initially calculated the frequency range assuming that the valves behave ideally when connected to the VDV6040p transformer.

What is meant by 'ideal behaviour' of the valves needs a short explanation. We have already stated that a valve may be modeled as a voltage source with a series resistance r_p. In this situation, the frequency range can be determined quite easily. The results of these calculations can be seen on the specification sheet that comes with each transformer, in the top graph on the second page. Note 3, at the bottom of the first page of the specification sheet, refers to these calculations: "assuming r_p and Z_L to be resistive". This means that the valve has been treated as an ideal voltage source. In reality, valve behaviour is more complex, but that is discussed further on.

The graphs shown in Figure 3.7 depict the frequency ranges of the triode, ultralinear and pentode configurations. We can see from these graphs that the frequency range is strongly dependent on the valve configuration, although that is not the only factor.

Using the same procedure, we can also calculate the frequency ranges for several different speaker impedances. These are illustrated in Figure 3.8. It's obvious that the frequency range also depends on the speaker impedance.

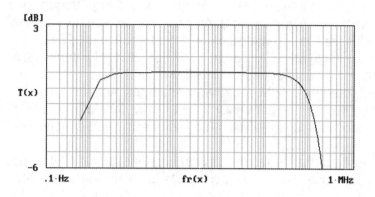

◀ Figure 3.7a
*Triode
transfer function
using an 'ideal'
voltage source.*

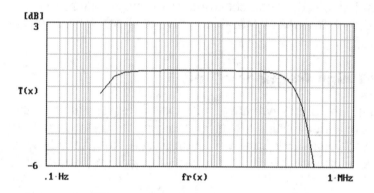

◀ Figure 3.7b
*Ultralinear
transfer function
using an 'ideal'
voltage source.*

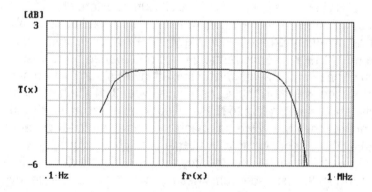

◀ Figure 3.7c
*Pentode
transfer function
using an 'ideal'
voltage source.*

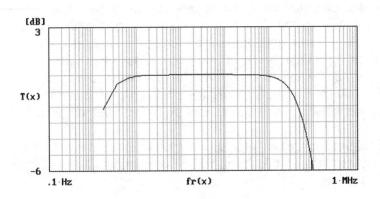

◀ **Figure 3.8a**
Transfer function
with Z_L = 8 Ω,
EL34 in ultralinear
mode.

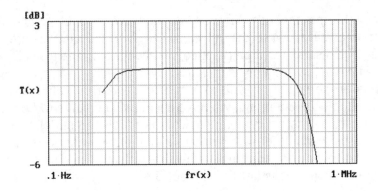

◀ **Figure 3.8b**
Transfer function
with Z_L = 5 Ω,
EL34 in ultralinear
mode.

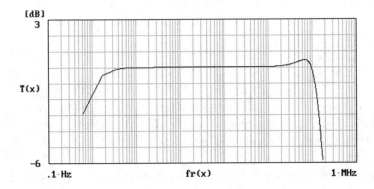

◀ **Figure 3.8c**
Transfer function
with Z_L = 2 Ω,
EL34 in ultralinear
mode.

On the basis of these two examples, we can conclude that we cannot specify the bandwidth of the transformer on its own. The final frequency range depends on the valves themselves, the configuration used and external factors such as the loudspeakers. For this reason, the specification sheet notes the measurement conditions (the valve configuration, the source resistance R_g and the impedance Z_L of the loudspeakers used). Using the total set of specifications (see Chapter 4), we can then predict how the transformer will behave if we use other valve types, configurations and loads.

The results of our calculations in this chapter are indicative, which means that we can predict, in general, how the transfer function will behave for a smaller or larger value of r_p and for different values of Z_L.

3.6 | High frequencies in the output valve

Now let's put all this into practice. Suppose we build a valve amplifier and, full of optimism, connect an oscilloscope to the output to see if our calculations are accurate. We will be sure to be disappointed. In practice, we always measure a smaller frequency range than what we predict. Why is this?

In order to explain this properly, we have to look inside the output valve and examine its construction. In our calculations, we have assumed the valve to be a voltage source with a constant internal resistance. This is much too simplistic, because the valve has internal capacitances between its elements (cathode, grids and anode). On top of this, the way we configure the valve influences its internal resistance, and this resistance is not constant throughout the entire power and frequency ranges.

Phase differences between the voltages on the anode and the grids also modify the behaviour of the valve, and the influence of the anode voltage on the control grid (especially in triodes) can produce an increased input capacitance, which is known as the Miller capacitance.

If we combine all these factors into a single, comprehensive mathematical model (which is not simple), then we can calculate the magnitude of the frequency range that will be achieved when we use the transformer with 'real' valves. The results of such calculations lead to a lower −3 dB frequency at the high end of the bandwidth. Since these results strongly depend on the 'vision' of the designer in the case of a real amplifier, we can't predict them in advance. We can only say what will happen under totally ideal conditions.

There is yet another factor that must be considered. A phase splitter is connected ahead of the output valves to ensure that the control grids of the output valves are driven in opposite phase to each other. Figure 3.9 indicates how the complete circuit now appears.

The operation of the phase splitter is not discussed here. What is important is that the phase splitter can be considered to be an additional voltage source whose output

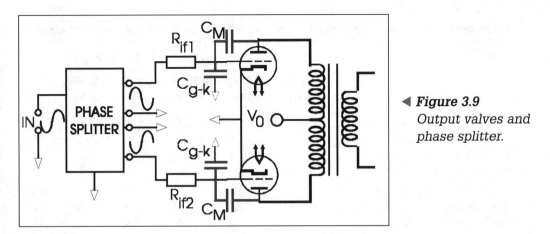

◀ *Figure 3.9*
Output valves and phase splitter.

impedance is Z_{if}, the internal resistance of the phase splitter valve. This output impedance acts together with the input capacitance of the power valves to form a low-pass filter that restricts the frequency range of the amplifier even more.

In conclusion, if you can take an ideal low-impedance phase splitter, load the output transformer in class A, assume that the power valves behave as voltage sources with a series resistance r_p and use a constant load impedance Z_L of 5 ohms, you can then verify the correctness of the calculated value of f_{-3H} (as long as there are no construction faults).

3.7 | **Summary and conclusions**

The frequency range of an output transformer is strongly dependent on the configuration of the valve amplifier that drives it. We have examined the most important factors and made indicative calculations to show how the frequency range changes with various valve configurations and speaker impedances. We have also seen that the phase splitter can be a potential trouble source. We have looked at the factors that affect the −3 dB points at both ends of the bandwidth (high frequency and low frequency). We have investigated the damping factor of the complete valve amplifier and shown how it influences the acoustic output of the connected loudspeaker.

The following pages contain new transformer specification sheets. They provide more detailed information, compared to the 'original' versions in Chapter 2. Chapter 5 addresses the complete theory and background information needed for frequency range calculations. The results of such calculations have been used to produce the specifications on the following pages.

Specifications of the standard series of Vanderveen balanced toriodal output transformers

	Model number: VDV (top), PAT (bottom)					
	1080PP 4008	2100PP 4006	3070PP 4004	6040PP 4002	8020PP 4000	
Primary impedance Z_{aa}	1239	1886	2757	5878	8000	Ω
Secondary impedance Z_L	5	5	5	5	5	Ω
Turns ratio N_p/N_s	15.74	19.42	23.48	34.28	40	
Ultralinear tap x	40	40	40	40	33	%
−0.1 dB frequency range[1,3]	105	112	70	29	60	kHz
−1 dB frequency range[1,3]	173	172	131	64	94	kHz
−3 dB frequency range[1,3]	251	243	202	116	134	kHz
Nominal power[1] P_{nom}	80	100	70	40	20	W
Power bandwidth lower −3 dB freqeuncy	20.5	20.7	22.7	25	28.5	Hz
Primary inductance[2] L_p	360	560	490	535	544	H
Primary leakage inductance L_{sp}	1.3	1.8	2.6	3.7	8.7	mH
Effective primary capacitance C_{ip}	593	475	495	518	240	pF
Primary internal resistance R_{ip}	37.8	104	174	68.1	155	Ω
Secondary internal resistance R_{is}	0.16	0.18	0.17	0.16	0.15	Ω
Insertion loss I_{loss}	0.263	0.379	0.40	0.184	0.211	dB
Valve plate resistance r_p	600	1000	1000	2650	8000	Ω
2nd-order filter Q factor	0.682	0.702	0.643	0.524	0.696	
2nd-order specific frequency f_o	261	245	224	169	136	kHz
Quality factor QF	2.74	3.11	1.91	1.45	6.29	x 10^5
Quality decade factor QDF	5.44	5.49	5.28	5.16	4.80	
Tuning factor TF	3.3	2.7	2.6	0.95	1.3	
Tuning decade factor TDF	0.518	0.434	0.42	−0.025	0.126	
Frequency decade factor[4] FDF	5.96	5.93	5.70	5.14	4.93	

1) Measured and calculated with balanced DC currents and AC anode voltages.
2) Measured across the entire primary winding at 230 V, 50 Hz.
3) Measured and calculated at 1 mW in Z_L, assuming r_p and Z_L to be resistive.
4) $FDF = \log (f_{h3}/f_{l3})$ = number of frequency decades transferred. See: Menno van der Veen, 'Theory and Practice of Wide Bandwith Toroidal Output Transformers', 97th AES Convention, San Francisco, 1994. Preprint number 3887-(G2).

VDV2100 balanced toroidal ouptut transformer frequency and phase response

[dB]   Frequency Response; Vertical 1 dB/div; Horizontal .1 Hz to 1 MHz   (3)

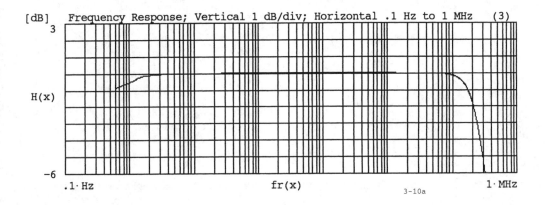

.1· Hz   fr(x)   1· MHz

3-10a

[degrees]   Phase Response; Vertical 30 deg./div; Horizontal .1 Hz to 1 MHz

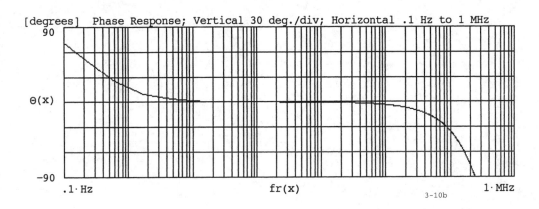

.1· Hz   fr(x)   1· MHz

3-10b

[degrees]   Differential Phase Response; vert 30 deg./div; hor .1 Hz to 1 MHz
            See: W.M.Leach, Differential Time Delay..; JAES sept.89 pp.709-715

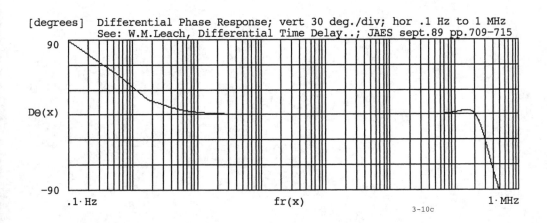

.1· Hz   fr(x)   1· MHz

3-10c

4

• • • | • • • • •

The Output Transformer in the Complex Domain

This chapter discusses the phase response and the differential phase response graphs on the transformer specification sheets. We hope to explain the term 'complex domain' and the total, real and imaginary parts of the transfer function.

4.1 | Calculations in the complex domain

Our concern in discussing the properties of the transformer is focused not only on the volume level produced by the transformer and the frequency range that it transfers, but also on the signal delay. The first two factors relate to the gain, while the last one relates to the phase characteristics of the transformer and its amplifier.

Why am I intent on dealing with these difficult subjects? It would be easier to just sit down and listen to some music instead, or to play one of my guitars. Or even better, to go sailing or jump into an ultra-light and test the warm-air thermals for a while. Both of these alternatives are very enticing, but the harsh realities of life must be faced, and we must center our attention on certain characteristics of the amplifier that can lead to very annoying effects.

◀ *Figure 4.1*
The author in the south of France, preparing an ultralight aeroplane for flight.

When amplifying a signal, we not only have to look at the volume produced, we also have to take another factor into account. This is the amount of time delay the signal experiences. What we will do now is to find a model that expresses this delay.

We can use an example to illustrate this delay. Figure 4.3 shows a test circuit in which a coil is connected to a power supply via a series resistance.

Suppose the power supply initially delivers 0 V, and that it then suddenly produces 10 V. What's going to happen? A current will immediately start to flow through the coil, and this in turn will produce a magnetic field in the coil. Lenz's law tells us that a changing magnetic field in a coil generates an induced current. In other words, we have to consider not only the current from the power supply but also the induced current (think of a bicycle dynamo). The induced current always works against the current that causes it, that is, it opposes the current from the power supply. This means that the full current from the power supply will not immediately flow through the coil; instead, the current will slowly increase. One way to describe this effect is to say that the current is 'delayed' and only reaches its maximum value 'later'. A similar effect can be seen with a capacitor, except that with a capacitor the voltage is delayed while the current immediately reaches its full strength.

▲ *Figure 4.2*
A jazz jam session in the garden.

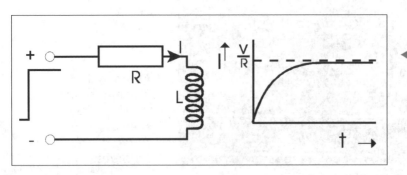

◀ *Figure 4.3*
Sample circuit for complex domain calculations.

The essence of these two examples is that it is easy to see that the current or voltage will be 'delayed' in time with a coil or a capacitor. What about the inductances and capacitances in transformers? They will all influence the time behaviour of the transformer. The complex domain, as used in mathematics, is well suited for investigations of this kind.

The diagram in Figure 4.4 depicts the complex domain, in which time delays can easily be visualized. A pair of axes is shown, drawn horizontally and vertically. The horizontal axis is called the *real* axis and the vertical axis is called the *imaginary* axis. This diagram also shows two arrows, which are called *vectors*.

Without going into too much detail, we will use this representation as follows:

- The *length* of the vector is proportional to the amount of amplification.
- The *angle* of the vector is proportional to the amount that the output current or voltage is delayed or advanced, relative to the input signal. A positive angle (with the vector above the positive real axis) means that the output signal is advanced, while a negative angle (with the vector below the positive real axis) means that the output signal is delayed.

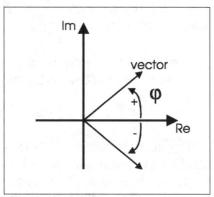

▲ *Figure 4.4*
Vectors represented in the complex domain.

We can now easily show two different properties in one simple diagram: the amount of amplification and the delay or advancement of the output voltage relative to the input voltage. Still, this diagram has a disadvantage: it is only valid for one frequency. What we would really like to know is how the transformer and amplifier behave at all frequencies. An extra refinement of the model is needed. This is shown in Figure 4.5.

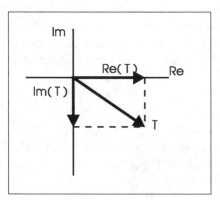

What's happened here is that we have enclosed the vector *T* in a rectangle, in which the vector itself is the diagonal. We have then drawn arrows along two sides of this rectangle, on the real and imaginary axes. Using this construction, we can see that if we know the real and imaginary arrows we can find the diagonal. We can also find the angle between the

◀ *Figure 4.5*
A vector can be broken down into its real and imaginary parts.

diagonal and the positive real axis. Thus if we know the real and imaginary parts, we can always determine the amplification (the diagonal) and the phase (the angle).

The above explanation of the complex domain does not deserve any prizes as a responsible mathematical description of how the complex domain functions. However, it is obvious that every given combination of amplification (vector length) and time delay (vector angle) can be broken down into real and an imaginary vectors. If we know the latter, then we can determine the phase angle.

4.2 | The real and imaginary components at different frequencies

The characteristic diagram for the VDV1080 transformer contains three curves, as shown in Figure 4.6.

The uppermost curve (labeled T) shows the amplification (the length of the vector) over the full frequency range. We can easily see that this curve drops above 100 kHz. This means that the transformer response decreases, but we knew this already.

The curve directly under T (labeled R) shows the real part of the vector, which is the length of the horizontal arrow in the rectangle diagram constructed in the complex domain. At high frequencies, this curve drops earlier than the T curve.

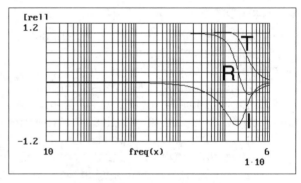

▲ *Figure 4.6*
VDV1080 frequency response in the complex domain.

The third curve, labeled I, shows the imaginary part. This curve is negative and reaches a minimum at approximately 120 kHz.

What does this behaviour mean and what causes it? The explanation for the real part is easy. For most of the frequency range, the voltage transfer T of the transformer is practically constant and the time delay is virtually zero. R is thus almost constant in this part of the frequency range. At high frequencies, above 100 kHz, T decreases and so does R.

Now comes the imaginary part. Above 20 kHz the imaginary part begins to increase (negatively), which is caused by the inductance L_{sp}. This annoying little 'extra' coil starts to delay the current through the transformer. It continues to do so up to the maximum (negative) value of the imaginary part at approximately 120 kHz. At this point, the capacitance C_{ip} starts to compensate for the delay caused by L_{sp}, and at even higher frequencies the imaginary part returns to zero.

In this type of graph, we can see the influence of C_{ip} and L_{sp} at a glance. If we had plotted only the total transfer function T then we could never determine the influences of C_{ip} and L_{sp}.

4.3 | The phase angle

There is yet a better method to demonstrate that time delays occur, which is by using the *phase angle*. What we mean by the phase angle is the angle between the positive real axis and the total amplification vector T. For each frequency, we can (in principle) drawn a rectangle using the known real and imaginary parts. From each of these, we can determine the angle between the positive real axis and the total amplification vector T. This angle, Q, is depicted in the middle graph on the specification sheet.

We can see that the delay is very small at 20 KHz, and that it only becomes significant at much higher frequencies.

The graph shows a positive phase delay at low frequencies. A positive delay indicates that the output signal is ahead of the input signal. As you can imagine, this situation is physically impossible (but please inform me if you actually manage it). This is simply the mathematical way of describing the low frequency behavior, and we had better just accept it for now.

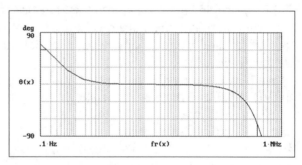

▲ *Figure 4.7*
VDV1080 phase angle versus frequency.

4.4 | Differential phase distortion

Even though we have highlighted many aspects of the transformer, some people have commented that a phase graph does not say anything significant about the quality of a transformer. They say, "We all know that the phase angle changes in transformers, but what is more important is the *shape* of the phase curve. Does it drop steeply and show irregularities, or does it change slowly and smoothly?"

Why is this important? It is because the shape of the phase curve indicates how the various frequencies are delayed relative to each other. This deserves a more detailed explanation.

Phase shifts are caused by time delays in the transformer. The time delay may be constant for all frequencies, in which case it is of no interest to us. Why? Try moving your head farther away from your speakers. The music will not change, and everything will sound just as good as before. Moving farther away from the speakers is however the same as introducing a small time delay, which in this case is the same (constant) for all frequencies. A constant time delay does not concern us, as it will cause no problems at all. It only results in a phase shift that varies linearly with frequency (this for the mathematicians among you). We can safely say that this type of phase shift is unimportant because it represents a constant time delay.

Thus, if we examine a phase graph and see that the phase shift changes, we need to know whether the phase shift is due to a constant, frequency-independent time delay or by a varying, frequency-dependent time delay. The latter will stretch the musical information apart, because the higher frequencies will be delayed more than the lower frequencies (or vice versa). A quick examination of a phase graph does not clearly show us whether the time delay is frequency-dependent or independent.

Many people have looked into this question in greater depth, and in the literature you will find theoretical discussions of a quantity that directly indicates phase shifts that are caused by frequency-dependent delays. This quantity is called the *differential phase distortion*.

We have calculated the differential phase distortion for our example transformer, the VDV1080, and the results are shown in Figure 4.8.

What can we see in this graph? The differential phase is equal to zero up to far above the audio limit. This means all frequencies are equally delayed, so that we will not hear or notice this delay. The differential phase is significantly different from zero only for frequencies above 100 kHz, where the high frequencies are delayed more than the middle and low frequencies. Because this all happens far outside the audio range, we will not notice any degradation of the transient behaviour of this transformer.

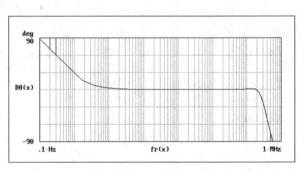

▲ *Figure 4.8*
VDV1080 differential phase distortion with eight KT88 valves operating in the ultralinear mode..

4.5 │ The limitations of complex analysis

Those who have waded through the preceding chapters will have received the impression that toroidal transformers are a godsend. This is obviously what is intended, and please feel free to carry on thinking this way. We wouldn't say no to a bit of free advertising, either.

Unfortunately, honesty forces us to add a small remark to the previous discussions. All the calculations for the phase and differential phase graphs are based upon an ideal situation, in which the transformer and amplifier are connected optimally. If we choose another connection method (the pentode mode, for example), the differential phase will deviate from zero at an earlier stage. One objective in designing these transformers was to ensure that this deviation only occurs above 20 kHz, and in this we were successful. Still, the best results are obtained when the output tubes are connected in the triode or ultralinear configuration.

This can be considered to be an explanation of why test amplifiers built with VDV transformers deliver superlative transient behaviour when configured in triode mode. In this configuration, they do not introduce any errors in the audio frequency range or the time domain. In the ultralinear mode, it is still possible to stay in the error-free domain if proper coupling is used, but in the pentode mode errors may just creep in at the upper end of the audio range, where the differential phase starts to deviate from zero.

4.6 | Summary and conclusions

The complex domain behaviour of a transformer is complicated and requires extensive calculations. The conclusions gleaned from complex domain analysis show that the output signal, by definition, is delayed relative to the input signal. This is represented by a negative phase angle that increases at high frequencies. In addition, the differential phase is important because it indicates the relative delays between different frequencies. The differential phase is also related to the quality of the transient response. We have indicated that the designer should connect the output tubes in triode or ultralinear mode to obtain the best results.

• • • | • • • • •

Frequency-Domain Calculations for Toroidal Output Transformers

This chapter deals with calculating the −3 dB bandwidth of a transformer. We develop an equivalent circuit to investigate the effects that output transformers and power valves have on each other. We discuss a transfer function based on the equivalent circuit of the output transformer, and we use the resulting information to calculate the −3 dB bandwidth for the combination of the power valves and transformer. At the end of this chapter, we apply all the theory we have discussed so far to a real-life example.

5.1 | The power valve as a voltage source

For this discussion, we replace the output valve(s) by a simplified equivalent circuit. Figure 5.1 shows the I_a–V_{ak}–V_{gk} characteristics of a well-known power valve (EL34 or 6CA7) in the pentode mode.

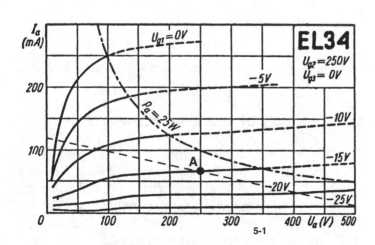

No matter whether two valves are used in a balanced configuration or only one valve is used in a single-ended configuration, the valve(s) are set up to work at a certain operating point (point A in Figure 5.1).

At this operating point, each valve can be replaced by an

▲ *Figure 5.1* *EL34 characteristics (source: Elektor).*

equivalent voltage source that provides an alternating voltage V_p via a series source resistance R_g.

For a single-ended configuration, R_g is equal to the plate resistance r_p of the valve. For a balanced configuration in class A, R_g is equal to $2r_p$. When two valves are used as cathode followers, R_g is equal to $2/s$. We could also model the valve as a current source with R_g in parallel. However, to simplify our calculations we use the voltage source model, with the knowledge that both models will lead to the same results.

5.2 | Matching the valve and transformer impedances

The valves are loaded by the primary impedance of the transformer, Z_{aa}, which mainly represents the speaker impedance Z_L transformed back to the primary side of the output transformer. If the transformer is constructed with N_p primary turns and N_s secondary turns, the turns ratio a is given by:

$$a = \frac{N_s}{N_p} \qquad \text{[5-1]}$$

The relationship between Z_{aa} and Z_L is then given by:

$$Z_{aa} = \frac{Z_L}{a^2} \qquad \text{[5-2]}$$

For maximum power transfer from the output valves to the loudspeaker, the total source resistance of the valves, R_g, should equal Z_{aa}. This is by no means always the case. We therefore define the load ratio β as:

$$\beta = \frac{R_g}{Z_{aa}} \qquad \text{[5-3]}$$

In most valve amplifiers, the value of β is greater than 1. In triode amplifiers, β is less than or equal to 1.

5.3 | The equivalent circuit of the transformer

Many equivalent circuits are available for transformers. In valve amplifiers the transformer is a *step-down* transformer, in which N_p is greater then N_s. If we first introduce the low-frequency and high-frequency behaviour into an equivalent circuit on the primary side of the transformer, and then convert this circuit together with the valve source resistance R_g to the secondary side where the load Z_L (the loudspeaker) is connected, we end up with the equivalent circuit shown in Figure 5.2.

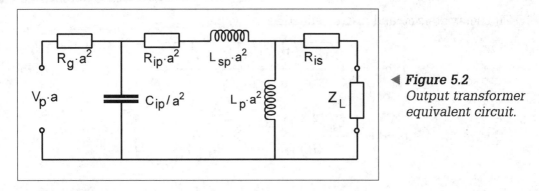

◀ *Figure 5.2*
Output transformer
equivalent circuit.

This equivalent circuit forms the basis for our analysis. Refinements to this circuit are possible. However, the results of calculations with this simple circuit, applied to the new toroidal output transformers, are in good agreement (better then 90%) with measured values. The advantage of this relatively simple circuit is that it allows us to easily understand the specifications and frequency-range determining elements of the output transformers used in valve amplifiers.

5.4 │ The transfer function

The total transfer function of the circuit in Figure 5.2 is given by Formula 5-4, where ω is the circular frequency ($\omega = 2\pi f$) and $j = \sqrt{-1}$.

$$H(\omega) = \frac{V_{load}}{V_p} = aI_{los}LH \qquad\qquad [5\text{-}4]$$

$$I_{los} = \frac{Z_L}{(R_g + R_{ip})\cdot a^2 + (R_{is} + Z_L)} \qquad\qquad [5\text{-}4a]$$

$$L = \frac{j\omega}{j\omega + \dfrac{(R_g + R_{ip})\cdot a^2 \cdot (R_{is} + Z_L)}{[(R_g + R_{ip})\cdot a^2 + (R_{is} + Z_L)]\cdot L_p \cdot a^2}} \qquad\qquad [5\text{-}4b]$$

$$H = \frac{1}{1 + a_2(\dfrac{j\omega}{\omega_o}) + (\dfrac{j\omega}{\omega_o})^2} \qquad\qquad [5\text{-}4c]$$

The parameters ω_o and a_2 are defined as follows:

$$\omega_o = \sqrt{\frac{(R_g + R_{ip})a^2 + (R_{is} + Z_L)}{R_g a^2 L_{sp} C_{ip}}} \qquad [5\text{-}5]$$

$$a_2 = \omega_o \left[\frac{L_{sp}a^2 + C_{ip}R_g(R_{ip}a^2 + R_{is} + Z_L)}{(R_g + R_{ip})a^2 + (R_{is} + Z_L)} \right] \qquad [5\text{-}6]$$

We can recognize four terms in the transfer function of Formula 5-4, each with its own specific function and effects.

The first term, a, represents the downwards transformation of the primary voltage V_p to the secondary side of the transformer.

The second term, I_{los}, represents the losses in the transformer due to the internal resistances of the primary and secondary windings, together with the 'losses' due to the combination of the source resistance R_g and the load impedance Z_L. The standard definition of the 'insertion loss' (I_{loss}) of a transformer includes only the transformer losses that relate to the load impedance Z_L and ignores those related to R_g, and also expresses the loss in decibels. We use the term I_{los} (with only one 's') to indicate that it is nearly the same as the standard loss term.

The third term, L, describes the low frequency behaviour of the valves, transformer and loudspeaker by means of a first-order high pass filter that is formed by the transformed resistances together with the primary inductance L_p.

The fourth term, H, describes the 'high frequency' behaviour of the circuit by means of a second-order low pass filter with a characteristic corner frequency ω_o (see Formula 5-5) and a tuning factor a_2 (see Formula 5-6). The Q factor is often used instead of a_2, where $Q = 1/a_2$.

Fortunately, real-world considerations allows us to simplify this transfer function. First, we can use the term β as defined in Formula 5-3. Second, we can conclude from measurements on a number of output transformers that for almost all transformers $R_{ip} \ll R_g$ and $R_{is} \ll Z_L$. We can therefore usually ignore the winding resistances without introducing a significant error. The total transfer function can in this case be written as:

$$H(\omega) = a\left(\frac{1}{1+\beta}\right)\left[\frac{j\omega}{j\omega + (\frac{\beta}{\beta+1})(\frac{R_{aa}}{L_p})}\right]\left[\frac{1}{1 + a_2(\frac{j\omega}{\omega_o}) + (\frac{j\omega}{\omega_o})^2}\right] \qquad [5\text{-}7]$$

In this case, ω_0 also becomes easier to handle:

$$\omega_0 = \sqrt{\frac{1}{L_{sp}C_{ip}}} \cdot \sqrt{\frac{\beta + 1}{\beta}} \qquad\qquad \text{[5-8]}$$

The formula for a_2 becomes simpler as well :

$$a_2 = \omega_0 \left[\frac{\dfrac{L_{sp}}{R_{aa}} + C_{ip}\beta R_{aa}}{\beta + 1} \right] \qquad\qquad \text{[5-9]}$$

Further analysis reveals that it is advantageous to express a_2 differently by introducing the term α, which is the ratio of the characteristic primary impedance Z_{ip} to the 'nominal' primary impedance Z_{aa}. This is shown in Formulas 5-10 and 5-11:

$$a_2 = \alpha \sqrt{\frac{1}{\beta(\beta + 1)}} + \frac{1}{\alpha} \cdot \sqrt{\frac{\beta}{\beta + 1}} \qquad\qquad \text{[5-10]}$$

$$\alpha = \frac{1}{Z_{aa}} \cdot \sqrt{\frac{L_{sp}}{C_{ip}}} \qquad\qquad \text{[5-11]}$$

Here the high frequency behavior of the transformer is described by a simple LC resonant circuit formed by L_{sp} and C_{ip}, damped by the combination of Z_{aa}, the valve source impedance and the loudspeaker impedance (as effectively represented by β). Clearly, this provides an excellent description of the high frequency behavior of the transformer.

Using Formulas 5-7 through 5-11 makes calculating the transfer function much easier. However, it should be noted that Formulas 5-4 through 5-6 must be used for a complete analysis without any approximations. They can best be implemented in a computer program (for example), due to their complexity.

5.5 | The –3 dB frequency range

Now we can calculate the –3 dB bandwidth of the valves plus transformer. Only the filter sections of the transfer function need to be considered, because the turns-ratio element and the 'loss' element are independent of frequency .

■ The lower –3 dB frequency

The transfer function (the third part of Formula 5-7) yields the lower –3 dB frequency directly, as expressed in Formula 5-12:

$$f_{-3L} = \frac{Z_{aa}}{2\pi L_p} \cdot \frac{\beta}{\beta + 1} \tag{5-12}$$

As expected, the lower –3 dB frequency is determined by the primary inductance L_p together with Z_{aa} and the load ratio β.

■ The upper –3 dB frequency

The upper –3 dB frequency f_{-3H} is not so easily calculated, because two poles are present (see the fourth part of Formula 5-7).

We can determine f_{-3H} by first calculating the length of the second-order filter vector in the complex domain, and then finding the –3 dB frequency at which its length is $1/\sqrt{2}$ times as large. This requires two formulas:

$$f_{-3H} = \frac{1}{2\pi} \cdot \sqrt{\frac{1}{L_{sp}C_{ip}}} \cdot f(a_2) \cdot \sqrt{\frac{\beta + 1}{\beta}} \tag{5-13}$$

$$f(a_2) = \sqrt{\frac{(2 - a_2{}^2) + [(a_2{}^2 - 2)^2 + 4)]^{1/2}}{2}} \tag{5-14}$$

Figure 5.3 shows $f(a_2)$ for various values of a_2. Most output transformers are used with Q values between 1 and 0.5 (a_2 between 1 and 2). In this region $f(a_2)$ is almost a straight line, so it can be approximated by the linear function $ff(a_2)$ shown in Formula 5-15, with less then 5% deviation from the value of the actual function $f(a_2)$.

$$ff(a_2) = 1.950 - 0.668\,a_2 \tag{5-15}$$

This function can be easily calculated by hand, but for a complete analysis without approximations $f(a_2)$ is the better choice.

In summary, we can say that the primary inductance determines the low-frequency behaviour, while the leakage inductance and the primary capacitance determine the high-frequency behaviour. However, the degree to which these elements affect the frequency range depends on the impedances connected to the transformer.

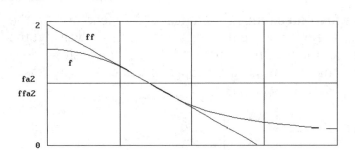

◀ **Figure 5.3**
*The function f(a₂)
and its straight-line
approximation ff(a₂).
The deviation from
f(a₂) is less than 5%
for 1 ≤ a₂ ≤ 2.*

5.6 | The tuning factor and the frequency-decade factor

Now we want to introduce the tuning factor and then calculate the -3 dB bandwidth, using this factor in combination with the quality factor of the transformer. These two factors can be combined into the frequency decade factor.

■| Introducing the tuning factor

If we divide Formula 5-13 by Formula 5-12, we effectively compare the upper -3 dB frequency to the lower -3 dB frequency. This yields the formula:

$$\frac{f_{-3H}}{f_{-3L}} = f(a_2) \cdot \left[\frac{\beta+1}{\beta}\right]^{3/2} \cdot \left[\frac{1}{Z_{aa}}\sqrt{\frac{L_{sp}}{C_{ip}}}\right] \cdot \frac{L_p}{L_{sp}} \qquad [5\text{-}16]$$

This formula has several interesting aspects.

The first term represents the influence of the the *tuning factor* (Q or a_2) at the high-frequency end.

The second term shows the how the relationship of valve source impedance R_g to the load impedance Z_L affects the -3 dB bandwidth.

The third term is the ratio of the characteristic primary impedance Z_{ip} (as given in Formula 5-17) to the effective primary impedance Z_{aa} (due to Z_L and a).

$$Z_{ip} = \sqrt{\frac{L_{sp}}{C_{ip}}} \qquad [5\text{-}17]$$

The fourth term is the well-known *quality factor* of the transformer:

$$QF = \frac{L_p}{L_{sp}} \qquad [5\text{-}18]$$

We can conclude that the first three terms of Formula 5-16 depend on how the transformer is used, the load, the effective source resistance of the valves and the value of the Q factor chosen for the high frequency end. These factors thus determine the tuning of the transformer when it is used under certain conditions. Based on these factors, we can now define the *tuning factor* TF as:

$$TF = f(a_2) \cdot \left[\frac{\beta + 1}{\beta} \right]^{3/2} \cdot \frac{Z_{ip}}{Z_{aa}} \qquad [5\text{-}19]$$

We can now construct a basic formula for the ratio of the upper and lower −3 dB frequencies, by introducing the tuning factor and the quality factor into Formula 5-16:

$$\frac{f_{-3H}}{f_{-3L}} = TF \cdot QF \qquad [5\text{-}20]$$

■ | Tuning factor examples

We initially investigated the value of the tuning factor for various types of valves and valve configurations. To do this, we varied R_g and kept Z_{aa} constant (which means that the turns ratio a and the load impedance Z_L were held constant).

The results of these calculations are presented in Figures 5.4, 5.5 and 5.6. The value of a is 0.5, 1 and 2, respectively. The value of α ranges from 0.1 through 10, and the value of TF is shown on the left-hand vertical scale. The Q factor (= $1/a_2$) is shown in the same figures on the right-hand vertical scale.

We next examined the values of the tuning factor with various loads. Figures 5.7, 5.8 and 5.9 show the results (see overleaf). To make these results more generally useful, we have used a normalized load $Z_{L,n}$. In Figure 5.7, $Z_{L,n}$ equals 1 ohm when $R_g = Z_{aa}$. This is practically equivalent to a balanced pair of triodes driving the output transformer. In Figure 5.8, $Z_{L,n} = 1\,\Omega$ when $R_g = 3Z_{aa}$ (balanced ultralinear configuration). Figure 5.9 shows the results for a balanced pentode configuration, for which R_g is very nearly equal to $10Z_{aa}$ when $Z_{L,n} = 1\,\Omega$. For the normalization, we have assumed that $\alpha = 1$ when $Z_{L,n} = 1\,\Omega$.

Note that normalizing Z_L allows Figures 5.7, 5.8 and 5.9 to be used for load impedances other that 1 ohm. For instance, if $Z_L = 5\,\Omega$ then Figure 5.7 shows the results for $R_g = 5/a_2$, with $\alpha = 1$ and Z_L ranging from 0.5 Ω to 50 Ω on the horizontal axis.

We can draw the following conclusions:

1) The tuning factor changes considerably with varying loading and tuning conditions. It ranges from approximately 0.1 to almost 10. This means that the

value of the quality factor alone is not enough to indicate the –3 dB frequency range of the transformer.

(A quick reading of the relevant literature might give the impression that the quality factor alone is the major determining factor for the frequency range. However, our calculations show that both C_{ip} and the impedances of the speaker and the valves also have a major influence on the frequency range. They can cause it to vary by a factor of at least 100.)

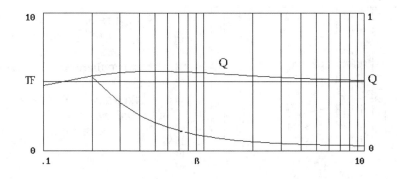

◀ **Figure 5.4**
*Tuning factor
(left scale)
and Q factor
(right scale)
for α = 0.5.*

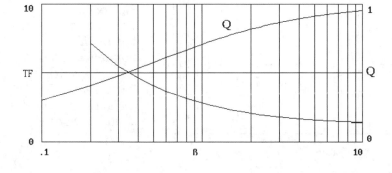

◀ **Figure 5.5**
*Tuning factor
(left scale)
and Q factor
(right scale)
for α = 1.*

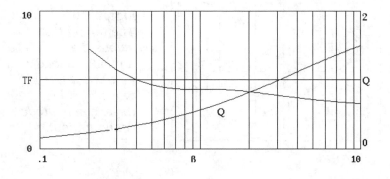

◀ **Figure 5.6**
*Tuning factor
(left scale)
and Q factor
(right scale)
for α = 2.*

2) The **Q** factor is surprisingly stable in Figure 5.4. Calculations show that if α = 0.65, **Q** has a constant value of 0.66 if β > 1.

(A constant **Q** factor means that the square wave response at 1 kHz is independent of the impedance of the speaker. With **Q** = 0.66, the ringing of the square wave will be negligible.)

3) A rather stable frequency response, almost independent of the valve plate resistance, is present when $\alpha \geq 2$.

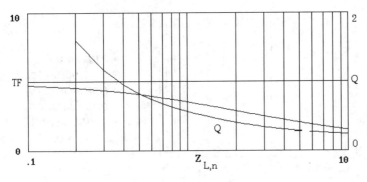

◀ **Figure 5.7**
The tuning factor versus the normalized load $Z_{L,n}$ for $\alpha = 1$ & $\beta = 1$ when $Z_L = 1\ \Omega$ (balanced triode configuration).

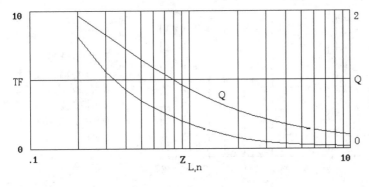

◀ **Figure 5.8**
The tuning factor as versus the normalized load $Z_{L,n}$ for $\alpha = 1$ & $\beta = 3$ when $Z_L = 1\ \Omega$ (balanced ultralinear configuration).

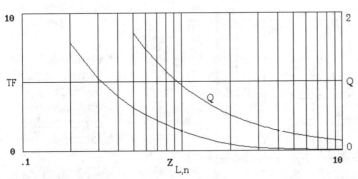

◀ **Figure 5.9**
The tuning factor versus the normalized load $Z_{L,n}$ for $\alpha = 1$ & $\beta = 10$ when $Z_L = 1\ \Omega$ (balanced pentode configuration).

(The plate resistance changes as the valve ages. If $\alpha \geq 2$, this aging will not affect the -3 dB frequency range.)

4) In the pentode mode in particular (Figure 5.6), the tuning factor decreases rapidly as the load impedance increases. In practice, the impedance of some speakers increases at higher frequencies due to the inductance of the speaker coil. This *partially* explains why some valve amplifiers transfer less high-frequency information when connected to such speakers.

(Most amplifiers are measured on the test bench with dummy loads that behave like frequency-independent resistors. An amplifiers can show excellent frequency-bandwidth behaviour on the bench but produce a muffled sound when a real loudspeaker is connected. The formulas above partially explain this behaviour. With guitar amplifiers in particular, this effect gives a nice, warm sound that is highly appreciated.

The reason for emphasizing that this factor only provides a partial explanation is that negative feedback is employed in most valve amplifiers. The combination of negative feedback and a restricted open-loop frequency range (without feedback) causes the output impedance to rise for frequencies above the upper -3 dB open-loop frequency. The increased output impedance is a second reason why the reproduction of high frequencies may be weak.)

■ | Introducing the decade factors

The ratio of f_{-3H} to f_{-3L} usually turns out to be a fairly large number. What does this quantity tell us? It gives a general impression of the -3 dB frequency bandwidth. However, this quantity is much easier to handle and to interpret if we express it as a *logarithmic* value. We then have a clear indication of how many frequency decades are spanned by the transformer and its tuning.

For this purpose, we define the *frequency decade factor* as:

$$FDF = \log \frac{f_{-3H}}{f_{-3L}} \qquad\qquad [5\text{-}21]$$

Rearranging this produces:

$$FDF = \log(TF \cdot QF) = \log TF + \log QF = TDF + QDF \qquad [5\text{-}22]$$

where we define the *tuning decade factor* as

$$TDF = \log TF \qquad\qquad [5\text{-}23]$$

and the *quality decade factor* as:

$$QDF = \log QF \qquad\qquad [5\text{-}24]$$

■ | Frequency decade factor examples

The following examples demonstrate the usefulness of the previously-described decade factors.

Example 1: suppose $L_p = 100$ H and $L_{sp} = 5$ mH. Then $QF = 20,000$. The number of frequency decades that can be spanned by this transformer, based on the quality decade factor, is 4.30.

Proper tuning can expand this range. If Butterworth tuning (optimally flat) is used with $a_2 = \sqrt{2}$ and $\alpha = 1$ (which means that $\beta = 1$), the tuning factor is 2.83 and the tuning decade factor is 0.452. The total number of frequency decades spanned is then 4.75. If $f_{-3L} = 1$ Hz, then $f_{-3H} = 10^{4.75} = 56$ kHz. Further calculations show that Z_{aa} must be 1257 Ω and C_{ip} must be 3.16 nF.

Example 2: using the same transformer ($\alpha = 1$), we will now tune for optimum constant time behaviour ($a_2 = \sqrt{3}$). In this case $\beta = 0.5$ (Formula 5-10). The tuning factor is 4.12 and $TDF = 0.61$. The total number of decades spanned is now: $FDF = 4.91$.

Using the formulas in Section 5.5, we calculate f_{-3L} and f_{-3H} to be 0.67 Hz and 55 kHz, respectively. Because α equals 1, C_{ip} should still be 3.16 nF. However, the source resistance R_g now has to be 629 ohms. This means that the number of power valves must doubled, compared to Example 1. Surprisingly enough, this example shows that the reduced value of R_g does not affect the upper −3 dB frequency, but instead the lower −3 dB frequency!

5.7 | New toroidal wide-bandwidth output transformers

In this section we introduce a new toroidal output transformer for valve amplifiers. We apply the theory from the previous chapters to this transformer and compare the calculated results to actual measurements.

■ | General description

In 1984 we constructed our first toroidal output transformer for push-pull valve amplifiers. This was a simple design that nevertheless had rather good specifications. Research showed that a optimized toroidal design would have some very interesting advantages compared to standard EI-core designs. By using toroidal cores and special winding techniques, we were able to produce very high coupling factors between the primary and secondary windings. This

▲ *Figure 5.10* *An example of the standard series of Vanderveen toriodal-core output transformers.*

resulted in small leakage inductance values. We noticed that a high primary inductance L_p could be achieved as well. Combining high L_p values with small L_{sp} values allowed us to achieve very high quality factors. Research also showed that low values of internal capacitance C_{ip} could be achieved by using special winding techniques and carefully arranging the winding layers.

The power capacity of our new transformers ranges from 20 watts to 100 watts, with the lower –3 dB power frequencies lying between 20 and 30 Hz. However, f_{-3L} is close to 1 Hz, due to the high L_p values (see Table 5.1).

We were able to achieve a high degree of symmetry for alternating currents and voltages. For example, the leakage inductance between the two halves of the primary is small; it is less than or equal to the (already small) total leakage inductance. This indicates a high degree of symmetry. Thanks to this symmetry, these transformers can handle high power levels with relatively small cores without entering into core saturation.

Compared to the original designs of the first generation (1984), we have now achieved higher primary inductances, higher coupling factors, lower leakage inductances, internal capacitances that are the same or even lower, a higher degree of

	Model number: VDV (top), PAT (bottom)					
	1080PP 4008	2100PP 4006	3070PP 4004	6040PP 4002	8020PP 4000	
Primary impedance Z_{aa}	1239	1885	2756	5878	8000	Ω
Turns ratio N_p/N_s	15.74	19.42	23.48	34.29	40	
Nominal power P_{nom}	80	100	70	40	20	W
Power bandwidth						
lower –3 dB frequency	20.5	20.7	22.7	25	28.5	Hz
Primary inductance L_p	360	530	490	535	485	H
Primary leakage inductance L_{sp}	1.312	1.8	2.6	3.7	8.0	mH
Effective primary capacitance C_{ip}	593	585	558	613	250	pF
Primary internal resistance R_{ip}	37.8	104	173.7	68.1	155.4	Ω
Secondary internal resistance R_{is}	0.16	0.18	0.168	0.158	0.161	Ω
Source resistance R_g	1200	2000	2000	5300	16000	Ω
2nd-order filter Q factor	0.682	0.695	0.639	0.496	0.671	
Lower –3 dB frequency f_{-3L}	0.278	0.304	0.400	0.847	1.793	Hz
Upper –3 dB frequency f_{-3H}	251	217	187	99	132	kHz
Quality decade factor QDF	5.44	5.47	5.28	5.16	4.78	
Tuning decade factor TDF	0.52	0.38	0.39	–0.09	0.09	
Frequency decade factor FDF	5.96	5.85	5.67	5.07	4.87	

▲ **Table 5.1** *Specifications for the standard series of toroidal-core transformers.*

balance and smaller core losses (by using a 'quiet', fast core material), and we have even reduced the heat losses in the windings by using windings with lower internal resistances.

■ Specifications

At present, five standard transformer types are available, with primary impedances of 1 to 8 kΩ. Their parameters are listed in Table 5.1. For other models, refer to the specifications of the 'Specialist' and 'SE' series of transformers in the following chapters.

Each of these transformers has primary taps for ultralinear valve configurations. This means that they can be used for triode, ultralinear and pentode configurations. All these transformers are intended for push-pull amplifier circuits.

Let's take a detailed look at the model with the lowest primary impedance, the VDV1080. The same calculations can also be performed for the other models as well, using the theory presented in this chapter. The necessary parameters are listed in Table 5.1.

■ Secondary impedance

The secondary impedance of this transformer is optimized for driving 5 Ω loudspeakers. The impedance of any loudspeaker varies with frequency, as illustrated in Figure 5.11. The value of the secondary impedance has been chosen to work well with the majority of available loudspeakers.

■ The quality factor and the quality decade factor

The primary inductance L_p is measured at 200 V, 50 Hz or 240 V, 60 Hz (to achieve the same flux density). If this measurement is repeated with lower or higher primary voltages L_p will differ slightly from the specified value, since the relative magnetic permeability μ_r depends the magnetic field strength.

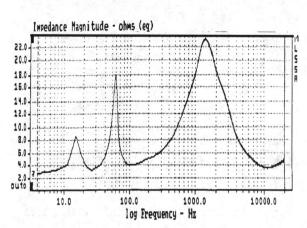

◀ *Figure 5.11*
Sample impedance
characteristic of an
electrodynamic loudspeaker.

The quality factor of the VDV1080 is 274,390. We use a value of 2.74E5 (2.74×10^5) for our calculations, since the use of more significant digits would not make sense. The quality decade factor is 5.44. This means that if everything is properly tuned, we can expect the frequency bandwidth to span at least 5.44 decades.

■ Winding resistances

The values of R_{ip} and R_{is} are 37.8 Ω and 0.16 Ω, respectively. We will drive the transformer with a source resistance R_g of 1200 Ω. The primary heat loss is thus only 3% of the transferred power, and the secondary loss is also 3%. We neglect these losses in our calculations so that we can use the simplified formulas, starting with Formula 5-7. We also use the linear approximation $ff(a_2)$.

■ Calculating the –3 dB bandwidth

With this transformer, C_{ip} is chosen so that the characteristic impedance Z_{ip} of the primary is aapproximately equal to the primary impedance Z_{aa}. We calculate the value of Z_{ip} as 1487 Ω. On the secondary side, the transformer sees a 5 Ω load, which produces a value of 1239 Ω for R_{aa}. The value of α is 1.200 and β is 0.969.

Using Formula 5-10, we find that $a_2 = 1.453$ and $Q = 0.688$. This is a healthy tuning, lying between optimally flat tuning ($Q = 0.577$) and Butterworth tuning ($Q = 0.707$).

Formula 5-15 yields a value of 0.979 for $ff(a_2)$. Now we can calculate the tuning factor and tuning decade factor: $TF = 3.40$ and $TDF = 0.53$.

Combining the quality decade factor and the tuning decade factor, we find that the –3 dB bandwidth spans 5.97 decades. Now we can use formulas 5-12 and 5-13 to calculate the lower and upper –3 dB frequencies. These are 0.270 Hz and 252 kHz, respectively. If we repeat these calculations without any approximations, we obtain 0.278 Hz and 251 kHz. Neglecting R_{ip} and R_{is} causes only very slight errors (2.9% and 0.4%, respectively). The results of these calculations are listed in Table 5.1.

Finally, we calculate the –3 dB frequencies with and without approximations: $\log_{10}(f_{-3H}/f_{-3L}) = 5.97$ and 5.96 decades, respectively. This again shows a good correlation (and so it should!).

Figure 5.12 shows the calculated and measured frequency responses (without approximations). The measurements were made by replacing each of the valves by a resistor equal to 0.5 R_g and driving the transformer primary from an oscillator with a 20 V peak to peak signal level. A 5 Ω load resistor was also used. The measurement setup is shown in Figure 5.13.

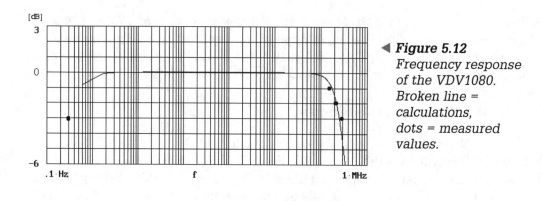

◀ **Figure 5.12**
*Frequency response
of the VDV1080.
Broken line =
calculations,
dots = measured
values.*

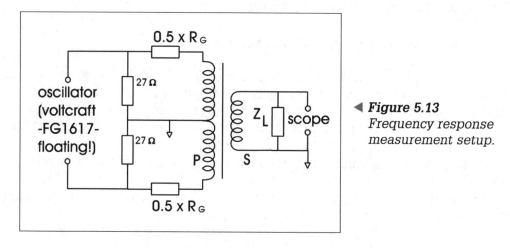

◀ **Figure 5.13**
*Frequency response
measurement setup.*

5.8 | Summary and conclusions

The approximate formulas and the complete formulas yield the same end results. The toroidal transformers discussed have an extremely wide frequency range, assuming that the valves act as voltage sources with series resistances.

It is now up to the designer to make full and optimum use of the excellent properties of these transformers, and to design fantastic valve amplifiers that fit the voltage-source model.

6
Theory of Overall Negative Feedback

We can calculate the frequency range of a valve amplifier, using the theory presented in the previous chapters. This chapter adds a new element: how does overall negative feedback affect the behavior of an amplifier? By feedback, we mean that the input and output signals are somehow compared to each other, and the difference between these signals is used to change the characteristics of the amplifier. For example, negative feedback broadens the frequency range and increases the damping factor. This chapter discusses the various aspects of overall negative feedback using an example amplifier, and works through all the calculations involved. By extending the models and theories in this chapter, the designer can use these results for his or her own particular designs. I would advise you to implement the formulas given here in a computer program, to save you from exhausting yourself with endless manual calculations.

6.1 | Defining the transfer function

Chapter 5 deals with the transfer function for the output section of a valve amplifier, which means the transfer function of the power valves and the output transformer. If we concentrate on the frequency-dependent part of the transfer function (see Formula 5-7), we have the following formula:

$$H(\omega) = \frac{j\omega}{j\omega + (\frac{\beta}{\beta + 1})(\frac{Z_{aa}}{L_p})} \cdot \frac{1}{1 + a_2(\frac{j\omega}{\omega_o}) + (\frac{j\omega}{\omega_o})^2} \qquad [6\text{-}1]$$

The first part of this function describes the low-frequency 6 dB/octave rolloff. The −3 dB frequency where this rolloff occurs, referred to as f_{-3L}, is given by the following formula (this is essentially the same as Formula 5-12):

$$f_{-3L} = \frac{\beta}{\beta + 1} \cdot \frac{Z_{aa}}{2\pi L_p} \qquad [6\text{-}2]$$

In Formula 6-1, we can use normal frequencies instead of circular frequencies. The transfer function then looks like this:

$$H(\omega) = \frac{jf}{jf + f_{-3L}} \cdot \frac{1}{1 + a_2(\frac{jf}{f_o}) + (\frac{jf}{f_o})^2} \qquad [6\text{-}3]$$

All we have to do now is to calculate f_{-3L}, a_2 and f_o. Using these values, we can calculate the absolute value of the transfer function $H(f)$ and plot it versus frequency. I use an example amplifier in the following sections to show you how to do this.

6.2 | Defining our example amplifier

At this stage we have a huge amount of freedom, which means we have a lot of choices to make. For our example, we will build an amplifier with four 6550WA power valves operating in triode mode. The effective plate resistance r_p for each set of two valves in parallel will be approximately 600 Ω; this depends on the high voltage used (V_o) and the quiescent current (I_o). We will use the VDV2100 transformer (refer to its specification sheet for details). Finally, we will assume that a perfect speaker with an impedance $Z_L = 5\ \Omega$ is connected to the secondary of the output transformer. All this information (plus that in Chapter 5) allows us to calculate the complete transfer function of this section of the amplifier.

Let's start with f_{-3L}:

$$Z_{aa} = \left[\frac{N_p}{N_s}\right]^2 \cdot Z_L = (19.42)^2 \cdot 5 = 1886\ \Omega \qquad [6\text{-}4a]$$

$$\beta = \frac{R_g}{Z_{aa}} = \frac{2 \cdot 600}{1886} = 0.636 \qquad [6\text{-}4b]$$

$$f_{-3L} = \frac{\beta}{\beta + 1} \cdot \frac{Z_{aa}}{2\pi L_p} = \frac{0.636}{1.636} \cdot \frac{1886}{2\pi \cdot 530} = 0.220\ Hz \qquad [6\text{-}4]$$

The next step in our calculation is to find the value of a_2. We have to calculate α first, and then a_2:

$$\alpha = \frac{1}{Z_{aa}} \cdot \sqrt{\frac{L_{sp}}{C_{ip}}} = \frac{1}{1886} \cdot \sqrt{\frac{0.0018}{585 \times 10^{-12}}} = 0.930 \qquad [6\text{-}5]$$

$$a_2 = \alpha \sqrt{\frac{1}{\beta(\beta + 1)}} + \frac{1}{\alpha} \cdot \sqrt{\frac{\beta}{\beta + 1}} = 0.912 + 0.670 = 1.58 \qquad [6\text{-}6]$$

The choices we have made are acceptable, because with this value of a_2 no ringing will occur ($Q = 1/a_2 = 0.632$).

The last element to be calculated in this example is the characteristic second-order rolloff frequency f_o:

$$f_o = \frac{1}{2\pi} \cdot \sqrt{\frac{\beta + 1}{\beta}} \cdot \sqrt{\frac{1}{L_{sp}C_{ip}}} = 249 \text{ kHz} \qquad [6\text{-}7]$$

We now know what the transfer function looks like, and we can implement it in a computer program. The frequency response plotted in Figure 6.1 shows the result of such an implementation.

Comparing these results with the transfer function graphs on the transformer specification sheets, we can see some striking similarities. This is nothing to be amazed about, since the same theory was used to calculate the transfer functions for the specification sheets.

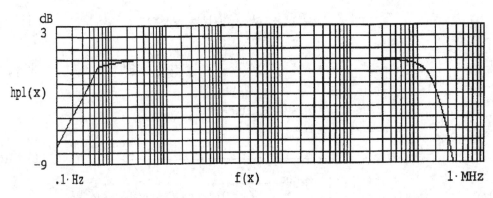

▲ **Figure 6.1** *The frequency response of the output section.*

6.3 Defining the phase splitter and preamplifier sections

The transfer function we have just discussed is definitely not complete, because in the real world a phase splitter and a preamplifier are always placed ahead of the power valves. These produce additional high frequency poles. To simplify our calculations, we introduce only one first-order pole frequency, f_{-3HIGH}:

$$f_{-3HIGH} = 150 \text{ kHz} \tag{6-10}$$

Now we have to extend the transfer function of Formula 6-3 by incorporating the expression shown in Formula 6-11:

$$\text{HF filter} = \frac{1}{1 + \dfrac{jf}{f_{-3HIGH}}} \tag{6-11}$$

When the phase splitter and preamplifier are added, coupling capacitors are used. These capacitors, together with the input resistors in the following amplifier stage, cause additional (or stronger) low frequency rolloffs. We will choose only one, with a −3 dB frequency of:

$$f_{-3LOW} = 10 \text{ Hz} \tag{6-12}$$

We have to extend the transfer function again, this time with Formula 6-13:

$$\text{LF filter} = \frac{jf}{jf + f_{-3LOW}} \tag{6-13}$$

The full transfer function for our complete amplifier now looks like this:

$$H(f) = H(f)_1 \cdot H(f)_2 \tag{6-14}$$

$$H(f)_1 = \frac{jf}{jf + 10} \cdot \frac{1}{1 + \dfrac{jf}{150 \times 10^3}} \cdot \frac{jf}{jf + 0.220} \tag{6-14a}$$

$$H(f)_2 = \frac{1}{1 + 1.58 \cdot \dfrac{jf}{249 \times 10^3} - \dfrac{f^2}{(249 \times 10^3)^2}} \tag{6-14b}$$

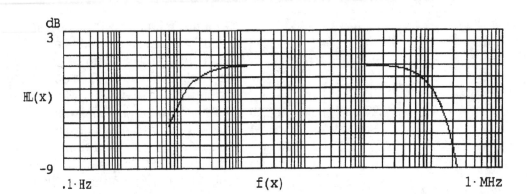

▲ **Figure 6.2** *The complete transfer function for the example amplifier.*

Figure 6.2 shows the the results of calculating this transfer function in the frequency domain. If we compare this to the transfer function shown in Figure 6.1, we see that the phase splitter and preamplifier sections significantly restrict the frequency range of the amplifier. In our example amplifier, the output transformer is thus not the limiting factor.

6.4 | The complete amplifier under load, with no overall negative feedback

Obviously, in practice a real amplifier amplifies, but up to now we haven't discussed this in detail. Let's start by assuming that the total open loop amplification of the combination of the preamplifier, phase splitter, power section and transformer with no load (that is, with no speaker connected) is:

$$A_o = 800 \qquad\qquad [6\text{-}15]$$

The last step needed to complete our model of the amplifier is to calculate the output impedance, Z_{out}, on the secondary side of the output transformer:

$$Z_{out} = \left[\frac{N_s}{N_p}\right]^2 \cdot R_g = \frac{2 \cdot 600}{(19.42)^2} = 3.18\ \Omega \qquad\qquad [6\text{-}16]$$

Note that this formula for Z_{out} is not complete, because it ignores the effects of L_p, C_{ip} and L_{sp} at the low and high frequency limits. On top of this, the speaker load Z_L is also complex. This last factor can make the calculation of the output impedance considerably more complicated. This is sufficient justification for using a simplified formula for Z_{out}.

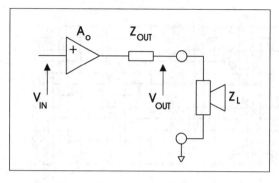

▲ **Figure 6.3**
*Equivalent circuit of the sample
amplifier without feedback.*

Figure 6.3 shows the equivalent circuit of our example amplifier without feedback. This diagram clearly shows that voltage division occurs at the output due to Z_{out} and Z_L.

Taking all these elements into account, we can now construct the complete transfer function for our valve amplifier. This is given in Formula 6.17. Figure 6.4 shows how this transfer functions looks when it is plotted in the frequency domain.

$$H_T(f) \;=\; \frac{V_{out}}{V_{in}} \;=\; A_o \cdot H(f) \cdot \frac{Z_L}{Z_{out} + Z_L} \qquad [6\text{-}17]$$

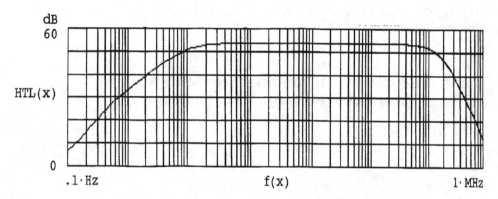

▲ **Figure 6.4** *The frequency response of the complete amplifier without feedback.*

It is interesting to see that the broad frequency range of the output transformer is not being used to full advantage, due to the limitations of the phase splitter and pre-amplifier. Note in particular the scale of the vertical axis. Its 60 dB range clearly indicates how much this gain amplifier has. You can also see the slopes of the low-frequency and high-frequency filter elements.

6.5 | Applying overall negative feedback

We will now introduce overall negative feedback (ONF), with the aim of reducing the no-load gain from 800 to 20. Feedback is achieved by connecting the 'in phase' output terminal to the cathode of the preamplifier valve via a resistor, as

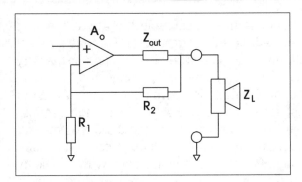

▲ Figure 6.5
Equivalent circuit of the sample amplifier
with negative feedback via R_2 and R_1.

shown in Figure 6.5. Here the feed-back resistor is shown as R_2, while the cathode resistor is shown as R_1. The practical aspects of negative feedback are dealt with in Chapter 15. Here we only want to investigate the theoretical conse-quences.

In Figure 6.5, we can see that the output signal is attenuated by R_2 and R_1. This attenuation can be expressed using the factor γ, as shown in Formula 6.18.

$$\gamma = \frac{R_1}{R_1 + R_2} \qquad [6\text{-}18]$$

The values of R_1 and R_2 are discussed and explained in Chapter 15. If we assume that $R_1 = 1 \text{ k}\Omega$, then R_2 should be 19.5 kΩ for an open loop amplification of 20 (with ONF):

$$\gamma = 0.004875 \qquad [6\text{-}19]$$

We can now calculate the transfer function of the unloaded amplifier with feed-back, using Formula 6-20. This is designated $H_{FU}(f)$: H for transfer, F for feedback and U for unloaded. The results are shown in Figure 6.6.

$$H_{FU}(f) = \frac{H(f)A_o}{1 + \gamma H(f)A_o} \qquad [6\text{-}20]$$

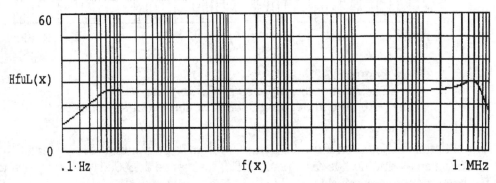

▲ Figure 6.6 *The frequency response of the unloaded amplifier with overall negative feedback.*

This graph shows a bandwidth that is more than acceptable, but at the high end we can see the first indications that something might go wrong. There is a rise of almost 4 dB, which may cause oscillations. There is a little bit of ringing at the very low end as well, but this will disappear when the loudspeaker is connected.

Since our amplifier will never be operated with no load, we now include Z_L in our model. Note that the impedance of most speakers shows a steep rise at high frequencies, due to the inductance of the speaker coil and wires. In practice, a real speaker may thus emulate a no-load condition for an amplifier. We will not discuss this point now, but it is understandable that the amplifier should be stable even without a load. Not all valve amplifiers meet this requirement, and tried-and-true wisdom reflects this in the adage, 'never operate a valve amplifier without a load'.

Formula 6-21 shows the transfer function of the loaded amplifier with overall negative feedback:

$$H_{FL}(f) = \frac{H(f)A_o}{1 + \gamma H(f)A_o} \cdot \frac{Z_L}{\dfrac{Z_{out}}{1 + \gamma H(f)A_o} + Z_L} \qquad [6\text{-}21]$$

Figure 6.7 shows the calculated shape of the new transfer function in the frequency domain.

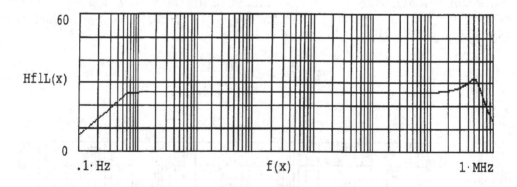

60

HflL(x)

0

.1· Hz   f(x)   1· MHz

▲ *Figure 6.7*
The frequency response of the amplifier
with overall negative feedback and a loudspeaker load.

The differences between Figure 6.6 and Figure 6.7 are minimal. However, at the low end the small ringing has disappeared. The resonance at 600 kHz is still present, so we have to try to compensate for this.

6.6 | Stabilization in the frequency domain

In Chapter 15, we discuss various methods that can be used to remove resonances. There we introduce C^* and C^{**}, as well as the method of increasing the values of the screen grid and control grid resistors. Unfortunately, in this case slightly increasing these resistor values will not help much, since our problem is fundamental and not caused by a badly designed component layout. Therefore, we will try to alleviate the problem by using C^* and C^{**}. To make things simple, we will concentrate on implementing C^{**}. The value of γ will change, since R_2 will be replaced by the parallel combination of R_2 and C^{**} (see Figure 6.8).

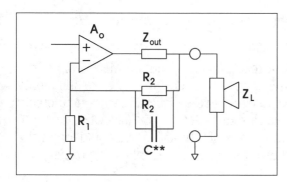

▲ **Figure 6.8**
*Implementation of C^{**}
in the sample amplifier.*

The factor γ is now frequency dependent, so we have to redefine it as shown in Formula 6-22. If we replace γ by $\gamma(f)$ in Formulas 6-20 and 6-21, we can recalculate the frequency response. The result is shown in Figure 6.9 for $C^{**} = 68$ pF. At first everything looks fine, but if we look carefully at the portion above 1 MHz we can see a 'lift'. To examine this in detail, we calculate the response between 10 Hz and 100 MHz, as shown in Figure 6.10.

$$\gamma(f) = \frac{R_1}{R_1 + \dfrac{R_2}{1 + 2\pi j f R_2 C^{**}}} \qquad [6\text{-}22]$$

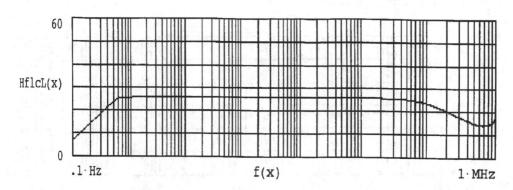

▲ **Figure 6.9**
*The frequency response of the loaded amplifier
with overall negative feedback and $C^{**} = 68$ pF.*

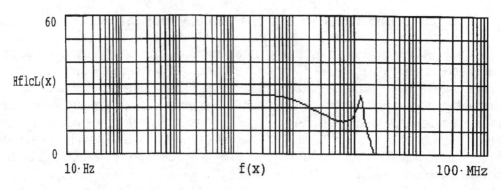

▲ *Figure 6.10*
The frequency response between 10 Hz and 100 MHz.

It is clear from this plot that there is a resonance around 1.3 MHz. This is not desirable, and it should be removed. At this stage of our design, there are still plenty of different ways to do this. For example, we could add series grid resistors to create an extra pole at high frequencies, we could introduce R^* and C^* (see Chapter 15) to create a compensating pole and a zero in the transfer function, we could lower the open loop gain A_o and so on. This is where the designer can place his or her own stamp on the design by skillful optimization.

I suggest, as an example, that an extra pole be introduced by using series resistor for the control grids of the power valves. These resistors will work with the Miller capacitances of the valves to form an additional first-order filter. I suggest setting the −3 dB frequency to 70 kHz and then repeating all the calculations. It follows that the resistance will be large (in the range of 1 to 10 kΩ). This means that we are not just making small changes in the grid resistor values to prevent local oscillations due to component placement; instead, we are consciously introducing a pole at this point. The results can be seen in Figure 6.11.

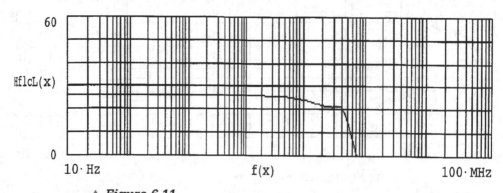

▲ *Figure 6.11*
The effect of using grid resistors to remove the resonance.

This works fairly well, as you can see, and we can imagine that this extra filter section can be optimized through careful calculation and experimentation. This is something that you can do yourself. Aside from this, it is interesting to note that the series grid resistors do indeed function as 'stop' resistors, preventing oscillations.

This completes our discussion of the example amplifier in the frequency domain. There are too many possible choices to allow us to fully discuss all the aspects involved. Our choices have highlighted the advantage of using a computer for amplifier research and design In practice, matters will usually be even more complicated due to numerous additional poles and zeros. However, once they have been identified and measured you can make fundamental changes to remove them, all just sitting at your desk with a keyboard at your fingertips.

6.7 | Comments about the damping factor

The formulas given so far can also be used for a few interesting calculations regarding the frequency dependence of the damping factor. The official definition of the damping factor is:

$$DF = \frac{\text{loudspeaker impedance}}{\text{output impedance}} = \frac{Z_L}{Z_{out}} \qquad [6\text{-}23]$$

Without feedback, this calculation is easy. Our load impedance is 5 Ω, and Formula 6-17 yields a value for Z_{out} of 3.18 Ω. The damping factor DF is thus 1.57. Assuming that Z_L and Z_{out} are frequency independent, the damping factor will be constant for all frequencies. However, we have already seen that this is not a very realistic assumption, because both of these impedances are in fact frequency dependent. For this reason, most manufacturers choose to define Z_L as constant and measure Z_{out} at 1 kHz, and then calculate the damping factor on this basis.

Now let's look at how the output impedance changes with frequency when we apply ONF. For the moment, we again assume that Z_{out} and Z_L are frequency independent. As soon as we apply ONF, the effective value of Z_{out} changes according to the formula:

$$Z_{out,e} = \frac{Z_{out}}{1 + \gamma(f)H(f)A_o} \qquad [6\text{-}24]$$

Because both $\gamma(f)$ and $H(f)$ are frequency-dependent, $Z_{out,e}$ is frequency dependent. It therefore follows that the damping factor is also frequency dependent:

$$DF_{eff} = \frac{Z_L}{|Z_{out,e}|} \qquad [6\text{-}25]$$

Taking the absolute value of $Z_{out,e}$ is a choice that I have made. I do not know whether this is consistent with the rest of the world, but it seems to be logical, even though the damping factor could be defined to be complex. However, we have to use its absolute value to see how big DF is, so it makes sense to exploit this fact in the definition.

We can now incorporate all these factors in our example amplifier, including C^{**} and the extra pole at 70 kHz, to study the frequency dependence of the damping factor in our model. This is shown in Figure 6.12.

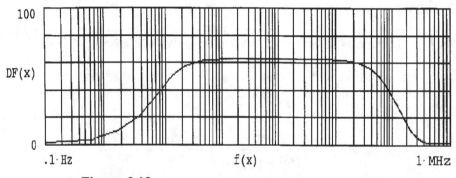

▲ **Figure 6.12**
The effective damping factor as a function of frequency.

The frequency dependence is now clearly shown, and DF can be seen to be relatively constant between 20 Hz and 20 kHz (the audio range). Any changes in the zeros and poles in the design will greatly influence the frequency dependence of the damping factor. Particular care should be taken at the low frequency end, due to the damping needed for the woofers.

This concludes this discussion of the frequency dependence of the damping factor. The same technique can also be applied to distortion calculations.

6.8 | Summary and conclusions

This chapter mathematically models the frequency-dependent aspects of an example amplifier with overall negative feedback, using the theory discussed in Chapter 4. The choice of zeroes and poles influences the stability of the amplifier, and some of these effects have been shown. Finally, the frequency dependence of the damping factor has been illustrated by means of calculations.

7

Output Transformer Low-Frequency Tuning

The previous chapters show how the frequency range of the amplifier is determined by the close interaction of the power valves, the output transformer and the loudspeaker load. This chapter addresses the low-frequency behaviour of a valve amplifier. We study the influence of the primary-winding inductance of the output transformer on the bass response, and we look at how to achieve optimum low frequency coupling between the power valves, the output transformer and the loudspeaker. We also consider how to minimize low frequency distortion.

7.1 | Measuring the primary inductance

The value of the primary inductance L_p of an output transformer is not constant. It depends on the frequency and the voltage of the signal applied to the primary winding. This varying inductance affects the response of the amplifier. To study this, we start with measuring the primary inductance.

Figure 7.1 shows the measurement setup. We measure the secondary inductance, which can be converted into the primary inductance by using the square of the transformer turns ratio A sine wave oscillator is used to make the measurement, along with a good amplifier having a large damping factor.

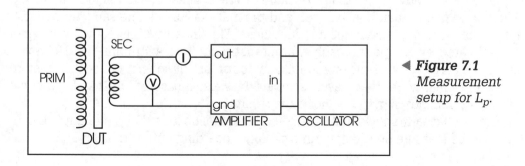

◀ *Figure 7.1*
Measurement setup for L_p.

A sine wave voltage at a frequency of 20 or 25 Hz is connected to the secondary winding of the transformer. The voltage across the secondary is measured, together with the current that flows in the secondary. There is no load on the primary side of the transformer. Be very careful not to touch the primary leads during the measurement, since they can carry a high voltage! The measurement results are shown in Figure 7.2 for several different output transformers (see Table 7.1 for the associated model numberss).

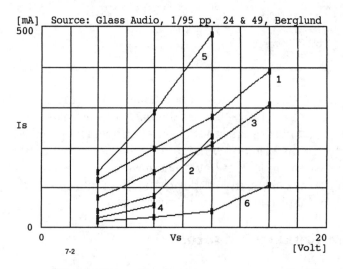

No.	Model	
1	Copland	—
2	Dynaco	ST70
3	Dynaco	MK III
4	Luxman	MQ-360
5	Luxman	MQ-80
6	VDV2100	
	(PAT4006)	

▲ **Table 7.1**
Output transformer model numbers.

▲ **Figure 7.2**
Measurement results for several models of output transformers (see Table 7.1).

Measurements 1 through 5 were made with a 25 Hz test voltage connected to the 8 Ω secondary taps. Measurement 6 was performed with a 20 Hz test voltage connected to the 5 Ω secondary taps. The lower frequency compensates for the lower secondary impedance, so that the core loading is equal for all measurements.

Figure 7.2 clearly shows that the various sample transformers behave differently. The reason lies in their construction and the materials used. The samples with the lowest currents have the highest inductances. The linearity of the $i_s - v_s$ curves can be estimated by comparing each characteristic curve to a straight line. However, since the currents were measured for only four test voltages, it is not that easy to check the linearity. For that reason, sample 6 was also measured at several additional secondary voltages. Figure 7.3 shows the results.

Figure 7.3 clearly shows that the $i_s - v_s$ characteristic looks like a straight line over most of the measurement range. An old adage regarding output transformers is that

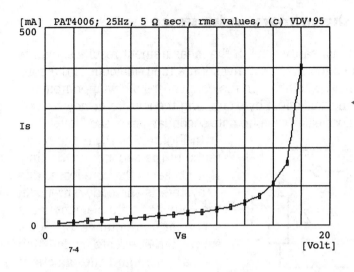

◀ Figure 7.3
*Detailed measurement
results for sample
transformer 6.*

the transformer with the highest and most nearly constant primary inductance will
have the best bass performance.

Sample 6 seems to best meet this criterion. However, we can more precisely
investigate its linearity. If the i_s–v_s characteristic is absolutely linear, then the ratio
of v_s to i_s will be the same for each measurement point in Figure 7.3. Figure 7.4
shows the calculated values of Z_s ($= v_s/i_s$), plotted as a function of v_s.

The secondary impedance is large, but it shows a clear variation. The curve plotted in Figure 7.4 is not a straight horizontal line, so the i_s–v_s characteristic is not
absolutely linear. This shows that the best way to test the linearity of an i_s–v_s characteristic is to plot the calculated value of the secondary impedance Z_s versus v_s.

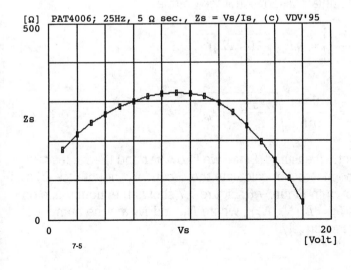

◀ Figure 7.4
*Secondary impedance Z_s
as function of v_s.*

7.2 | Calculating the primary inductance

What causes the nonlinearity seen in the measurement results shown in Figure 7.2? To answer this question, we must investigate the behaviour of the core. The measurements suggest that some effect in the core causes a deviation from linearity. We can start investigating this effect by examining the low-frequency equivalent circuit of the output transformer, as seen from its secondary side (see Figure 7.5).

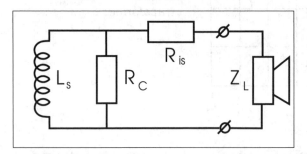

In Figure 7.5, R_{is} is the resistance of the secondary winding. R_C represents the core losses due to hysteresis and eddy currents in the core. The third element is the secondary inductance L_S. For a simple but adequate explanation we can disregard the effects of core losses, since they only become important at high output levels where the transformer approaches core saturation. If we keep to moderate power levels, R_C in Figure 7.5 can be ignored.

▲ **Figure 7.5**
Low-frequency equivalent circuit on the secondary side of the transformer.

The relationship between v_s and i_s at a frequency f is given by Formula 7-1:

$$\frac{v_s}{i_s} = R_{is} + j2\pi f L_s \quad \text{where } j = \sqrt{-1} \text{ and } \pi = 3.14... \quad [7\text{-}1]$$

The imaginary unit j can be eliminated by calculating the magnitude of v_s/i_s and then finding the value of L_s. Formula 7-2 shows how to do this:

$$\left|\frac{v_s}{i_s}\right| = \sqrt{R_{is}^2 + (2\pi f L_s)^2} \quad [7\text{-}2a]$$

$$L_s = \frac{1}{2\pi f} \cdot \sqrt{(\frac{v_s}{i_s})^2 - (R_{is})^2} \quad [7\text{-}2b]$$

The value of R_{is} can be directly measured. Since we know π, f and the values of v_s and i_s for each measurement point, we can calculate the secondary inductance L_s at each point. The results are shown in Figure 7.6. Figure 7.7 shows the inductance on the primary side, calculated as $L_p = L_s(N_p/N_s)^2$, where N_p and N_s are the number of primary and secondary turns, respectively.

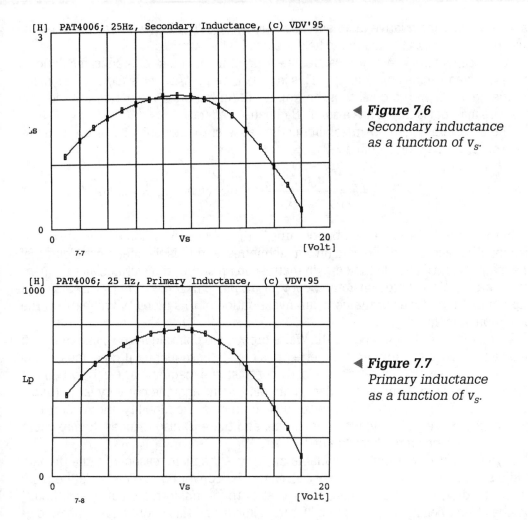

Figure 7.6
Secondary inductance as a function of v_s.

Figure 7.7
Primary inductance as a function of v_s.

These calculations clearly show that L_s is not constant. Since the value of R_{is} is very small (0.18 Ω), the L_s curve behaves identically to the v_s/i_s curve. We can now pose a more precise question regarding the cause of these variations in L_s.

7.3 | Exploring the core

When a current passes through a winding around a core it creates a magnetic field, and the magnetic field tends to cause the particles in the core (and groups of particles, called *Weiss groups*) to move and rotate (this effect is called *magnetostriction*).The more easily this can happen, the stronger is the magnetic field generated in the core, since the strength of the field depends on the extent to which the Weiss groups are aligned to the magnetic field lines. The mobility of the Weiss groups is indicated by the relative magnetic permeability (μ_r). The larger its value, the better the core responds to the magnetic field created by the winding.

All these moving Weiss groups create a kind of magnetic interference, resulting in a noise voltage across the winding. This is called the *Barkhausen effect*, and its magnitude depends on the quality of the iron used. An important selection criterion for the core material is that it has a small Barkhausen effect.

The relative magnetic permeability is the cause of the nonlinearity of L_s. Its influence on L_s is given by Formula 7-3:

$$L_s = \frac{\mu_0 \mu_r N_s^2 l_m}{A} \quad [H] \quad \text{where } \mu_0 = 4\pi \times 10^{-7} \quad [7\text{-}3]$$

In this formula N_s is the number of turns in the secondary winding, A is the cross-sectional surface area of the core (in square metres) and l_m is the mean path length of the magnetic field lines in the core (in metres). In an output transformer, all the quantities in Formula 7-3 are constant except for μ_r. Since μ_r represents the 'mobility' of the magnetic particles in the core, an investigation of this mobility will explain the deviation from linearity.

When the core is saturated, all the Weiss groups are pointing in the same direction and cannot move any further into 'better' positions. Consequently, μ_r becomes nearly zero. At very low magnetization levels, by contrast, the magnetic forces between the Weiss groups hold them more or less stationary, so μ_r again is not very large (*initial permeability*). At some point between these extremes, the mobility and responsiveness of the Weiss groups reach a maximum, and there μ_r also reaches its maximum value. This behaviour explains Figures 7.6 and 7.7.

If you now consider that this variable mobility is the main reason why the primary audio signal energy from the power valves can be converted into secondary energy at the loudspeakers, it becomes clear that output transformers can be 'difficult' devices. Their behaviour seems to be far from linear, and this might cause a lot of distortion. By comparison, valves (for which the anode current obeys strict and simple laws) and transistors (which conform to strict logarithmic relationships) are very 'clean' devices. So why not dispense with output transformers? The answer is that they are not really as bad as they seem, and actually they do sound nice. I shall explain why this is so by looking at their distortion behaviour.

7.4 | Output transformer distortion calculations

To learn how to calculate the distortion of an output transformer, let's look at a push-pull power amplifier. A standard circuit for such an amplifier is shown in Figure 7.8.

Each of the power valves has an effective plate resistance r_p. The secondary side of the transformer is connected to a loudspeaker with an impedance Z_L. We assume

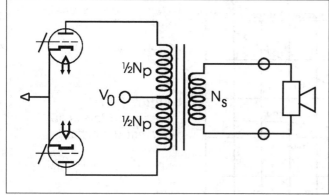

▲ **Figure 7.8** *Standard push-pull amplifier circuit.*

that Z_L is frequency independent and constant (have you ever met such a loudspeaker?). On the primary side of the transformer, Z_L is represented by Z_{aa}, which is almost 2 kΩ for the VDV2100. Figure 7.9 shows the low frequency equivalent circuit of this amplifier, seen from the primary side.

The two power valves can be replaced by a voltage source with a series resistor equal to $2r_p$. We can disregard the resistances of the primary and secondary windings in this analysis, since their influence on the distortion is minimal. Imagine that this amplifier now starts working. An alternating voltage v_{aa} appears between the two anodes, and this generates an alternating current in the circuit of Figure 7.9. The current passing through the primary inductance L_p generates a magnetic field in the core, resulting in a voltage at the secondary side of the transformer. It is now easy to understand how distortion might occur. Since L_p is not constant, the current is distorted. However, does the secondary voltage show the same distortion?

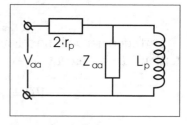

▲ **Figure 7.9**
Output transformer low frequency equivalent circuit (primary side).

This distortion phenomenon was researched by Partridge[3]. Figure 7.10 (overleaf) shows an example of the results of his measurement on cores made from 3.5% silicon steel[4]. The vertical axis shows the current distortion *ID* in percentage, while the horizontal axis shows the amplitude of the magnetic flux density B_{max} in the core (in Teslas). (The magnetic flux density is the number of magnetic field lines per square metre intersecting a surface *A*). The three curves show the levels of the second, third and fifth harmonics of the current.

To explain the distortion behaviour of an output transformer in general, I now assume that the sample transformers of Figure 7.2 use the same core material as that used for measurements in Figure 7.10. The secondary voltage v_s can be converted into B_{max} by using Formula 7-4:

$$B_{max} = v_s \cdot \frac{\sqrt{2}}{2\pi f A N_s} \qquad [7\text{-}4]$$

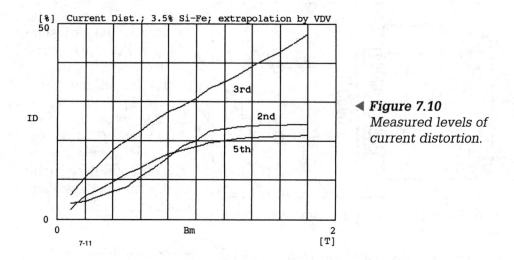

◀ Figure 7.10
Measured levels of current distortion.

Partridge derived the following formula (Formula 7-5) to calculate the voltage distortion **VD** (in percent):

$$VD = ID \cdot \frac{R_{eq}}{2\pi f L_p} \cdot (1 - \frac{1}{4} \cdot \frac{R_{eq}}{2\pi f L_p}) \qquad \text{[7-5]}$$

The resistance R_{eq} is given by Formula 7-6.

$$R_{eq} = v_s \cdot \frac{Z_{aa} \cdot 2 r_p}{Z_{aa} + 2R_p} \qquad \text{[7-6]}$$

Now we have all the information we need to calculate the voltage distortion at any frequency and any secondary voltage, assuming that the core material behaves as shown in Figure 7.10.

7.5 | How the valves affect the distortion

I have used the procedure described in the last section to calculate the distortion characteristics of the VDV2100 when driven by four 6550WA Sovtek valves. Two valves are paralleled on the upper side of the transformer primary and another two on the lower side. In pentode mode, the effective plate resistance is 7.5 kΩ, and in ultralinear mode (with the screen grids connected to 40% primary taps) the effective plate resistance is almost 2 kΩ. In triode mode, the plate resistance is 750 Ω. The calculated distortion characteristics for these three modes are shown in Figures 7.11, 7.12 and 7.13, respectively.

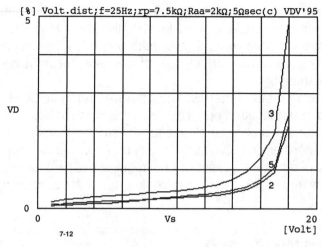

7-12

◀ Figure 7.11
*Voltage distortion at
25 Hz, pentode mode.*

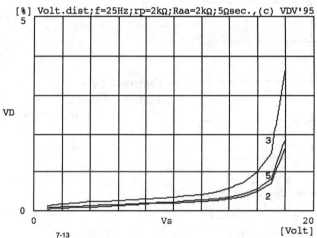

7-13

◀ Figure 7.12
*Voltage distortion at
25 Hz, ultralinear mode.*

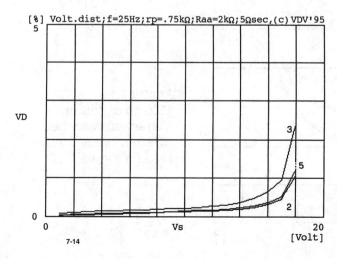

7-14

◀ Figure 7.13
*Voltage distortion at
25 Hz, triode mode.*

The general conclusion that can be drawn from the results of these calculations is that a lower effective plate resistance produces a lower level of distortion. Hodgson[4] uses this argument to explain why triodes sound better than pentodes. Based on these calculations, I find that the output transformer distortion is less in the triode mode, and I agree with his line of thinking.

Figure 7.14 shows the distortion characteristics when the frequency is 50 Hz instead of 25 Hz, with the valves in ultralinear mode. The distortion is much less that in the 25 Hz calculations. In general, the higher the frequency the smaller the amount of distortion caused by the core. Further on I show that this is important in explaining the specific sound character of a valve amplifier at low frequencies. At high frequencies, the leakage inductance and internal capacitance determine the distortion behaviour.

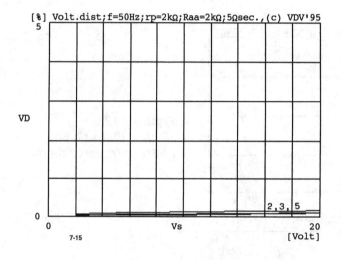

◀ *Figure 7.14*
Voltage distortion at 50 Hz, ultralinear mode.

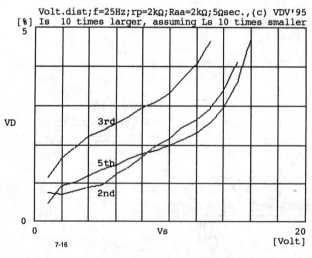

◀ *Figure 7.15*
Voltage distortion characteristics when L_p is ten times smaller than for Figure 7.12.

The results of the next exercise with these calculations are shown in Figure 7.15. Here I assumed the current in the VDV sample transformer to be 10 times larger than for Figure 7.12, which means that the effective inductance is 10 times smaller. The amount of distortion is strikingly large compared to the previous cases. This explains why a large L_p value is of utmost importance in producing undistorted sound at low frequencies. For this reason, our toroidal output transformers are designed to have large primary inductances.

7.6 | How bad is nonlinearity?

You can discern a striking similarity in all the distortion characteristics given above. The variation in μ_r is not evident in these graphs, nor does the nonlinearity of L_p or L_s seem to be an important factor. It seems as though the nonlinearity is canceled out in the voltage distortion equations. Only at the saturation limit, where L_p and L_s are very small, is the voltage distortion large. This is an unexpected result. How can we understand it?

It can easily be proven mathematically that the voltage distortion will be small and nearly independent of the behaviour of μ_r below saturation, as long as the condition given in Formula 7-7 is satisfied:

$$2\pi f L_p \gg R_{eq}, \text{ or otherwise stated: } L_p \gg \frac{R_{eq}}{2\pi f} \qquad [7\text{-}7]$$

If this condition is satisfied, the denominator of Formula 7-5 is so large that the voltage distortion is negligible. A large primary inductance is therefore absolutely essential to make the distortion as small as possible at low frequencies. As soon as $2\pi f L_p$ is (nearly) equal to R_{eq}, the distortion characteristics become very sensitive to variations in μ_r. We have seen an example of this in Figure 7.15, where L_p was made ten times smaller. Hence, a large inductance for the output transformer is an essential condition for a small voltage distortion figure.

However, it is sometimes necessary to design transformers with small primary inductances. This is the case for single-ended types, where a balance between DC and AC saturation must be achieved. This results in a much smaller value for L_p than in the push-pull case. The condition of Formula 7-7 is not satisfied by such transformers, so it is absolutely essential to provide constant-μ_r behaviour to prevent the voltage distortion from becoming very large. Constant-μ_r behaviour can be achieved by choosing special core materials and fine tuning the air gaps.

What is the final result of this investigation? The condition given in Formula 7-7 can be used to judge how much low frequency distortion an output transformer will produce in a specific amplifier circuit. You cannot judge the 'quality' of an output transformer on its own; you must first know the value of the equivalent source resistance R_{eq} (and thus the valves used and their operating mode) and the ratio of the lowest desired frequency f to the primary inductance L_p. Only after these have been defined can you determine whether a given output transformer is suitable for a particular application.

7.7 | The sound of a valve amplifier

With the information we have gathered thus far, it is possible to explain the specific sound of a valve amplifier, with particular attention to how it reproduces bass frequencies.

At low frequencies in particular, the transformer distortion overshadows that due to the valve circuitry. If the output transformer distortion becomes large at 40 Hz, for example, it will generate a second harmonic at 80 Hz, a third harmonic at 120 Hz and so on. These harmonics are closely related to the 40 Hz fundamental. When we listen to such an amplifier we hear a rich, strong bass, but we do not hear the distortion terms as distinct, separate components.

What we hear testifies to the amazing ability of our ears to convert harmonic components into fundamentals. We keep on hearing 40 Hz, and this 40 Hz tone sounds even stronger and louder due to the harmonics. Experiments[5] in which the fundamental was entirely removed, so that only the harmonics remained, have shown that the fundamental will actually be heard even when it is not present. The harmonic components thus strongly reinforce the auditory perception of the fundamental.

Harmonic distortion components are produced only at low frequencies, while the midband and high frequency spectrum remains undistorted. This type of distortion therefore does not sound harsh or nasty; instead, it is fully acceptable to our ears. We can conclude that this particular sort of output transformer distortion enriches the reproduced sound, especially at low frequencies.

However, what happens when you use an output transformer with a very large inductance? It might surprise you, but the bass will sound weaker. No distortion components are produced, and you hear only the pure bass tones. This can be explained with reference to the VDV2100.

While making tests, I noticed that this toroidal transformer's bass sounded softer than that of an EI-core output transformer with a low primary inductance (30 H). Due to its large L_p value, the toroidal transformer has a frequency range that extended farther at the low end than that of the EI-core output transformer. The bass should therefore have sounded fuller with the toroidal output transformer, but this was in fact not the case. The above theory fully explains this subjective observation. I leave it to you to decide whether extra harmonics of low bass tones are desirable.

This bass distortion theory clarifies why a given output transformer can 'sound' completely different in different amplifier environments. It also explains why the output transformer of a guitar amplifier plays a major role in creating a special tonal balance. It clearly shows that 'oversized' cores should not be used in guitar amplifiers, because the warm sound character produced by a transformer with a small primary inductance is a major factor in creating the specific 'guitar' sound. This theory also explains why we find huge cores in sophisticated high-end equipment. They are there to keep the low frequency distortion as small as possible. The toroidal output transformers that are central to this book are designed for clean, undistorted low frequency behaviour, rather than for a 'rich' or 'warm' bass sound.

7.8 | References

1) Rickard Berglund, 'Quick, Simple Output Transformer Tests', *Glass Audio*, Vol. 7/1, pp 24 & 49.
2) Menno van der Veen, 'Measuring Output Transformer Performance', *Glass Audio*, Vol. 9/5, pp 20–34.
3) Dr N. Partridge, 'Distortion in Transformer Cores', *Wireless World*, June 22 & 29, July 6 & 13, 1939. (This reference and other sources are listed in Reference 5.)
4) Tom Hodgson, 'Single-Ended Amplifiers, Feedback and Horns: Some History', *Sound Practices*, Spring 1994, pp 39–42.
5) *Auditory Demonstrations*, IPO, NIU, ASA. Demonstration 20: virtual pitch (track 37). Philips CD1126-061.

8

Special Output Coupling Techniques

The standard push-pull tube amplifier design is well known. It consists of a push-pull output transformer, two power valves and a phase splitter, and it utilizes external negative feedback from the output to the input. This arrangement can be used for pentodes or beam power pentodes, with the screen grids and anodes connected to the output transformer. The implementation is not difficult, and high output power can be achieved with wide bandwidth and low distortion. This chapter deals with other, more advanced ways of coupling the power valves to the output transformer, and it introduces the 'specialist' series of toroidal output transformers, which have been developed to work with these techniques.

8.1 | From pentode to Super-Pentode

The development of the new output transformers discussed in this chapter is based on two facts. The first of these is that a pentode can deliver more output power than a comparable triode. Triodes, on the other hand, have lower internal resistance, which results in higher damping factors. If we could combine the best aspects of both configurations – the high output power of a pentode and the low output impedance of a triode – we would have something quite remarkable. How can we convert pentodes into triodes without sacrificing output power? To answer that question, we have to review existing methods of local feedback and consider the Child-Langmuir current–voltage relationships of a pentode.

8.2 | The I_a–V_{ak}–V_{gk} formula

For the sake of this discussion, a beam-power pentode is considered to be equivalent to a 'normal' pentode — which it is not, of course. In Figure 8.1 we see a representation of the currents and voltages as they normally appear in a pentode.

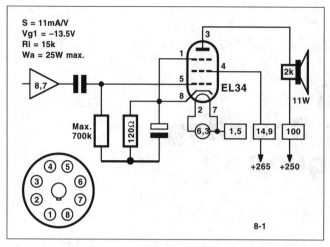

The anode current I_a largely depends on the control grid voltage V_{gk}, the screen grid voltage V_{g2k} (or V_{g2k0} if the screen grid is connected to a DC voltage) and the anode voltage V_{ak}. The screen grid draws a current I_{g2}. The cathode current I_k, which is defined by the well-known Child-Langmuir formula, is the sum of the screen grid current and the anode current.

▲ Figure 8.1

Currents and voltages in a pentode
(courtesy De Muiderkring[9]).

We need a formula for the anode current for our analysis, but a number of researchers have concluded that there is no straightforward relationship between I_k, I_a and I_{g2}[1, 2, 10]. For that reason, we have used measurement data to develop an *ad hoc* formula for the current division between the anode and the screen grid. With this relationship, which we designate as $\alpha(V_{ak}, V_{g2k})$, we can then determine the value of the anode current that flows in the output transformer.

$$I_a = \alpha(V_{ak}, V_{g2k}) \cdot K \cdot (V_{gk} + D_{g2}V_{g2k} + D_a V_{ak})^{3/2} \qquad [8\text{-}1]$$

$$\alpha(V_{ak}, V_{g2k}) = \frac{I_a}{I_k} = \alpha_o \cdot \left[\frac{2}{\pi} \cdot \left| a\tan(\frac{V_{ak}}{V_{g2k}}) \right|\right]^{1/n} \qquad [8\text{-}2]$$

where $1 < n < 10$ and $0.8 < \alpha_o < 1$

The constants in these formulas can be calculated from valve handbook information. In this chapter I use the characteristics of an EL34 as an example. Its constants are $\alpha_o = 0.87$, $V_{g2k} = 360$ V (fixed), $K = 2.766 \times 10^{-3}$, $D_{g2} = 0.09179$, $D_a = 4.706 \times 10^{-3}$ and $n = 4$ (all quantities in SI units).

Figure 8.2 shows the calculated EL34 characteristics, while Figure 8.3 shows the measured characteristics[3]. In these plots V_{gk} changes in steps of $\Delta = -4$ V, starting at 0 V. The close match between the calculations and the measurements is certainly encouraging.

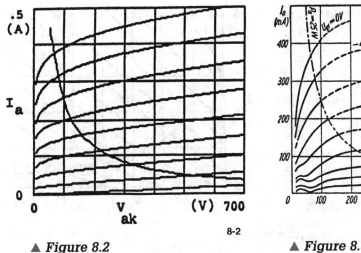

▲ *Figure 8.2*
Calculated EL34 characteristics.

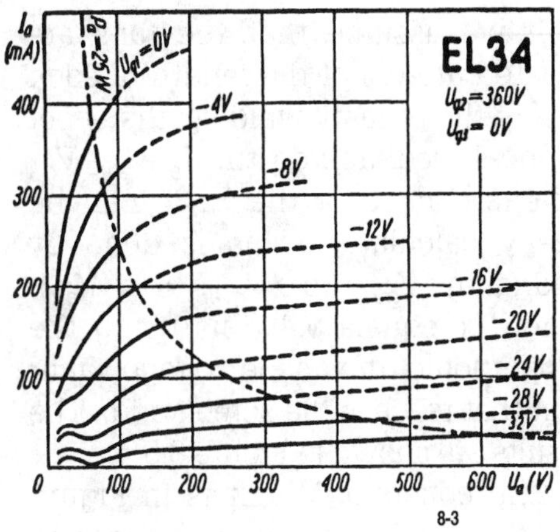

▲ *Figure 8.3*
Measured EL34 characteristics[3].

8.3 | Local ultralinear feedback

In 1951, Hafler and Keroes (Acro-Sound, Dynaco, Hafler) introduced the ultralinear local feedback technique (see Reference 3, p 131). In this configuration, both halves of the output transformer primary winding are tapped, and the taps are connected to the screen grids of the power valves. Figure 8.4 shows this arrangement.

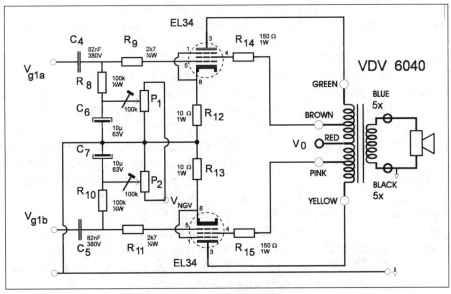

▲ *Figure 8.4* *Amplifier power stage with ultralinear feedback.*

If we assume that the taps are located at 40% of the length of each half of the primary winding, the effect of local feedback on the I_a–V_{ak}–V_{gk} characteristics of the EL34 can be easily calculated. This is done by changing V_{g2k} to $(V_{g2k} + x \cdot V_{ak})$, where x equals 0.4 (this being the proportion of the anode voltage variation that reaches the screen grid). The results are shown in Figure 8.5.

The constant–V_{gk} lines in Figure 8.5 are much steeper than those in Figures 8.2 and 8.3, indicating that the effective plate resistance is lower. This technique thus increases the damping factor. The available output power is somewhat less than with the pentode configuration.

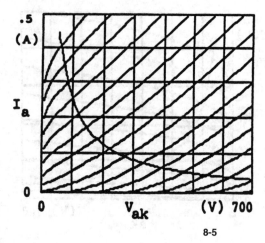

8-5

▲ *Figure 8.5*
EL34 ultralinear characteristics for Δ = –4 V, V_{g2k} = 360 V and x = 0.4.

8.4 | Specialist SSCR toroidal output transformers

The standard range of Vanderveen toroidal output transformers (VDV1080 through VDV8020) allows the ultralinear local feedback technique to be used. It cannot be used with all types of power valves, however, because not all valves can handle having the same DC voltage on the screen grid and the anode. Some valves require a lower DC voltage on the screen grid, especially with high anode voltages. For example, when a 6L6GC or 6550WA is used at 600 V, the screen grid must be at 325 V (see Reference 3, pp 146–147). For this reason I have developed a new series of transformers with separate screen grid windings (see Reference 3, pp 127–130, and Reference 4). Figure 8.6 shows the winding arrangement of these SSCR (Separate SCReen) toroidal output transformers.

This type of transformer can be used in a standard ultralinear configuration, but it allows the screen grid voltage V_{g2k0} and the anode voltage V_{ak0} to be set independently. This also allows V_{g2k0} to be stabilized, making the characteristics of the power valve independent of the instantaneous output power.

This last statement requires some explanation. Figures 8.7 and 8.8 show the I_a–V_{ak}–V_{gk} characteristics of the EL34 for V_{g2k0} = 250 V and 265 V, respectively. This simulates a 'collapse' of the supply voltage when excessive current is drawn from the power supply. The differences between these two figures are significant, indicating the need to stabilize the screen grid supply voltage[4, 10].

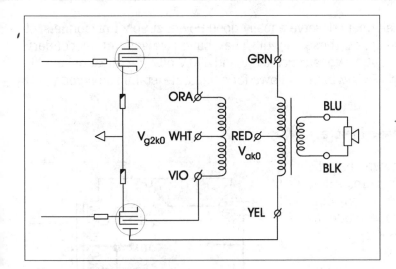

◀ **Figure 8.6**
*The SSCR winding
arrangement.*

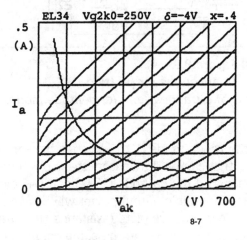

8-7

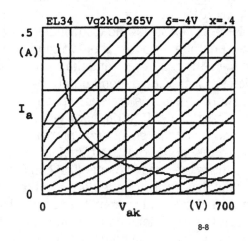

8-8

▲ **Figure 8.7**
*EL34 characteristics
for V_{g2k0} = 250 V.*

▲ **Figure 8.8**
*EL34 characteristics
for V_{g2k0} = 265 V.*

The specifications for these new SSCR transformers are provided at the end of this chapter. They are available with primary impedances of 2000 and 4000 ohms and power ratings of 100 watts and 70 watts, respectively. Briefly, they employ extra large cores, which extends the −3 dB nominal power frequency to 14 Hz while maintaining a full frequency bandwidth from 0.3 Hz to 180 kHz. Large diameter wires are used for the windings to minimize insertion losses. The primary inductance has been designed to be as large as possible, in order to keep core distortion small at low frequencies. A special winding technique lowers the effective internal primary capacitance, thus creating an extremely large quality factor (well over 200,000).

Excellent output transformers deserve equally good power supply transformers, of course, and we have designed these as well. They have two separate secondary windings, which provide output voltages of 450 V and 490 V after rectification and filtering. The independent 490 V winding allows for a separate, stabilized screen grid supply at 450 V or lower.

8.5 | The power issue

It is well known that the available output power increases as we go from the triode mode through ultralinear to the pentode mode, as illustrated in Figure 8.9. For example, a pair of EL34s with V_{ak0} = 480 V yields P_{triode} = 25 W, P_{UL} = 50 W and P_{pent} = 70 W.

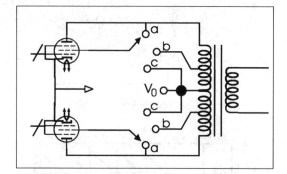

▲ *Figure 8.9*
Connections for (a) triode,
(b) ultralinear and (c) pentode mode.

Now let's consider the following: in the pentode mode, the voltage between the screen grid and the cathode (V_{g2k0} or V_{ak0}, depending on the transformer used) is constant. In the ultralinear mode, V_{g2k} changes when the anode voltage changes, in proportion to the tap ratio of the transformer. In the triode mode, V_{g2k} changes the same amount as the anode voltage. The conclusion that can be drawn from these observations is that if the voltage between the screen and the cathode (V_{g2k}) can be held constant during music amplification, the highest possible output power will be available. If this condition can be combined with a low effective plate resistance, then we can have triode behaviour together with high output power in the same configuration. This best-of-both-worlds concept is used in the following sections, which explain the features of our new cathode-feedback toroidal output transformers. These also have ultralinear taps on their primary windings.

8.6 | Cathode feedback techniques

In 1946, a new concept of local feedback was formulated by McIntosh. Designs were published that featured feedback circuitry at the cathodes of the power valves. In 1949 McIntosh implemented his ideas in the Model 50-2 amplifier, which was the first commercial product to use the famous Unity Coupled design (see Reference 3, p 127). In 1954 Bogen also developed a cathode feedback design, followed by Peter Walker (Quad) in 1958 (see Reference 3, p 138). Audio Research combined several feedback techniques in their famous D40 and D79 designs, and even today their

amplifiers still use cathode feedback circuitry[5].

How does cathode feedback
actually work? First, it requires
extra windings on the output
transformer. Figure 8.10 shows a
cathode feedback (CFB) transformer, with the phases of the
windings marked by dots. As you
can see, the signals at the cathodes are in phase with the control
grid signals and antiphase to the
anode signals (which produces
negative feedback).

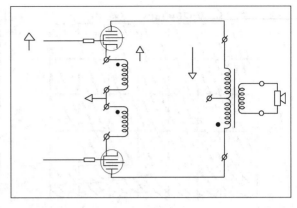

▲ *Figure 8.10*
Cathode feedback circuit
with transformer coupling.

Now, let us take a look at the
upper half of the amplifier circuit.
Suppose that the CFB winding connected to the cathode has N_{CFB} turns, while the
upper half of the primary has $0.5N_p$ turns. The ratio between the signal reaching the
cathode and the anode signal is given by the formula $\Gamma = (N_{CFB}/0.5N_p)$. The formula
for I_a can now be adapted for this situation. Figure 8.11 defines the relevant terms.
Notice that the control grid signal is referred to ground, rather than to the cathode as
in previous circuits.

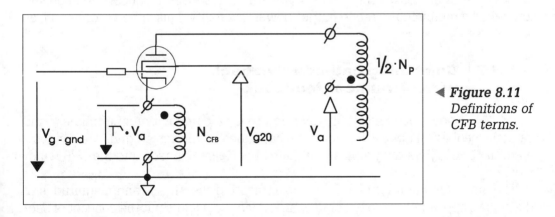

◀ *Figure 8.11*
Definitions of
CFB terms.

Figure 8.12 (overleaf) shows EL34 valve characteristics with cathode feedback
when $\Gamma = 0.1$ and $V_{g20} = 360$ V. For comparison, Figure 8.13 shows calculated characteristics for the EL34 without any feedback and with the screen grid connected to
the anode, to convert the EL34 pentode into a triode.

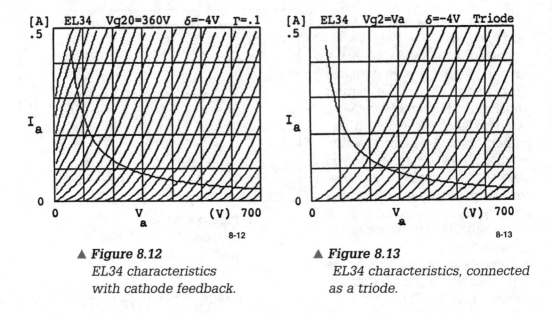

▲ *Figure 8.12*
EL34 characteristics
with cathode feedback.

▲ *Figure 8.13*
EL34 characteristics, connected
as a triode.

These calculations yield interesting results. With cathode feedback the curves have the same slopes as in the triode configuration, and therefore the same damping factor results. However, the CFB configuration allows a much larger variation in the maximum anode voltage than the triode configuration (compare the left hand sides of Figures 8.12 and 8.13). This proves that cathode feedback produces triode behaviour while maintaining pentode output power capability. This is however not all, as we will see!

8.7 │ Combining cathode feedback with ultralinear feedback

It now becomes highly tempting to try a combination of ultralinear and cathode feedback. Figure 8.14 shows the basic idea — the screen grids are connected to the primary winding taps, while the cathodes are connected to the CFB windings.

The arrows in Figure 8.14 are vectors, indicating the phases and magnitudes of the signals appearing at the winding connections. Now let us put the concept of Section 8.5 to work. The upper screen grid must be connected to the lower tap of the primary to keep V_{g2k} constant. When the tap ratio is matched to the number of turns on the cathode feedback winding, maximum power can be combined with a maximum damping factor. We have performed experiments based on these simulations, and as a result we have developed two new output transformers. These are described in the next section. The experimental results are reviewed in Sections 8.9 and 8.10.

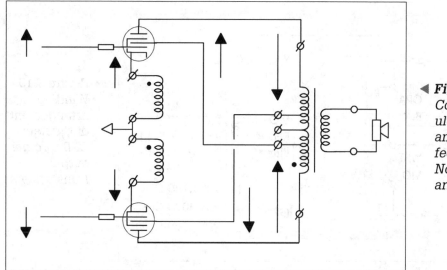

◄ *Figure 8.14*
Combined
ultralinear
and cathode
feedback.
Notice the
arrows.

8.8 | Toroidal cathode feedback output transformers

There are three new CFB toroidal output transformers, with primary impedances of 2000 and 4000 ohms. Their power bandwidths extend down to 14 Hz and 23 Hz. The 23 Hz type (VDV2100-CFB/H) is intended for applications where coutinuous, full power is not required at low frequencies, as is often the case with high fidelity amplifiers, while the two 14 Hz types are intended for applications such as subwoofer amplifiers. The 5-ohm secondary winding is centre tapped, allowing symmetrical external negative feedback or cathode feedback to be used as described above, and there are also ultralinear taps on the primary. Each half of the balanced transformer has its own separate CFB winding. Figure 8.15 (overleaf) shows the winding arrangement for all CFB transformers and illustrates the extra features of this configuration, such as the possibility of measuring the quiescent cathode current by using a resistor connected to ground. The complete transformer specifications, located at the end of this chapter, describe the wide bandwidths and other features of these transformers.

8.9 | Experiments with cathode feedback and ultralinear configurations

Experiments with these new transformers strongly confirm the concept formulated in Section 8.5. The circuit diagrams of Figure 8.16 show the various experimental configurations, in which the CFB output transformer was connected to the power valves in various ways. This does not exhaust the set of possibilities, since the centre-tapped secondary can be also be used as a CFB winding.

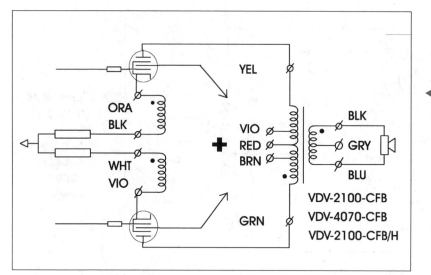

Figure 8.15
Winding
arrangement
of the new
CFB toroidal
output
transformers.

In the experiments, the power valves were driven by a low impedance, wide band-width amplifier, to avoid influencing the measurements by source bandwidth limita-tions. We measured the output power, damping factor, frequency response and gain. The gain was defined as $A_L = V_{load}/V_{g1-gnd}$, where V_{load} is the AC voltage across the 8 Ω load and V_{g1-gnd} is the AC voltage between one of the control grids and the ground. The control grids were held at −40 V to set the quiescent current to 50 mA for each valve. The power valves were two single EL34s. The quiescent anode supply voltage was 475 V; this dropped to 468 V under maximum load. The transformer was a model VDV2100-CFB/H with the following relevant specifications: $x = 0.33$ (UL tap); $\Gamma = 0.1$ (CFB). Each amplifier was connected to a 8-ohm resistive load, thus creating an effective primary impedance of 3200 Ω. Figure 8.16 shows all configurations by number, and the associated measurement results are listed in Table 8.1.

8.10 | From the pentode and triode to the Super-Pentode ®©

The measurement results from Table 8.17 are briefly explained in the following paragraphs.

Configuration 1 ($x = 0$, $\Gamma = 0$) is the normal pentode amplifier configuration.The output power is large, the damping factor is low and the frequency range is relatively restricted due to the high plate resistance — although −3 dB at 140 kHz is still pret-ty decent.

Configuration 2 ($x = 0.33$, $\Gamma = 0$) is the well-known ultralinear configuration. Some power is lost compared to Configuration 1, but the damping factor is higher due to negative feedback applied to the screen grids. V_{g2k} decreases when V_{ak} decreases, so these results fit with the concept presented in Section 8.5.

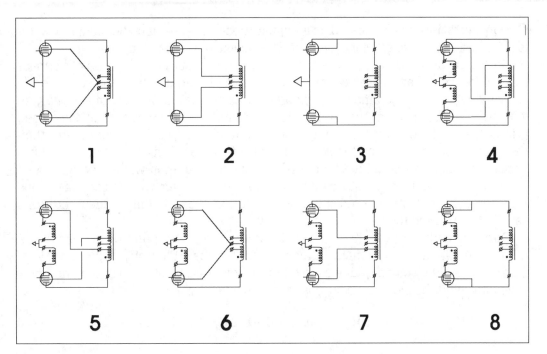

▲ **Figure 8.16**
Amplifier configurations using the VDV2100-CFB/H toroidal output transformer.

circuit	1	2	3	4	5	6	7	8	
$x^{(1)}$	—	0.33	1	−1	−0.33	—	0.33	1	
$\Gamma^{(2)}$	—	—	—	0.1	0.1	0.1	0.1	0.1	
P_{nom}	74	55	27	—	80	63	49	27	W
Z_{out}	157	23.9	8.4	14.9	12.3	8.3	6.1	4	Ω
$DF^{(3)}$	0.05	0.33	0.95	0.55	0.65	0.96	1.31	2	
$A_L^{(4)}$	0.77	0.62	0.47	0.50	0.47	0.41	0.36	0.30	
f_{-3dB}	140	160	170	—	164	170	175	180	kHz

Notes: 1) x = screen grid negative feedback ratio; 2) Γ = cathode negative feedback ratio; 3) $DF = 8/Z_{out}$; 4) $A_L = V_{load}/V_{g1-gnd}$

▲ **Table 8.1** *Test results for the amplifier configurations of Figure 8.16.*

Configuration 3 ($x = 1$, $\Gamma = 0$) is a regular triode. As expected, the damping factor is large and the power efficiency is poor. This has already been explained.

Configuration 4 ($x = -1$, $\Gamma = 0.1$): the maximum output power could not be measured because the amplifier became unstable at high output levels; the screen grids got very hot and a huge amount of distortion was generated. What happened? There was negative feedback at the cathode ($\Gamma = 0.1$) and positive feedback at the screen grid ($x = -1$). The effective amount of positive feedback was however greater than the amount of negative feedback, so the net effect was positive, and the amplifier oscillated. Since this could not be remedied, this configuration will not be discussed any further, and building this design is not advised. However, we can see in Sections 8.11 and 8.12 that this configuration will function properly only if the conditions established by McIntosh are used, meaning $x = -1$ and $\Gamma = 1$.

Configuration 5 ($x = -0.33$, $\Gamma = 0.1$) is very interesting and deserves a more detailed explanation, given its unusual capabilities. When V_a decreases, V_{g2k} *increases*! As the screen grid is coupled to the lower ultralinear tap of the primary, x is negative and the increase in V_{g2k} is therefore given by:

$$\Delta V_{g2k} = (x + \Gamma) \cdot \Delta V_a = (-0.33 + 0.10) \cdot \Delta V_a = -0.22 \Delta V_a \qquad [8\text{-}3]$$

In keeping with our ideas in Section 8.5, we have a configuration here in which we can expect more output power than in the regular pentode mode. Why is this? Regular pentode operation requires V_{g2k} to be constant. Power is lost if V_{g2k} and V_a decrease together (in the triode and ultralinear configurations). In this configuration, though, V_{g2k} *increases* when V_a decreases, so we have crossed the 'pentode barrier'. The result is increased maximum output power (80 watts) compared to the pentode mode (74 watts in Configuration 1). This is not the only goodie! The damping factor is 13 times as great as in the pentode mode, and although the amplification has decreased somewhat – no problem here – the frequency range has increased. These are remarkable properties, and reason enough to give this configuration a special name. I call it the Super-Pentode® circuit (© 1995 Ir. buro Vanderveen).

These results explain why the primary is not tapped at $x = 10\%$ in these CFB output transformers, which would have been logical according the concept in Section 8.5. With 10% taps V_{g2k} would be constant during the amplification of audio signals. A tap at the 33% point, combined with the illustrated feedback arrangement, yields a Super-Pentode configuration with higher output capabilities than a regular pentode. Of course, Super-Pentode operation is not restricted to the x and Γ values used in this example. The Super-Pentode condition occurs whenever the voltage between the screen grid and the cathode increases when the anode to cathode voltage decreases. The CFB transformers have been designed such that the screen grid taps will produce stable Super-Pentode behaviour for almost all available power valves. The decisive factor here is the use of screen grid amplification instead of control grid amplification, together with suitable values of x and Γ.

Configuration 6 ($x = 0$, $\Gamma = 0.1$) is the well-known cathode feedback configuration, but with improved performance. Compare for instance the measured results for Configuration 3 and Configuration 6. The amplification and damping are nearly identical. However, the output power of Configuration 6 is more than double — a clear advantage of this type of amplifier (see Reference 3, pp 142, 146 & 147). It is also not necessary to connect the screen grids to the anode supply V_{a0}; they can be connected to a separate, stabilized power supply that provides V_{g20}. For this reason, the new cathode feedback transformers do not have separate screen grid windings.

Configurations 7 & 8 ($x = 0.33$ & 1, $\Gamma = 0.1$): what happens here is directly implied by the original concept. The screen grid voltage decreases more and more with respect to the cathode, raising the damping factor (due to increased negative feedback) while decreasing the available output power. However, the output power in Configuration 7 is larger than the output power in a standard triode circuit (Configuration 3), while the linearity and damping factor are much improved compared to Configuration 3. For these reasons circuit 7 has also been given a special name. I call it the Super-Triode ® circuit (© 1998 Ir. buro Vanderveen).

In conclusion, Configurations 5, 6 and 7 offer elegant 'new' ways to apply local feedback while maintaining large output power and a high damping factor (as was intended) . Measurements on amplifiers that use the new CFB output transformers corroborate the concept formulated in Section 8.5.

8.11 | The next logical step: unity coupling

When I studied the relevant literature, the McIntosh unity coupled circuit (1946 – 1949) clearly stood out, since it provides elegant solutions for many long-standing problems. These amplifier designs are still so advanced that it is understandable that they are reused even today. While studying McIntosh's work, I came to the conclusion that new winding techniques were needed to realize effective unity coupled transformers. The unity coupled configuration is a logical next step in the concept described in Section 8.5, as will be seen. Figure 8.17 (overleaf) depicts the unity coupled circuit, which uses a combination of negative cathode feedback and positive screen grid feedback.

The first important factor is the number of turns connected to the anode, which must equal the number of turns connected to the cathode. This implies that $\Gamma = 1$, yielding strong cathode feedback (much stronger than for the amplifiers in the previous section). The screen grids are connected to the opposite ends of the of primary. Notice the arrows (vectors) in Figure 8.18 — it should be clear that when the cathode voltage increases, the screen grid voltage increases by exactly the same amount (in other words, $x = -1$). This is the condition under which V_{g2k} remains constant during the amplification of audio signals, which explains why the McIntosh design delivers such high output power. As the transformer is driven by the anodes as well as the cathodes, both the plate resistance and cathode output impedance must be taken

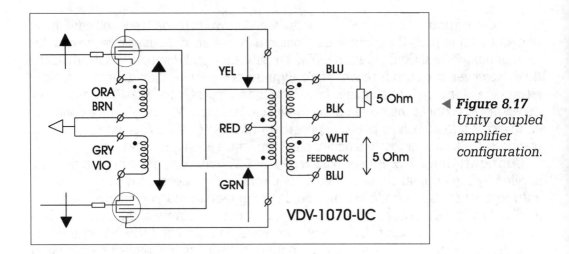

◀ *Figure 8.17*
Unity coupled
amplifier
configuration.

into account. The relatively small cathode output impedance is nearly equal to $1/s$, where s is the transconductance of the power valve. This all implies that the output transformer is driven by a low impedance, thus yielding wide bandwidth.

Because the anode and the cathode together deliver the drive voltage to the output transformer, each providing at most half of the supply voltage, the number of primary turns can be much smaller than for a comparable regular output transformer. The consequence is that the transformer can be bifilar wound, with half as many turns on the primary winding as a standard output transformer. This means, for example, that if the primary impedance should normally be 4 kΩ in a circuit with two EL34 valves, here we can give the bifilar primary an equivalent impedance of 1 kΩ.

In most circuits it is not necessary to consider the current flowing via the screen grids, as it does not pass through the output transformer and therefore creates no problems. However, in the unity coupled configuration the screen grid is connected to the output transformer, so its current must be taken into account. The screen grid current plus the anode current equals the cathode current. All these currents pass through the output transformer in a complementary fashion, thus contributing to the power output.

The next issue is of great importance in the McIntosh designs. Amazingly enough, the power valves operate almost in class B, so that the quiescent currents are very low. These amplifiers drive their valves 'cool'. Normal class B circuits generate large crossover distortion components, as well as notch distortion caused by the partial unloading of the transformer when one of the power valves switches off. The leakage inductance and the internal capacitance of the primary form an undamped circuit that oscillates whenever a power valve switches off. Notch distortion and crossover distortion both occur at the same location, but the frequency of the former is very high. According to McIntosh, the quality factor of the output transformer should be at least 72,000. As the leakage inductance has been nearly eliminated in the toroidal output transformers for unity coupled designs, they have a quality factor of 2,342,000. This value generously exceeds the strict demand set by McIntosh.

The last issue is that this arrangement makes heavy demands on its drive circuit. Large drive voltages are needed, with amplitudes up to 200 V. The drive signal at each control grid equals the voltage across the cathode winding plus the voltage needed to drive the valve itself. McIntosh developed elegant solutions to this problem (see References 6, 7 and 8).

8.12 | Experimental results with the VDV1070-UC toroidal output transformer

The experiments described in Section 8.9 have been repeated with the new VDV1070-UC transformer. Two EL34 power valves were used, each set to a 42 mA quiescent current. The measurement conditions were identical to those in Section 8.9, except that the secondary load was changed to 5 Ω to create an optimum primary load. The configurations described in Section 8.9 were tested. Wide bandwidth driver amplifiers were again used for measuring the effective bandwidths of the experimental amplifiers. For measuring the maximum output power, a high voltage setup was used, consisting of a centre-tapped step-up transformer (1:75 ratio) and a Quad 306 power amplifier. Table 8.2 shows the results of the experiments. Only configurations 4, 6 and 8 of Figure 8.16 are applicable to unity coupled amplifiers.

Configuration 4 ($x = -1$, $\Gamma = 1$) is the classic unity coupled configuration, as invented by Frank McIntosh. The output power is high, as expected, while the output impedance is low — much less than any value seen in Section 8.9. The amplification is low, also as expected. A simple calculation shows us what is going on. Suppose

circuit	1	2	3	4	5	6	7	8	
x	—	—	—	−1	—	—	—	1	
Γ	—	—	—	1	—	1	—	1	
P_{nom}	—	—	—	65	—	43	—	22	W
Z_{out}	—	—	—	1.34	—	1.106	—	1.06	Ω
$DF^{(1)}$	—	—	—	3.73	—	4.52	—	4.72	
$A_L^{(2)}$	—	—	—	0.113	—	0.106	—	0.097	
f_{-3dB}	—	—	—	494	—	—	—	—	kHz

Notes: 1) $DF = 5/Z_{out}$; 2) $A_L = V_{load}/V_{g1-gnd}$

▲ **Table 8.1** Test results with the VDV1070-UC toroidal output transformer.

the amplifier delivers 65 watts in 5 Ω, equivalent to $\sqrt{(65 \cdot 5)} = 18$ Vrms across the load. At the control grid of each power valve, the drive voltage is $(18 \div 0.113) = 159$ Vrms. This indicates the need for a special driver, as is further explained in References 3, 6, 7, 8 and 10.

The frequency response is impressive: the −3 dB points are 0.09 Hz and 494 kHz, without any external negative feedback! What causes this? At low frequencies, the cutoff point is substantially shifted down by the combination of the low output impedance of the power valves – due to unity coupled feedback – and the high primary inductance of the output transformer, due to the improved toroidal winding. The high frequency response is also extended by the low output impedance of the power valves, which together with the combination of the small leakage inductance and small effective capacitance of the transformer primary yields a whopping 494 kHz.

Configurations 6 & 8 ($x = 0$ & 1, $\Gamma = 1$): these configurations do not require a detailed explanation. The important factor is that the output power is reduced while the damping is slightly increased. However, as the screen grid current does not pass through the output transformer, Configuration 6 worsens the notch distortion. Configuration 8 yields the highest damping factor but relatively little output power, and it must be considered to be a difficult amplifier to build due to the high drive voltages needed on the control grids.

8.13 | Summary and conclusions

We have introduced several new toroidal output transformers and explored the use of local feedback to increase the damping factor, as is required by present-day audio developments. We have presented formulas for calculating the anode current in a power valve and the effects of local feedback. Two transformers with separate screen grid (SSCR) windings have been introduced, with primary impedances of 2 and 4 kΩ. These allow stabilized power supplies to be used for the screen grids, with voltages lower than the anode supply voltage. We have explored the concept that the voltage between screen grid and the cathode should be held constant during amplification in order to obtain maximum output power. We have introduced new cathode feedback (CFB) output transformers with extra ultralinear taps. These transformers are optimized for a wide range of advanced amplifier configurations, featuring the Super-Pentode and Super-Triode configurations. We have described experiments with unity coupled output transformers. Finally, a new toroidal unity coupled transformer that offers extremely wide bandwidth and a very high damping factor has been introduced. References for further study are listed in Section 8.14.

8.14 | References

1) H. de Waard, *Electronica*, fourth printing, 1966, pp 36 – 41. W. de Haan, Hilversum.
2) W. Marshall Leach, Jr, 'SPICE Models for Vacuum-Tube Amplifiers',
    J. Audio Eng. Soc., Vol. 43/3, March 1995, pp 117 – 126.
3) J. Hiraga, *Initiation Aux Amplis a Tubes*. Eyeroles, second edition.
4) B. Perkins, 'A Little Input on Audio-Output Transformers'; *Audio Note 2.1*
    plus update. Calgary, Alberta, Canada T2T 4X3.
5) M. Colloms, 'Audio Research Reference Series'; *HiFi News & Record Review*,
    February, 1994, pp 30 – 33.
6) P.G. Sulzer, 'Survey of Audio-Frequency Power-Amplifiers Circuits',
    Audio Engineering, May 1951.
7) R.F. Scott, 'Circuit Features of High-Fidelity Power Amplifiers',
    Radio Electronics, Aug. 1955, pp 44 – 46.
8) N.H. Crowhurst, 'Realistic Audio Engineering Philosophy', *Audio*, Oct. 1959.
9) Muiderkring, *Tube and Transistor Handbook, Volume 1*, Nov. 1964, p 279.
    De Muiderkring NV.
10) Menno van der Veen, 'Modeling Power Tubes and their Interaction with Output
    Transformers', 104th Audio Engineering Convention, Amsterdam 1998.
    Preprint 4643.

8.15 | Transformer specifications and wiring diagrams

The specifications of the Specialist series of toroidal output transformers are listed in Table 8.3, overleaf. The wiring diagrams are shown in Figure 8.18, following Table 8.3.

Specifications of the Specialist series of Vanderveen balanced toroidal output transformers

	Model number: VDV						
	4070-SSCR	2100-SSCR	4070-CFB	2100-CFB	2100-CFB/H	1070-UC	
Primary impedance Z_{aa}	4000	2000	4000	2000	2000	4000	Ω
Secondary impedance Z_L	4	4	5	5	5	5	Ω
Turns ratio N_p/N_s	31.6	22.4	28.3	20.0	20.0	28.3	
Ultralinear tap ratio x	40	40	33	33	33	-100	%
Cathode feedback ratio Γ	—	—	7.1	10	10	100	%
-0.1 dB frequency range[1, 3] $f_{-.1dB,H}$	84	102	67	84	131	110	kHz
-1 dB frequency range[1, 3] $f_{-1dB,H}$	131	134	136	149	204	244	kHz
-3 dB frequency range[1, 3] $f_{-3dB,H}$	185	177	222	224	290	451	kHz
Nominal power P_{nom}	70	100	70	100	100	70	W
-3 dB power frequency $f_{-3dB,P}$	14	14	14	14	23	14	Hz
Primary inductance[2] L_p	1163	675	1056	663	505	1574	H
Leakage inductance L_{sp}	3.2	2.1	3.1	1.4	1.5	0.67	mH
Effective primary capacitance C_{ip}	345	660	358	638	400	388	pF
Primary internal resistance R_{ip}	114	57	120	63	56	78.4	Ω
Secondary internal resistance R_{is}	0.10	0.13	0.15	0.17	0.10	0.18	Ω
Insertion loss I_{loss}	0.23	0.26	0.25	0.28	0.20	0.24	dB
Effective plate resistance[4] r_p	4000	2000	1000	1000	1000	530	Ω
2nd-order filter Q factor[4]	0.699	0.745	0.607	0.659	0.698	0.500	
2nd-order specific frequency[4] f_o	188	167	266	242	294	697	kHz
Quality factor[4] QF	3.63	3.21	3.41	4.74	3.37	23.49	x 10^5
Quality decade factor[4] QDF	5.56	5.50	5.53	5.68	5.53	6.37	
Tuning factor[4] TF	1.35	1.71	3.13	1.91	2.67	2.14	
Tuning decade factor[4] TDF	0.134	0.232	0.495	0.282	0.427	0.330	
Frequency decade factor[5] FDF	5.70	5.47	6.03	5.96	5.95	6.70	

1) Measured and calculated with balanced DC currents and AC anode voltages.
2) Maximum value of the primary inductance, measured across the secondary with a 50 or 60 Hz sine wave.
3) Measured and calculated at 1 mW in Z_L, assuming r_p and Z_L to be resistive.
4) See: Menno van der Veen, 'Theory and Practice of Wide Bandwidth Toroidal Output Transformers', 97th AES Convention, San Francisco, 1994. Preprint number 3887-(G2).
5) $FDF = \log (f_{-3dBH}/f_{-3dBL})$ = number of frequency decades transferred.

▲ **Table 8.3** Specifications of the Specialist toroidal output transformers.

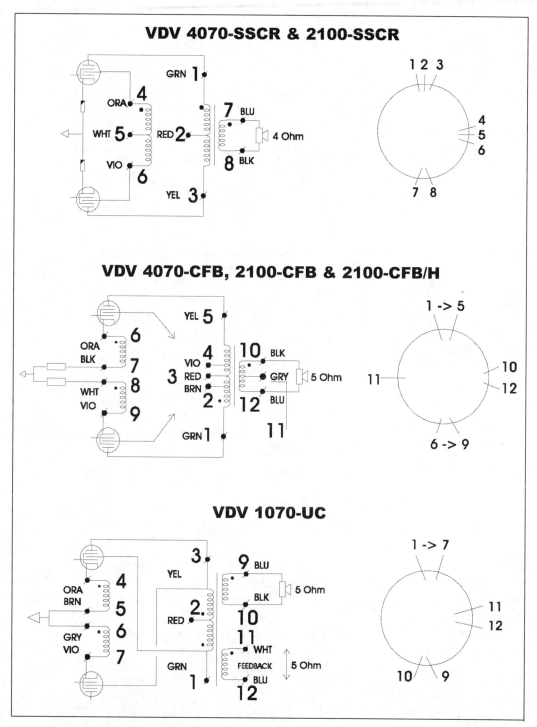

▲ *Figure 8.18* Wiring diagrams of the Specialist toroidal output transformers.

Single-Ended Toroidal Output Transformers

As the name already suggests, a single-ended (SE) valve amplifier utilizes a single power valve to drive the output transformer. There is no compensation for the quiescent current that flows through the output valve and the transformer, so the core of the transformer has a persistent 'static' magnetization. On top of this static magnetization, the core must be able to accommodate the fluctuating magnetic field induced by the varying current that flows through the output valve when it is driven by an audio signal. In order to accomplish this, the construction of the output transformer must be more complex than usual. In this chapter I discuss what is required from an SE transformer and how to fine tune its interaction with the output valve. In addition, I introduce three special SE toroidal output transformers, together with calculations of their frequency responses and power bandwidths.

9.1 | You can't argue about taste

Single-ended (SE) amplifiers are hot — again! These amplifiers are very popular and can be found in the most exquisite high-end installations. As always, the enthusiasts and their opponents are equally vociferous. Those who dislike SE amplifiers are quick to point out that they do not show up well in measurements: the power yield and damping factor are both relatively small, and the distortion percentages are downright unflattering. In most designs, not even the vaguest attempt is made to reduce distortion by means of feedback. Harmonic distortion levels of a few percent are not uncommon. In spite of all these objections, these amplifiers are finding more and more appreciation. Compared to the 'tight' sound of a transistor amplifier or a balanced valve amplifier with negative feedback, the sound of SE amplifiers tend to more spacious and 'open', with outstanding tonal balance. The combination of highly detailed reproduction and a total absence of aggressiveness is something that particularly impresses listeners.

One aspect of the discussions between fans and opponents that particularly strikes the weary observer is the language used. The first group tends to talk about

SE amplifiers in terms suitable for describing a musical instrument, idiosyncrasies and all. The opponents, on the other hand – adherents of the 'straight wire with gain' philosophy – point out that the predominantly second harmonic distortion adds a phoney lustre to the sound, so goodbye hi fidelity, there it goes out the window.

Most people do not realize that we have been raised on SE amplifiers. In the old days nearly everybody owned a wireless set, which contained a single power valve and a tiny output transformer to boot, yielding 'miniwatts'. In spite of that, our parents kept telling us to 'turn it down!' — just when we were listening to the latest Beatles tune! And guess what — did anyone ever complain about the sound quality of those radios? Complaints came only later, when transistor amplifiers arrived on the scene. It has taken decades of improvement before these amplifiers have finally started to sound right.

The old-timers who liked the good sound of SE amplifiers were not overly impressed by measurements and 'wire-with-gain' theories. Their number has not diminished; on the contrary, this group is more alive than ever before. In this light, discussions about the intrinsic worth of SE amplifiers – distortion and all – are just senseless; what counts is that people like their sound, and yes, you cannot argue about taste!

9.2 | The basic circuit diagram of an SE amplifier

Figure 9.1 depicts the essential parts of an SE amplifier, which are the components around the output valve and transformer. A triode is often used in the power stage of an SE amplifier. Types such as the 300B, 845 and 211, which are readily available at present, are commonly used. In this introductory diagram, the triode is biased by a cathode resistor shunted by a high quality capacitor. The quiescent current I_0 through the valve flows through this resistor, causing a voltage drop across it and therefore a positive voltage on the cathode. The grid is connected to ground potential via the grid resistor R_g. This means that the grid is negative with respect to the cathode. The magnitude of the negative voltage determines the quiescent or bias current through the valve.

The bias current can also be set by connecting the cathode to ground and feeding the grid resistor from a negative power supply, thereby generating the negative grid voltage. Whatever method is used, the general principle depicted in Figure 9.1 still holds. The

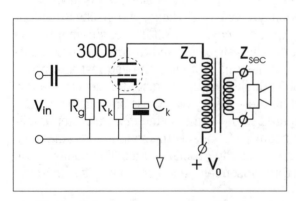

▲ **Figure 9.1**
Basic circuit diagram of an SE amplifier.

anode is connected to the primary of the output transformer. The 'top' of the primary is fed from the high voltage power supply V_0. The quiescent current of the power valve thus flows through the entire primary, producing a static magnetization of the transformer core. This is very different from the situation in a balanced amplifier, where the equal quiescent currents of the two amplifier halves flow in opposite directions through the primary to yield a net magnetic effect of zero. The core of an SE transformer has a static magnetization, while in a properly adjusted balanced amplifier it does not.

When an AC voltage – here comes the music! – is connected to the grid of the power valve, the anode current starts to vary around its quiescent value I_0. The core of the SE transformer must now accommodate a combination of two magnetic fields without saturating: the static field, generated by the bias current, and the alternating field that results from the AC voltage. I have more to say about this further on.

9.3 | Characteristics of a single-ended power valve

A triode valve amplifies due to the variation of the anode current as a function of the grid potential. This holds true for both balanced amplifiers and single-ended amplifiers. Figure 9.2 depicts the 'calculated' characteristics of a 300B power valve. In this diagram, the voltage between the anode and the cathode (V_{ak}) is plotted against the anode current I_a. Each ascending curve corresponds to a constant negative grid voltage V_{gk}, as can be read from the small numerals at the top.

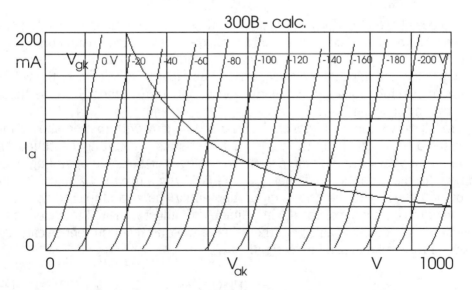

▲ *Figure 9.2* *Calculated characteristics of a 300B triode.*

A single descending curve is also plotted in Figure 9.2. This depicts the maximum anode dissipation P_{max}. In the case of the 300B, this dissipation amounts to 40 watts. For every value of V_{ak} there is therefore a maximum allowable anode current $I_{a,max}$, given by:

$$I_{a,max} = \frac{P_{max}}{V_{ak}} \qquad [9\text{-}1]$$

Regardless of the bias current applied to the 300B, this dissipation limit may not be exceeded — at least not for a prolonged interval. Every selected combination of voltage and current must fit under the maximum dissipation curve; this is called the *safe operating area*.

9.4 | Calculating the operating point

Using a simple example, I will explain how to bias a triode power valve and what value to choose for the primary impedance of the SE output transformer. This example uses a 300B, as in the previous section.

Designing an amplifier is always a matter of making choices, and here comes the first one: what are $V_{ak,0}$ and I_0 to be? The first quantity is the *quiescent voltage*, which is the voltage between the anode and the cathode when no input signal is present. The second quantity is the associated *quiescent current*.

In this example, I have chosen the quiescent operating point as:

$$V_{ak,0} = 400\text{ V}, \ I_0 = 80\text{ mA}; \ P_{a0} = V_{ak,0} \cdot I_{a0} = 32\text{ W} \qquad [9\text{-}2]$$

The values chosen for $V_{ak,0}$ and I_0 are based on the following considerations: (a) the valve must be biased somewhere in the middle of its characteristic curves, with ample room to move both 'up and down' and 'left and right'; (b) the anode dissipation must stay below the maximum dissipation limit and (c) I have to respect the voltage and current specifications of whatever power-supply transformer I have gathering dust on the shelf and can use for this project.

Figure 9.3 shows the characteristics of the 300B again, with the the chosen bias point marked by a dot. Using the valve characteristics, we can now estimate the value of the negative grid voltage needed to achieve the selected operating point. Reading from the graph, we see that $V_{gk,0} = -86$ V. If we use the basic circuit diagram of Figure 9.1, with the grid at ground potential, the next step is to determine the value of the cathode resistor R_k. Its voltage drop must be +86 V to generate the required bias. We combine this with the value of the quiescent current to calculate the value of R_k and its maximum dissipation:

$$R_k = \frac{V_{gk,0}}{I_0} = \frac{86\text{ V}}{80\text{ mA}} = 1075\ \Omega; \ P_{Rk} = I_0^2 R_k = 6.9\text{ W} \qquad [9\text{-}3]$$

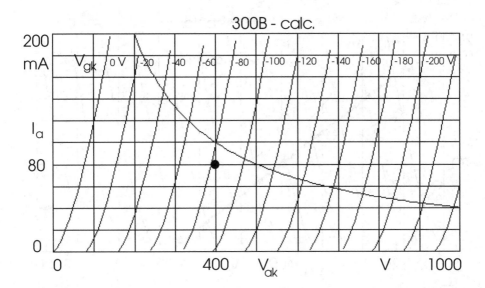

▲ **Figure 9.3** *300B triode characteristics with the quiescent operating point.*

Now we have all the information we need to calculate the power supply voltage. This amounts to:

$$V_0 = V_{ak,0} + |V_{gk,0}| = 400 + 86 = 486 \text{ V} \qquad [9\text{-}4]$$

Thus we see that the supply voltage and current for this amplifier – after rectification, filtering and perhaps stabilization – must be 486 V and 80 mA, respectively. If the available power transformer cannot supply these values, we must choose a new operating point and redo the calculations to fit the transformer. However, the power transformer is not the only factor to be considered when optimizing the design, as is shown below. Indeed, the design procedure is a kind of 'loop' that can be iterated numerous times to reach a closer approximation to the ideal. There is thus a sort of feedback in SE amplifiers after all — at least in the design phase!

The next calculation has a surprising result. It turns out that choosing the bias point determines both the primary impedance Z_a of the output transformer and the amplification of the power valve. This can be demonstrated by first considering that the current flowing through the triode will fluctuate between certain boundaries; it will never be less than 0 mA and it will never exceed $(2 \cdot 80) = 160$ mA. Why is this? As long as the current changes in direct proportion to the grid voltage, the amplifier will not distort. This proportionality implies that a decrease or increase of the grid voltage must produce a corresponding increase or decrease of the anode current. In real life, this relationship does not hold completely, especially at the extremes. This produces some distortion. However, it is prudent to assume a proportional relation-

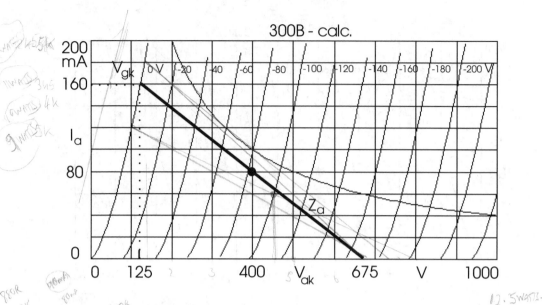

▲ **Figure 9.4** *Estimating the power limits and Z_a.*

ship between the grid voltage and the anode current when designing an amplifier, since this will minimize the distortion.

As a consequence, we know the maximum anode current to be 160 mA. We use this knowledge in Figure 9.4 to find the intersection point of the horizontal line at 160 mA and the leftmost triode curve, which corresponds to a grid voltage of 0 V. This intersection marks the second characteristic point of the amplifier-to-be. Notice that the corresponding anode-to-cathode voltage V_{ak} can also be read on the horizontal axis (via the dotted vertical line) This amounts to 125 V. The combined properties of the second characteristic point thus become:

maximum anode current point: I_a = 160 mA, V_{ak} = 125 V, V_{gk} = 0 V   [9-5]

We next estimate the third characteristic point by drawing a straight line starting at our newly found point and passing through the quiescent operating point. This line extends to the right, where it intersects the horizontal axis at the point where the anode current I_a has diminished to zero. We can read the following values from the graph:

minimum anode current point: I_a = 0 mA, V_{ak} = 675 V, V_{gk} = −172 V   [9-5]

The line between the maximum and minimum I_a points defines the primary impedance of the output transformer. If this impedance is constant, the anode current and voltage will both change proportionally. This implies that the secondary load, the loudspeaker, must have constant impedance as well! The slope of the line we have drawn shows this relationship: a change in the anode voltage corresponds to a change in the anode current, and the ratio of the voltage change to the current change is the impedance:

$$Z_a = \frac{675 - 125}{160 - 0} = \frac{550 \text{ V}}{160 \text{ mA}} = 3438 \ \Omega \qquad [9\text{-}7]$$

The primary impedance of the output transformer thus should be approximately 3.4 kΩ. This need not be exact (constant loudspeaker impedance anyone? That would be the day!). A suitable transformer would be the VDV-3035-SE, which has a primary impedance of 3.5 kΩ.

We have generated a lot of useful information by finding these values. If we assume that the losses in the output transformer can be ignored, we can now calculate the output power according to Formula 9-8:

$$P_{out} = (0.5)(400 - 125)(160 - 80) = (0.5)(275 \text{ V})(80 \text{ mA}) = 11 \text{ W} \qquad [9\text{-}8]$$

The output power equals the effective anode voltage multiplied by the effective anode current. The anode voltage varies between +275 V and –275 V, referred to 400 V. The effective value is thus $(275 \div \sqrt{2})$ V. In the same vein, the effective value of the AC current is $(80 \div \sqrt{2})$ mA. These two figures multiplied together give us Formula 9-8. There are other ways to calculate this, such as $P_{out} = V_{ak}^2/Z_a$ and so on.

There is yet more; we now know the amplification of the system as well. We can deduce from Figure 9.4 that it takes 86 volts on the grid to change the anode voltage by 275 V. The valve amplification is thus:

$$A_{ga} = \frac{V_a}{V_g} = \frac{275 \text{ V}}{86 \text{ V}} = 3.2 \qquad [9\text{-}9]$$

If we know the secondary impedance of the output transformer, we can calculate the voltage transformation ratio from the anode to the loudspeaker. This is equal to the square root of the ratio of the primary and secondary impedances. The VDV-3035-SE toroidal transformer has a secondary impedance of 4 or 8 Ω. If we assume that we use the 4 Ω tap, we can combine the transformer ratio with the result of Formula 9-9 to calculate the net amplification from the grid to the loudspeaker, as shown in Formula 9-10:

$$A_{tot} = A_{ga} \cdot A_{trf} = 3.2 \cdot \sqrt{\frac{4}{3500}} = 3.2 \cdot \frac{1}{29.6} = 0.108 \qquad [9\text{-}10]$$

$$\eta = \frac{P_{out}}{P_{a0}} = \frac{11 \text{ W}}{32 \text{ W}} = 34\% \qquad [9\text{-}11]$$

The efficiency η of the amplifier is defined in Formula 9-11:

We can now make some predictions regarding the distortion of the amplifier. Distortion occurs when the anode voltage does not change in exact proportion to the grid voltage. The amount of deviation is a measure of the distortion. In our example thus far, the proportionality is perfect, but in reality things are different. The main cause of this is the skewing of the valve characteristics at low anode currents. Some of this can be seen in the calculated response of the 300B, but as these curves are derived from a model and are therefore rather idealized, the distortion appears to be small.

We can estimate the internal resistance r_i of the 300B valve from the slope of its characteristic curves; this is approximately 700 Ω. We can combine this value with the primary and secondary impedances of the output transformer to calculate the output impedance Z_{out} and the damping factor DF of this SE amplifier. (Note that if $Z_{sec} = Z_L$ then $DF = Z_a/r_i$.)

$$Z_{out} = r_i \cdot \frac{Z_{sec}}{Z_a} = 700 \cdot \frac{4}{3500} = 0.8 \ \Omega \qquad \text{[9-12a]}$$

$$DF = \frac{Z_L}{Z_{out}} = \frac{4}{0.8} = 5 \qquad \text{[9-12b]}$$

This concludes our discussion of the calculations for a single-ended amplifier. Our example has shown that we can use a limited number of characteristic values for the valve and output transformer to calculate a myriad of properties before we actually start building. However, these calculations are just the initial phase in the process of designing a single-ended amplifier. We must verify that the calculated operating point is the best one possible for a given configuration. 'Massaging' the parameters, which means trying other values of the supply voltage, bias point and so on, may yield better results, depending on the requirements of the application. The design can be optimized for minimum distortion or maximum output power. With the calculation tools given here, you can choose any combination you like.

9.5 | Properties of single-ended output transformers

The requirements for single-ended output transformers are more numerous and more stringent than those for balanced output transformers. The primary consideration is that an SE output transformer must transform AC voltages, but there is also the factor of the static magnetization. In order to achieve good low frequency response, the primary inductance must be large. The high frequency response depends on the leakage inductance and the effective primary capacitance. The wiring resistances of the primary and secondary windings must be low to avoid losses, the flux density in the core cannot be made too high without causing distortion, the number of turns in the primary winding must be just right in order to properly transform the input power, the core metal must behave as linearly as possible — the list is virtually endless. Needless to say, all of these factors obey the law of conservation of aggravation, which means that collectively most of them represent diametrically opposed requirements! Developing a single-ended toroidal output transformer is therefore much more difficult than developing a similar balanced transformer. In this chapter I present an exposé of the properties of our 'specialist' series of single-ended toroidal output transformers.

Table 9.1, located at the end of this chapter, lists the specifications of three transformer models: the VDV-3025-SE, VDV-3035-SE and VDV-3050-SE. The last two digits of the model number indicate the primary impedance, which is thus 2.5 kΩ, 3.5 kΩ and 5.0 kΩ, respectively. The first two digits are production codes. Experiments with the 300B valve have shown that good operating conditions can be achieved with primary impedances in the range of 2.5 to 5 kΩ, which is why this transformer series has been designed for this range. In the future, the range will be extended with a high-impedance transformer – 10 kΩ! – that will also allow higher output power. For more information, refer to the list of importers and suppliers at the end of the book.

The properties of the single-ended transformer series are explained in the following subsections.

9.5.1 | Low frequency behaviour and power

In Chapter 5 I presented a method to calculate the frequency response for a given combination of power valve and output transformer. The formulas derived there can be used again, as long as we take into consideration that we have one output valve instead of two. As the total source impedance of a balanced amplifier equals the internal resistance of both valves, we have $R_g = 2r_i$. If we replace R_g with the internal resistance of a single triode, we have adapted the formula to the new configuration. The characteristics of the 300B valve and the VDV-3035-SE transformer are used in the following calculations.

The low frequency –3 dB point is determined by the primary inductance L_p, the primary impedance Z_a and the internal resistance r_i. This yields the following expression (see also Formulas 5-12 and 5-3):

$$f_{-3L} = \frac{Z_a}{2\pi L_p} \cdot \frac{\beta}{\beta + 1} \qquad \text{where } \beta = \frac{r_i}{Z_a} \qquad [9\text{-}13]$$

We know the following: $Z_a = 3.5$ kΩ; $L_p = 28$ H; $r_i = 700$ Ω. Inserting these figures into Formula 9-13 yields $f_{-3L} = 3.3$ Hz. The specification is 3.5 Hz, and the small difference is caused by roundoff errors. The frequency response thus starts at 3.3 Hz, a value that has been chosen deliberately low during the design to minimize distortion in the core.

The specifications show another low frequency figure: f_{Pnom} = 20 Hz. This relates to the power bandwidth of the transformer; at 20 Hz the transformer can handle a nominal power of 13 watts. This a conservative estimate; in practice the transformer can handle 1.4 times this amount (18 watts) before the core starts to saturate. Why the modest specification? Well, better safe than sorry! This way we have a wide safety margin, within which the transformer will operate cleanly. Unfortunately, deriving these figures with the given information is not possible; they are the outcome of a set of complex calculations made during the design process for the transformer, based on the magnetic properties of the core material.

Which frequency now limits the lower −3 dB power bandwidth? This is easy as pie; see Formula 9-14:

$$f_{-3dB,power} = \frac{f_{Pnom}}{\sqrt{2}}$$ [9-14]

Plugging in the numbers yields $f_{-3\,dB,\,power}$ = 14 Hz. Due to the large core size in the VDV-SE series, the power bandwidth starts at a low frequency. Clean, undistorted bass is a prime objective with single-ended amplifiers, just as with any other type.

9.5.2 | High frequency behaviour

At high frequencies, the behaviour of the transformer mainly depends on the leakage inductance L_{sp} and the effective internal capacitance C_{ip}. The primary inductance does not come into the picture here. Refer to Formulas 5-11, 5-10, 5-15 and 5-13. The result is:

$$\alpha = \frac{1}{Z_a} \cdot \sqrt{\frac{L_{sp}}{C_{ip}}} = \frac{1}{3500} \cdot \sqrt{\frac{7 \times 10^{-3}}{1.1 \times 10^{-9}}} = 0.721$$ [9-15]

$$a_2 = \alpha \cdot \sqrt{\frac{1}{\beta(\beta + 1)}} + \frac{1}{\alpha} \cdot \sqrt{\frac{\beta}{\beta + 1}} = 2.04$$ [9-16]

At this point I would like to make a small digression regarding the nature of Q. The high frequency part of the system response (due to the combination of the output transformer, the power valve and the loudspeaker) behaves like a second-order low pass filter in which the Q factor equals $1/a_2$. This yields Q = 0.491. Given roundoff errors and what have you, we can estimate the actual value to be Q = 0.5. In other words, the system is critically damped. In practice, this means placid high frequency behaviour, without overshoots and/or ringing, when the amplifier is driven by pulse-shaped signals. This was also a design goal for these transformers.

Now it's the end of the recess; let's get back to calculating the high frequency bandwidth:

$$ff(a_2) = 1.960 - 0.668\,a_2 = 0.587 \qquad\qquad [9\text{-}17]$$

Formula 5-15 can be applied under the condition that $1 \le a_2 \le 2$. The value of a_2 is just over 2 in this example, but Figure 5.3 shows that the deviation is small. As a check, we can compare the result of the estimation to the value given on the specification sheet, which is based on the exact relationships. The final result is:

$$f_{-3H} = \frac{1}{2\pi} \cdot \sqrt{\frac{1}{L_{sp}C_{ip}}} \cdot ff(a_2) \cdot \sqrt{\frac{\beta + 1}{\beta}} = 82.5 \text{ kHz} \qquad\qquad [9\text{-}16]$$

The value on the specification sheet is $f_{h3} = f_{-3H} = 89.9$ kHz. Is the difference serious? No; we already knew that Formula 5-15 can be applied under the condition that $1 \le a_2 \le 2$. If the value of a_2 is within the given range, the maximum error is 5%. The value of a_2 that we have here is slightly outside of this range, but the error is still only 8%. This matters very little for estimating the high frequency behaviour.

Figure 9.5 shows the calculated frequency response of the VDV-3035-SE output transformer in combination with the 300B power valve. Note that the actual response extends beyond 100 kHz — as noted, the specifications are conservative.

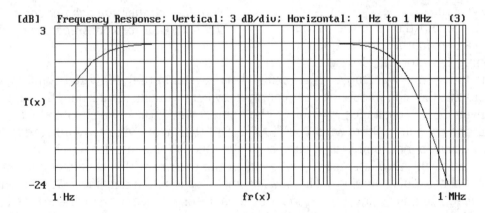

▲ *Figure 9.5*
Calculated frequency response of the 300B valve
with the VDV-3035-SE transformer

What if we use another power valve instead, such as the well-known EL34? Will this combination do equally well? The answer is no — the internal resistance of the EL34 is around 15 kΩ, and when we insert that value in the set of formulas we see the −3 dB point drop down to 35 kHz. The bottom line is that this series of transformers has been developed specifically for low-impedance power triodes. This fits the present trend, and the design has been optimized for such applications.

9.5.3 | Fine tuning the high frequency response

There is an extra item in the big bag of tricks that comes with the VDV-30xx-SE series of transformers. Every toroidal single-ended transformer allows the effective internal capacitance to be altered, thereby influencing its high frequency behaviour.

The primary winding is constructed to minimize the internal capacitance C_{ip} when the red lead is connected to the high voltage power supply and the yellow lead is connected to the anode of the power valve, as shown in Figure 9.6. However, if these connections are reversed – red to the anode and yellow to the power supply – the capacitance is increased by a factor of approximately 4. What is the purpose of this?

If the impedance of the power valve is high, the high frequency tuning Q factor will also be high,

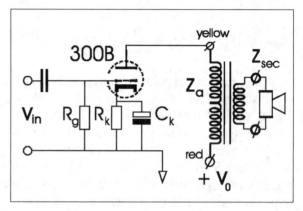

▲ *Figure 9.6*
Standard connection scheme for a VDV-30xx-SE toroidal transformer.

and the system will start to 'ring' somewhat. Reversing the yellow/red connections increases the high frequency damping, thereby substantially diminishing the ringing. If even more capacitance is required, the primary winding can be shunted by a high voltage capacitor. Start with 1 nF/1000 V and then work your way upwards. The valve-transformer combination can be exactly tuned in this manner, as a bit of experimenting will show. It is not correct to shunt the primary with a capacitor and resistor in series. This damping technique is sometimes found in amplifiers with external feedback. In this design, any need for external feedback has been deliberately eliminated, and a shunt capacitor alone will suffice. Once again, an external capacitor lowers the Q value and thus eliminates ringing.

9.5.4 | The insertion loss I_{loss}

Thus far, the quantity 'insertion loss' has been mentioned only in passing. The time has now come to discuss it in more detail. The windings of an output transformer have resistances of R_{ip} (primary) and R_{is} (secondary). When the amplifier drives an alternating current to the loudspeaker, this current also flows through the primary and secondary winding resistances, which results in dissipation. Your priceless hi-fi watts are being turned into ordinary heat! The insertion loss I_{loss} is the ratio of the effective power at the loudspeaker to the total power, expressed in dB. We can now derive the necessary formula with the aid of Figure 9.7.

The output transformer is seen from the secondary side in Figure 9.7. The primary resistance R_{ip} is thus transformed to the secondary by multiplying it by the square of the turns ratio to become $R_{ip} \cdot a^2$, where $a = N_s/N_p$ (see Formula 5-1). The total effective resistance at the secondary side is $R_T = (R_{ip}a^2 + R_{is})$. The loudspeaker impedance is Z_L.

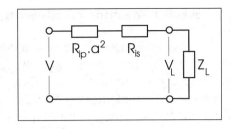

▲ **Figure 9.7**
Mid-band equivalent circuit of the transformer, for defining the insertion loss.

If we apply an AC voltage V to the transformer (as shown on the left in Figure 9.7), a current I will flow in the series circuit formed by R_T and Z_L:

$$I = \frac{V}{R_T + Z_L} \; ; \; R_T = R_{ip}a^2 + R_{is}; \; V_L = IZ_L = \frac{Z_L}{R_T + Z_L} \cdot V \qquad [9\text{-}19]$$

The resulting voltage across the loudspeaker is expressed in Formula 9-19 by V_L. The actual power developed in the loudspeaker is given by $P_L = V_L I$. The power P_{in} entering the transformer is given by $P_{in} = VI$. The efficiency η and the insertion loss are defined in Formula 9-20:

$$\eta = \frac{P_L}{P_{in}} = \frac{Z_L}{R_T + Z_L} \; ; \; I_{loss} = -10\log\eta \; [dB] \qquad [9\text{-}20]$$

These formulas can be applied to the data from the specification sheet of the VDV-3035-SE transformer, where we find the following values: $R_{ip} = 50 \; \Omega$, $R_{is} = 0.1 \; \Omega$, $a = 29.522$ and $Z_L = 4 \; \Omega$. Based on these values, we can calculate R_T to be $0.157 \; \Omega$. The efficiency is the ratio of the useful power to the total power, so $\eta = 0.962$. The insertion loss is therefore $I_{loss} = 0.168$ dB.

What does this all mean in practice? Let us assume an amplifier in which the output valve delivers 13 watts to the transformer-loudspeaker combination. Then 96.2% of 13 watts will end up in the loudspeaker, so that only 0.5 Watt is dissipated in the transformer. This is another mark of distinction of the VDV-30xx-SE series. The resistive losses are very small, thanks to the use of heavy wire. Most cheaper transformers have insertion losses of 1 dB or more. An insertion loss of 1 dB results in an effective output power $P_{out} = 10^{-0.1} \cdot P_{in} = 0.794 \cdot P_{in}$. That is a loss of almost 21%! As the output power of a single-ended amplifier is low to begin with, it is certainly not smart to waste more than absolutely necessary.

9.5.5 | Maximum allowable primary direct current

It is possible to base a design entirely on the valve characteristics, so that in principle you can choose any quiescent current you want as long as you stay below the maximum anode dissipation. However, there is a close relationship between the maximum power that the output transformer can handle, the primary impedance and the optimum quiescent current through the power valve. The most important consequence of this relationship can be found in the specification sheets of the VDV-SE output transformers. Let us again take the specifications of the VDV-3035-SE as an example. Under 'Saturation current' we find the value I_{DC} = 173 mA. When this much current flows through the primary of the transformer, the core is maximally magnetized, and actually just on the edge of saturation. The specifications are fairly conservative, as already noted, so there is probably some headroom left — but it will not be much. It is therefore not wise to choose a quiescent current that is as large as I_{DC}. The best idea is to bias the power valve at the 'optimum' quiescent current, which is defined as:

$$\text{optimum bias current} = I_0 = \frac{1}{2} \cdot I_{DC} \qquad [9\text{-}21]$$

In this case, half of the magnetic capacity of the core is used by the quiescent current and the other half is available for the audio program's currents and voltages. It is of course allowable to use a lower quiescent current than the optimum value given by Formula 9.21. Larger quiescent currents will however diminish the 'music' space. Note that with a constant output power of 13 watts, as the primary impedance Z_a increases from 2.5 kΩ through 3.5 kΩ to 5 KΩ, both I_{DC} and the optimal quiescent current I_0 decrease according to $1/\sqrt{Z_a}$.

9.5.6 | Phase distortion and differential phase distortion

Just as in the previous chapters that deal with balanced transformers, it is possible to calculate and measure the phase relationship between the primary and secondary voltages of the single-ended output transformer. Figure 9.8 depicts the phase response characteristics of the VDV-3035-SE transformer.

The phase characteristics of the SE transformers are similar to those of the balanced transformers. The phase excursions are however larger, especially at the low end. The main reason for this is the smaller primary inductance of the single-ended transformers. This results in a larger group delay at low frequencies, which causes the bass response to sound subjectively different. Time and space do not permit me to give an adequate explanation of this psychophysical phenomenon.

The differential phase distortion can be calculated for single-ended transformers as well; the results are plotted in Figure 9.9. If you recall, the differential phase distortion for balanced transformers is negligibly small up to 100 kHz, but single-ended

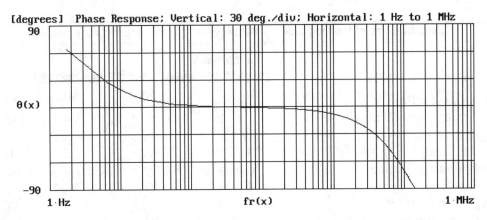

▲ *Figure 9.8* *Phase response of the VDV-3035-SE transformer.*

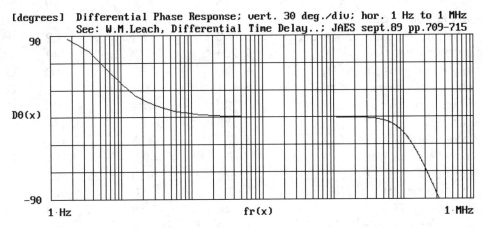

▲ *Figure 9.9* *Differential phase distortion of the VDV-3035-SE.*

transformers start to show noticeable deviations at around 50 kHz. Compared to typical audio ranges – 20 kHz standard, and around 50 kHz for high-end equipment with sampling rates of 98 kHz or even higher – this frequency is high enough that differential phase distortion can be considered negligible within the audio range. This, too, was an objective in designing this line of transformers.

9.6 | Summary

This chapter presents a series of toroidal single-ended output transformers, and explains their specifications. It also provides formulas for calculating significant factors relating to the operating bias, power and damping factor. Table 9.1 summarizes the specifications of the VDV single-ended toroidal transformers.

Specifications of the single-ended Vanderveen toriodal output transformers

	Model			
	VDV-3025-SE	VDV-3035-SE	VDV-3050-SE	
Primary impedance Z_{aa}	2491	3486	5055	Ω
Secondary impedance Z_L	4–8	4–8	4–8	Ω
Turns ratio $1/a = N_p/N_s$	24.957	29.522	35.551	
0.1 dB frequency range	23–22k	16–22k	12–20k	Hz
1 dB frequency range	10–49k	6.9–49k	5.3–45k	Hz
3 dB frequency range	5.1–91k	3.5–90k	2.7–84k	Hz
Nominal power[1] P_{nom}	13	13	13	W
Lower nominal power frequency f_{Pnom}	20	20	20	Hz
Primary inductance[2] L_p	18	28	40	H
Primary leakage inductance L_{sp}	5.5	7.0	10	mH
Effective primary capacitance Cip	1.0	1.1	1.2	nF
Saturation current I_{DC}	204	173	143	mA
Primary internal resistance R_{ip}	40	50	80	Ω
Secondary internal resistance R_{is}	0.1	0.1	0.1	Ω
Power valve plate resistance r_i	700	700	700	Ω
Insertion loss I_{loss}	0.175	0.168	0.174	dB
2nd-order filter Q factor[5] Q	0.487	0.493	0.491	
2nd-order specific frequency[5] f_o	147.2	142.5	134.1	kHz
Quality factor[5] $QF = L_p/L_{sp}$	3273	4000	4000	
Quality decade factor[5] QDF	3.5	3.6	3.6	
Tuning factor[5] TF	5.49	6.38	7.79	
Tuning decade factor[5] TDF	0.740	0.805	0.892	
Frequency decade factor[4, 5] FDF	4.26	4.41	4.49	

1) Measured and calculated for $I_0 = 0.5 I_{DC}$.
2) Measured across the entire primary winding at 230 V, 50 Hz.
3) Frequency ranges and ratios, and the secondary internal resistance, are for the 4 Ω secondary tap.
4) $FDF = \log (f_{h3}/f_{l3}) =$ number of frequency decades transferred.
5) Menno van der Veen, 'Theory and Practice of Wide Bandwith Toroidal Output Transformers', 97th AES Convention, San Francisco, 1994. Preprint 3887-(G2).

Note: specifications subject to change due to improvements resulting from ongoing research.

▲ **Table 9.1** *Specifications of the VDV-SE-30xx toroidal output transformers.*

10

Building a Push-Pull Valve Amplifier: the Phase Splitter

This chapter discusses the first of the basic circuits needed to build a push-pull valve amplifier. We examine the phase splitter, which drives the output valves, concentrating on how the phase splitter works and the limitations of our circuit. This chapter is especially useful for the DIYer, because it is full of practical tips. There are examples of various types of phase splitters at the end of the chapter.

10.1 | Avoiding core saturation

The reason that a push-pull amplifier (using valves) needs a phase splitter can be found in the construction of the output transformer. It is driven by a pair of output valves, whose anodes are connected to the ends of the primary winding, while the power supply for the output valves is connected to the middle of the primary winding. If you look at Figure 10.1, you will see that a number of direct and alternating currents are indicated by arrows and sine waves, respectively.

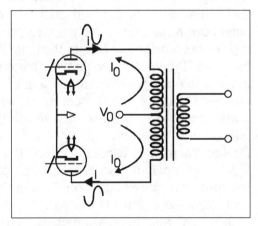

▲ *Figure 10.1*
Direct and alternating currents in the output transformer.

Examining the direct currents, we notice a few interesting things. Clearly, the direct current originates at the middle of the transformer. It then branches; one part flows up and the other flows down the winding. Both branch currents are equal if the output valves are set up properly, and obviously both currents create magnetic fields in the two halves of the primary winding. Now comes something remarkable: the magnetic fields oppose each other, because the currents flow in opposite directions. If everything is set up properly, we can even reduce the total effective magnetic field to zero.

This leads to the following important conclusion: the direct currents needed to operate the output valves create a zero net magnetic field in the primary winding. It follows that (in principle) we can use a small core, because saturation cannot take place without a magnetic field. Saturation occurs, as shown in Figure 10.2, when the magnetic particles in the core are all pointing in the same direction. This means that the core cannot be magnetized any further, because all the particles are already facing the same way. Saturating the core is an undesirable effect, since it means that we have reached the limits of the transformer. We then cannot put any more into it or take any more out.

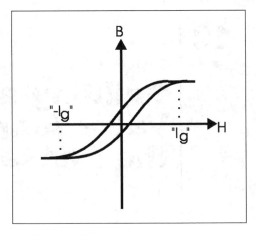

▲ *Figure 10.2*
Core saturation occurs when the current level exceeds I_g.

Now for the second remarkable fact: if we can ensure that the 'music' creates a net magnetic field in the core, then a current will flow in the secondary winding, and this in turn will drive the loudspeaker. In order for this to happen, the 'music' current must flow in the same direction through both halves of the primary winding, so that it produces a magnetic field in the core. This situation is depicted by the sine waves in Figure 10.1. We can see directly that the sine wave at the top of the primary winding and the sine wave at the bottom of the winding are opposite to each other. In other words, if the current from the upper anode increases then the current from the lower anode decreases (and vice versa). The top will then become more positive and the bottom will become less positive. In this situation, an alternating current will flow through the primary winding, causing the core to be magnetized.

We can conclude from this that in a push-pull amplifier, the direct currents from the output valves pass through the transformer such that their magnetic fields cancel each other, while the alternating voltages (the music) should be applied to the ends of the transformer in opposite phase to each other. The alternating voltages will then produce an effective magnetic field, which will induce a secondary voltage to drive the loudspeakers.

10.2 | The function of the phase splitter

The phase splitter has to divide the alternating voltage audio signal into two equal and opposite alternating voltage signals. This is illustrated in Figure 10.3.

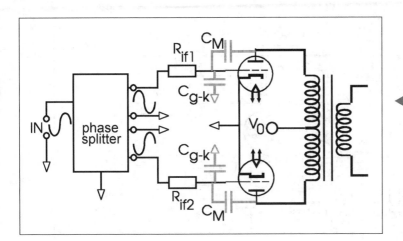

◀ *Figure 10.3*
The phase splitter
generates opposite-
phase signals.

If the output signals of the phase splitter are connected to the control grids of the output valves, signals will be produced on the anodes that are opposite to each other. This is exactly what is needed to drive the output transformer as it should be.

There are plenty of circuits available that can perform the task of phase splitting. In the early days, transformers with opposed windings were employed to 'automatically' produce opposite-polarity signals. Later on, valve circuits were used, and a lot of clever tricks were developed. We do not intend to discuss all these different circuits, but we will discuss one circuit which the do-it-yourselfer can use as a basis for his or her own designs. This circuit has proven its worth in many amplifiers over the years. It has a wide frequency range and can provide large output voltages (which are necessary for driving the output valves in the best manner). We would like to stress again that this is not the only circuit capable of doing this. Many tricks and clever feats are possible, but the circuit discussed in this chapter amply serves its purpose, and it sounds fantastic.

10.3 | Phase splitter circuit diagram

The circuit diagram of the phase splitter is shown in Figure 10.4 with component values, including resistor power ratings. The numbers next to the valve symbols in the diagram refer to the pin numbering of the valve base.

We employ a type ECC82 (12AU7) valve, which is widely available and has several good qualities needed for its function here. In principle, we could also use an ECC81 (12AT7). The latter type can amplify signals up to four times as much as the ECC82. This amount of amplification may be needed for some applications.

One half of the ECC82 is configured as a preamplifier, with an amplification factor of 14. The anode of the first triode is connected directly to the grid of the second triode. This grid thus carries exactly the same DC voltage and alternating voltage as the anode of the first triode.

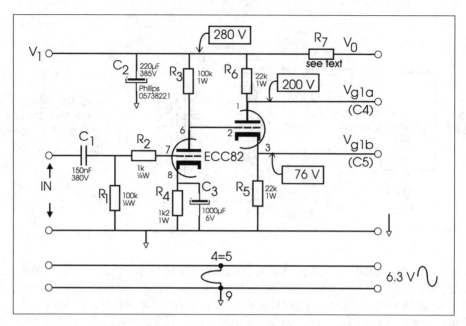

▲ **Figure 10.4** *Phase splitter circuit diagram.*

In the diagram, we can see that the values of the anode and cathode resistors of the second triode are equal. This is the little secret that makes this circuit perform so well. How does it work? When an alternating current flows through the second triode, it also flows through the anode and cathode resistors. Since these resistors are equal, the alternating voltages across them will also be equal but opposite. If the valve has been properly set up, no current will ever flow through the grid. This is different from a transistor, which always has a base current that can produce aberrations in this type of circuit. It is clear that the alternating voltages at the anode and the cathode are equal by design. We can easily use this circuit for a phase splitter.

10.4 | Requirements and adjustments: the supply voltage

Certain conditions must be met if this circuit is to work properly. A number of output valve configurations that can be driven by the phase splitter are discussed in Chapter 11. The output valves require various supply voltages, while the phase splitter works best at 280 V (see also Sections 10.9 and Chapter 14 for a version of this phase splitter with a 350 V supply). Now, how can we ensure that this requirement will be satisfied?

The phase splitter is powered via resistor R_7, located at the top right of Figure 10.4. We know the supply voltage and current needed by the phase splitter. Suppose we have already selected a set of valves and an associated output transformer (see

Chapter 11), so that the value of the supply voltage is defined. If we label this supply voltage V_0, we can calculate the value of R_7 as follows:

$$R_7 = \frac{V_0 - 280}{0.0057} \quad [\Omega] \qquad\qquad [10\text{-}1]$$

The denominator, 0.0057, is the current in ampères that flows through the phase splitter. The amount of power that the resistor must be able to handle is:

$$P_{R7} = (V_0 - 280)(0.0057) \quad [\text{W}] \qquad\qquad [10\text{-}2]$$

For example, suppose we choose a 30 watt amplifier using two EL34s. The supply voltage is then 380 V. R_7 is then equal to:

$$R_7 = \frac{380 - 280}{0.0057} = 17{,}544 \ \Omega \qquad\qquad [10\text{-}3]$$

In practice, the value of the resistance is not critical, so a value of 18 kΩ will do. The power dissipated by the resistor is then:

$$P_{R7} = (380 - 280)(0.0057) = 0.57 \ \text{W} \qquad\qquad [10\text{-}4]$$

To minimize the risk that the resistor will burn out (in the long term), it is a good idea to 'overspecify'; thus a 1 W, 18 kΩ resistor is a sensible choice in this case. Other examples can easily be calculated using this method.

10.5 | The capacitors

The input capacitor C_1 is shown at the far left side of the circuit diagram in Figure 10.4. Its function is to block any DC voltage coming from the preamplifier (see Chapter 15; if the preamplifier described there is used then this capacitor is essential). Most modern preamplifiers do not have DC voltages at their outputs, which means that C_1 is not necessary in most cases. If we take the attitude that any capacitor can affect the signal quality, then it is a good idea not to use C_1 if it is not needed.

Now on to the most important capacitor, C_2. The make and type number of this capacitor are given. Here we employ modern capacitors developed by Philips for a new series of switching power supplies, types 05738221 and 05758221. These capacitors have excellent frequency response and a relatively large capacity to volume ratio. Capacitor C_2 works in conjunction with R_7 to eliminate the ripple voltage originating from the power supply. This aspect is very important, since this circuit is asymmetrical with regard to ground and the supply voltage. Every ripple voltage component from the power supply will lie in the audio range, so the large capacitance of C_2 is vital.

Capacitor C_3 acts together with the cathode resistor R_4 to short circuit any AC voltage at the cathode. There are many complicated mathematical models that can be used to calculate the value of C_3. The value of R_4 as well as the internal resistance and conversion conductance of the ECC82 must be taken into account in these calculations. We have chosen a value of 1000 µF to guarantee that the necessary conditions will be met. Aside from this, even good capacitors are still cheap, so a bit of overkill won't do any harm.

The phase splitter ouputs are connected to the power stage via capacitors C_4 and C_5, which are not shown in Figure 10.4. The quality of these capacitors must be excellent, since they carry the signals to the grids of the output valves and thus have a significant effect on the sound quality. Experimentation and optimization are thus recommended. See Chapter 11 regarding the values and placement of C_4 and C_5.

10.6 | Some remarks about grounding

The phase splitter circuit can be constructed on a PCB, but here we assume that the phase splitter will be hand wired. This means we will use 'real' wires and define our own ground points. Fortunately, the latter is easily done with this phase splitter. The ground connections (including that for C_2) should all be gathered together to form a single 'star' ground point located next to the base of the ECC82 valve. The influence of this star ground is significant (and positive) — in other words, this is an important aspect!

10.7 | The filament supply

It is a good idea to also ground the filament (pin 9 of the valve base) to the star ground point. The ECC82 filament is powered by a 6.3 V, 50 Hz AC voltage. The connoisseurs among you will change this to a DC voltage, a choice we will not argue with. This type of change falls into the category of 'optimization', which is covered later on in this book. In this area the do-it-yourselfer can implement his or her own creative ideas, and the I do not wish to deprive the reader of his or her enjoyment.

Recently, circuits and constructions have appeared in which the voltage across the filament has been lowered to 4 V instead of the usual 6.3 V. The argument used to defend this is that life of the valve is extended with a lower voltage. The author strongly disagrees with this reasoning. It may be true that the life of the *filament* is lengthened, but a lower filament voltage has additional consequences, such as lower emission and a different internal resistance (and therefore a different amplification factor). This cannot be what was intended. What is even worse, and seems to have been overlooked, is that the cathode has an optimum working temperature at which the effects of residual gases in the valve can be held in check. The residual gases are gradually removed by the silver-coloured 'getter' material that coats the inside surface of the glass. If the cathode is at the wrong temperature then the getter material is also at the wrong temperature, which means that the cathode may become poisoned. This can lead to total valve disfunction. Of course, voltages exceeding 6.3 V are not beneficial, because the filament's life may be shortened. To summarize: just use the recommended 6.3 V. In any case, the manufacturer has optimized the valve's construction and characteristics for this voltage.

10.8 | Caution: high frequencies

Suppose that we have just finished constructing our amplifier and everything is working smoothly. We then carefully select several pieces of measuring equipment from the abundant supply scattered around the room, just to check whether the author has been telling us the truth. Suppose we want to measure the frequency range of the signals that drive the grids of the output valves. We naturally use a 10:1 probe with a very small internal capacitance, to avoid loading the circuit. With our eyes glued to the oscilloscope screen, we expectantly await the first results.

What do we see? To our amazement, it appears that someone has been pulling our leg all along. At high frequencies, the cathode output voltage V_{g1b} is greater than V_{g1a} (see Figure 10.4). This cannot be true, since it was explicitly stated that the AC voltage across R_6 is equal to the AC voltage across R_5. What's going on?

Although this riddle has a simple solution, it could easily be put in the puzzle section of a periodical, with a trip around the world for the lucky winner. Unfortunately, there is no prize to win. In order to quiet the chorus of questions, I present the answer here.

The output impedance of the phase splitter is higher at the anode (V_{g1a}) than at the cathode (V_{g1b}). In fact, we can imagine this higher output impedance to be equivalent to a 10 kΩ resistor in series with the output (V_{g1a}). This resistor forms a low pass filter in conjunction with the input capacitance of the power valve connected to V_{g1a}. This attenuates high frequencies (above 100 kHz). The cathode connection V_{g1b} has a low output impedance, so the input capacitance of the output valve has less effect. We cannot eliminate this effect by modifying the valve setup, but we can clear it up by simply placing a 10 kΩ resistor in series with V_{g1b}. This will make the phase splitter source resistances equal for both of the output valves, so that the asymmetry at high frequencies will disappear. If you are bothered by this effect (which is hardly noticeable), then you can alleviate the problem by simply adding a single resistor to the circuit.

10.9 | The phase splitter with a different supply voltage

Chapters 11 and 14 discuss the most recent developments regarding this phase splitter, as build on a PCB for the 70 W and 100 W push-pull power amplifiers. While developing these amplifiers, we noticed that we could improve the phase splitter circuit. The amplitude of the phase splitter output signals can be increased by raising its supply voltage from 280 V to 350 V, thus improving the drive capabilities of the circuit. With a 350 V supply voltage, the current drawn by the phase splitter is 7.1 mA. For the 70 W power amplifier configuration, this means:

$$R_7 = 3.9 \text{ k}\Omega, 1 \text{ W} \qquad \text{(70 watt amplifier)}$$

With the 100 W amplifier, the supply voltage of the power section is higher, so the optimum value for R7 is:

$$R_7 = 12 \text{ k}\Omega, 1 \text{ W} \qquad \text{(100 watt amplifier)}$$

A value of 12 kΩ is also the best choice for the 80 Watt triode amplifier.

10.10 | Examples of other types of phase splitters

A few examples of various types of phase splitters are shown in Figure 10.5, to help you if you want to make your own phase splitter. I do not want to cover all possible phase splitter designs, but I would like to point you in the right direction by illustrating a few ideas and concepts. The resistor values are indicative; you must work out the details for yourself. Good luck!

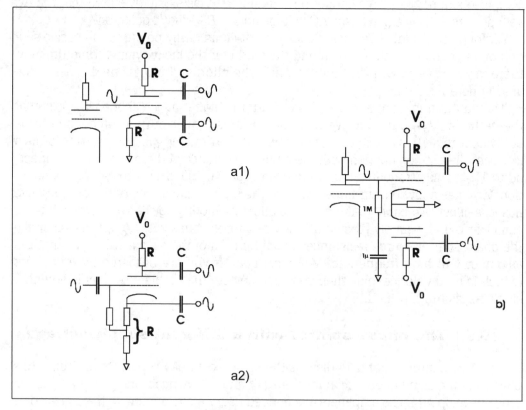

▲ **Figure 10.5** *Alternative phase splitter circuits (part 1 of 2).*

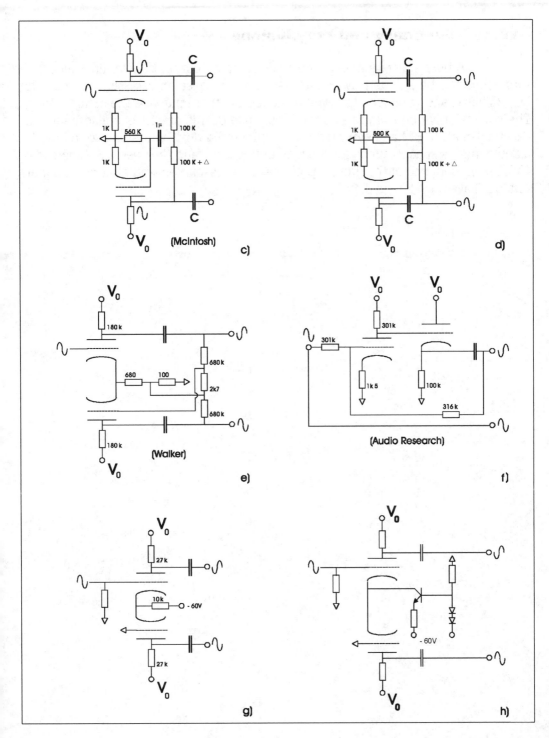

▲ **Figure 10.5** *Alternative phase splitter circuits (part 2 of 2).*

10.11 | Summary and conclusions

A push-pull circuit is very beneficial for the output transformer, since core saturation can be avoided. We have discussed a phase splitter that employs an ECC82 valve, and we have highlighted the factors that influence the sound quality. The surprisingly good high frequency response of this circuit has also been discussed. An attempt has been made to convince the do-it-yourselfer to follow the manufacturer's specifications for the filament voltage (and thus use 6.3 V instead of 4 V). The importance of the ground point has been discussed, and alternative supply voltages have been touched on.

11

Building a Push-Pull Valve Amplifier: from 10 to 100 Watts

This chapter is especially useful for the DIYer. It presents several power amplifier circuits that can be built using the standard series of VDV transformers. For each transformer model, an amplifier circuit that can be driven by the phase splitter described in Chapter 10 is discussed.

11.1 | Decisions, decisions, decisions

It is impractical to give a detailed description of each power amplifier. A much thicker book would be needed for this (and a lot more reading!). We take a more general approach, which is to first describe the basic amplifier circuit and the output transformer connections. After this, we describe the individual amplifiers in turn, with attention to component values and specific features.

When choosing the basic circuit, the general design is not much of a problem. Selecting the method used to set the optimum operating point of the output valves is more difficult. Many different approaches are possible, such as:

- using a negative grid voltage (NGV),
- using a cathode resistor, so the valve automatically finds its optimum working point (auto-bias),
- automatic setup, using a current source in the cathode lead,
- automatically adjusting the negative grid voltage varied according to the measured cathode current,
- combinations of the above methods, and
- last but not least: clever solutions thought up by the individual designer.

Clearly, there are many possible solutions. I have chosen the first approach, which is to use a negative grid voltage to set the operating point. This has several advantages: the circuitry is simple and exactly the same for every type of power amplifier, any type of valve can be used, and the valves need not be matched. These arguments should be enough to convince us that this approach is the most elegant solution.

We must make another choice that will significantly influence the sound quality. This choice has already been discussed in previous chapters: should we use triode, ultralinear or pentode mode? The advantage of using NGV biasing is that this choice can be left entirely up to the builder. As you will see, this choice does not affect the circuit, since the crux of the matter is how the screen grids are connected to the output transformer. In the following circuit diagrams, the ultralinear mode is shown for reasons of simplicity.

And now for a final argument in favour of using a standard circuit. In the past, valves were readily available, and they could be obtained from the Netherlands, England, America, the East Block countries and the Far East. This is still essentially true, but what has changed is the prices — and unfortunately in the wrong direction. I recently heard that a certain standard but difficult-to-obtain valve could be had for the fine sum of £80 ($125) apiece. The situation will only get worse, and the prices of valves will continue to rise. That is why it is vital to use valves that are so standard that they are relatively cheap and will be widely available for many years to come. For this reason, we use the EL84 (6BQ5) for low power applications and the EL34 (6CA7) for high power applications. Some people like these valves and some do not, but my experience with them is good enough that I have no doubts about recommending them. Some people may comment that a real triode (such as a 300B) sounds much better than an EL34 configured as a triode. This is true, but your wallet will suffer heavily if you insist on the real triode. Other possibilities are the KT88, the KT99 (an improved version of the KT88), the KT90 and the 6550 WA. Here again, the drawback is the exorbitant prices of these valves. An experienced person who knows exactly what he or she is doing and can perform all the necessary optimizations may well consider using expensive valves, but a standard type is the wisest choice for the beginner, or for the music lover whose main interest is not the type of valve used.

11.2 │ The basic circuit: general design

Figure 11.1 depicts the basic circuit for the output valves. The component numbering and the connections shown on the left of the diagram are consistent with Figure 10.4, so you can easily place the two diagrams side by side. You can do the same with the power supply connections and the circuit diagram of the power supply described in Chapter 12. It is quite remarkable that this circuit contains so few components. This represents the absolute minimum that is needed, and it also keeps the diagram clear and simple. On top of this, this circuit has proven itself many times, and it works well.

11.3 │ The basic circuit: input requirements

In general, the input circuit works as follows: the phase splitter output signals V_{g1a} and V_{g1b} enter the amplifier on the left via capacitors C_4 and C_5. The sig-

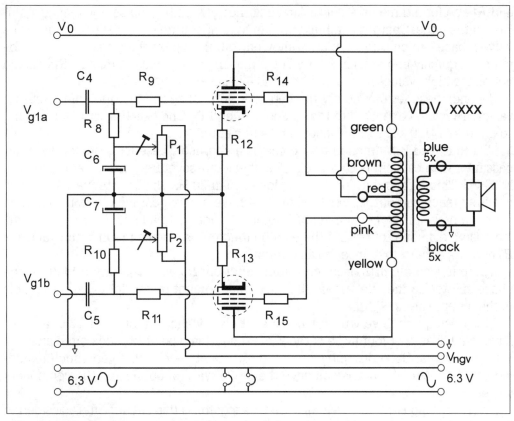

▲ **Figure 11.1** *Basic output circuit with a toroidal output transformer.*

nals then pass via the 'stop' resistors R_9 and R_{11} to the grids of the output valves, where they are further processed. The term *stop resistor* needs a bit of explanation.

An internal capacitance C_{gk} (not shown in the circuit diagram) is present between the control grid (G_1) and the cathode of every valve, due to their close proximity. Resistors R_9 and R_{11} and the internal capacitances form low-pass filters. These affect only very high frequencies, in the region of 1 MHz. If the amplifier is inclined to oscillate, these low-pass filters attenuate high frequencies and effectively stop the oscillation. This explains the name given to these resistors. R_9 and R_{11} are usually between 1 and 10 kΩ, so their influence will not be noticed below 100 to 200 kHz. This is however not true if the output valve is used in triode mode, because the anode then has a significant influence in the form of a relatively large Miller capacitance. In this case you should reduce the resistance of R_9 and R_{11}.

In the middle of the circuit diagram there are two grid resistors (R_8 and R_{10}) plus two variable resistors (P_1 and P_2). They supply the negative grid voltages (NGV). R_8

and R_{10} perform three different tasks. First, they ensure that no charge can accumulate on the grids. Charges can build up due to temperature effects and leakage at the valve's base. No charge should be allowed to build up on the grids, so it must be removed quickly and efficiently. It follows that the resistances of R_8 and R_{10} should not be too high. Values between 47 kΩ and 470 kΩ are acceptable.

Second, these resistors carry the negative grid voltage to the grids of the output valves. They are connected to the trimpots P_1 and P_2. The exact resistor value is not so important; 100 k Ω to 1 MΩ should be sufficient.

The third and last function may come as a surprise. These resistors form a high-pass filter with capacitors C_4 and C_5. The filter's crossover frequency is approximately 20 Hz. This means that frequencies lower than 20 Hz will be attenuated and will not fully reach the output valves. This can have a very positive effect if too much bass is a problem, as mentioned in Chapter 2. Incidentally, a low damping factor will increase the amount of bass. If there is too much bass, you can reduce the values of R_8 and R_{10} equally to reduce the amount of bass.

There is also a fourth, less important function: R_8 and R_{10} form a load for the phase splitter, so they determine the maximum amount of 'music' voltage available to the output valves.

This description is very useful, because it clearly shows that these two resistors have to fulfill at least four tasks at the same time. This type of situation often arises in valve amplifiers. Good designers do not disagree with each other very much regarding the basic circuit, but they all have their own ways of optimizing the component values.

I have consciously made several decisions regarding this circuit. After considering all the arguments, I have chosen 100 kΩ for R_8 and R_{10}. This represents an optimization. The values of capacitors C_4 and C_5 (82 or 100 nF each) put the −3 dB point of the high pass filter at 20 Hz. In other words, at 20 Hz there is a decrease of 3 dB relative to 1 kHz. This produces two distinct advantages: firstly, it removes rumble from phonograph playback signals and 'thumping' from CDs. Most speakers cannot even reproduce these sounds, so there is no point in amplifying them. Secondly, it avoids possible saturation of the output transformer core at full power, which is most likely with frequencies lower than 20 Hz. This also confirms that the choice of where to place the −3 dB point is sound. This all has not audible effect. If you insist on reproducing frequencies down to 1 Hz, then you only have to increase the values of C_4 and C_5 by 20 times (to about 2 µF).

In some of the circuits for the individual amplifiers that are described later on in this chapter, you will find several power valves connected in parallel. In such cases resistors R_8 and R_{10} are also duplicated and connected in parallel, which increases the load on the phase splitter. You will see that in this case different values have been chosen for C_4, C_5, R_8 and R_{10}, to achieve an optimum compromise with the phase splitter. In each case I have worked on the basis of putting the −3 dB point at 20 Hz.

11.4 │ The basic circuit: adjusting the NGV

The negative bias voltages for the control grids can be adjusted using the two trimpots P_1 and P_2. Capacitors C_6 and C_7 shunt any ripple voltages to ground.

The quiescent plate current for each output valve is specified for each amplifier circuit. There is no point in adjusting the NGV to a specific voltage, because the valves are never identical (even when they are sold as matched pairs, there are always small differences). The proper approach is to adjust the bias to achieve the correct plate current. This obviously means that this current must be measurable. For this reason, the two 10Ω resistors R_{12} and R_{13} are connected between the cathodes and ground. We can easily measure the voltage across each of these resistors with a simple voltmeter when the amplifier is on. Suppose that the plate current is 50 mA. The voltage across the cathode resistor is then:

$$V_k = R_k I_k = 10 \cdot 0.050 = 0.50 \, \text{V} \tag{11-1}$$

In practice, this method of setting up and adjusting the quiescent currents has a very elegant advantage. Suppose that we have adjusted the trimpots so that the voltages across the two cathode resistors (V_{k1} and V_{k1}) are nearly equal. We then connect the voltmeter between the two cathodes (V_{kk}) instead of across each individual resistor. If the plate currents in both output valves are equal, the measured potential should be zero volts. If this is not the case, then we can eliminate the difference by simply adjusting one of the trimpots. This means that the plate current balance can be very accurately adjusted. This shows up at the loudspeaker, where you will notice that the 50 or 60 Hz hum has been reduced to an inaudible level.

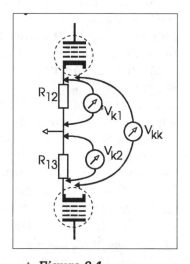

▲ *Figure 9.1*
Equalizing the plate currents using the cathode voltages V_{k1} and V_{k2} and the differential cathode voltage V_{kk}.

11.5 │ Stabilizing the output valves

It is a well known fact that new valves tend to drift away from their optimum working points. The following remarks can therefore be important. New valves need a certain amount of time to stabilize after they are first put into service. Manufacturers are aware of this, and many 'burn in' their amplifiers for a certain length of time. This is done by initially switching on the valve filaments for 30 minutes without applying any high voltages (in other words, with the amplifier in standby mode; see Chapter 12 for more information). The valves will then be well warmed up. After this, the high voltage is switched on and the NGV is adjusted for the optimum operating point. The amplifier is then loaded with a speaker, or preferably a dummy load, and a large signal (a sine wave or square wave at approximately 1 kHz, or even loud music) is then passed through it for several minutes. A small amount of drift may be observed after this. The NGV can then be readjusted. The whole process is repeated as necessary until an insignificant amount of drift is observed. Repeating the adjustment several times is usually enough to ensure that no further adjustment will be necessary for at least six months, since the valves will have arrived at a stable working point.

11.6 | Connecting the output transformer

There is very little to say about the connection of the output valves to the output transformer. We have already noted that the valves may be set up in triode, ultralinear or pentode mode. This can be realised by connecting the valves' screen grids (G_2) to the anode, the tap on the output transformer or the supply voltage, respectively. You may already have noticed that the screen grids are connected via the resistors R_{14} and R_{15}, each of which has a value of 150 Ω (see Figure 11.3). These resistors are essential in all the possible modes, which

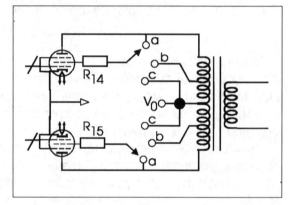

▲ **Figure 9.1**
Connections for the three different operating modes.

means that these resistors are always connected to the screen grids and then to different points in the circuit, depending on the mode used. Resistors R_{14} and R_{15} are employed to prevent oscillations and to ensure that the currents drawn by the screen grids do not become too large. In certain circumstances, it may be advantageous to add a switch to the amplifier so that you can easily change the mode.

Warning: never change the mode while the high voltage is applied to the valves! Otherwise, you may hear an enormous blast from the loudspeakers. First switch off the high voltage supply, then change the mode, and finally switch the high voltage supply on again.

You should also be careful with the colour coding of the wires. All VDV toroidal-core transformers are coded identically, which means that connecting the output transformers is clear and easy. Note however that the connections are different if an extra preamplifier is used, as described in Chapter 15.

11.7 | 10 watts using two EL84s with a VDV8020PP (PAT4000)

Figure 11.4 shows the circuit diagram of this amplifier, including the pin numbers of the EL84 (6BQ5). The valves are operated at a plate voltage of 330 V and a plate current of 40 mA. The voltage across R_{12} and R_{13} will thus be 0.4 V if the NGV is adjusted properly. With the values given here, the plate dissipation of each EL84 is slightly more than the specified maximum dissipation of 12 watts. My experience is that the valve can easily handle this, and it will not cause any problems at all. In fact, it gives the EL84 that little bit extra that ensures good high-power transient reproduction. A good 5 watts of audio power is possible in triode mode. Ultralinear mode will produce 10 watts, while pentode mode will yield 17 watts at 5% distortion (according to the specifications in the valve book). Information about the power supply is provided in Chapter 12.

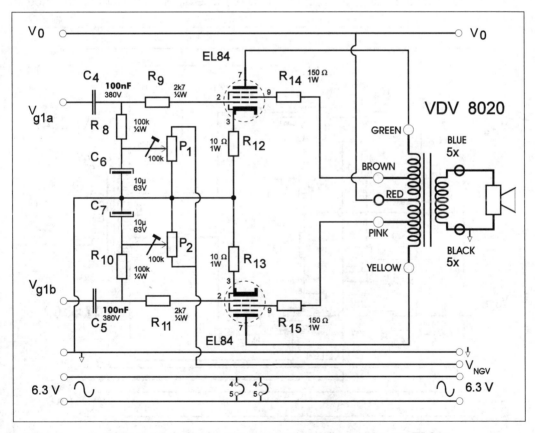

▲ *Figure 11.4* *A 10 watt power amplifier with two EL84s.*

11.8 | 30 watts using two EL34s with a VDV6040PP (PAT4002)

In this amplifier, the EL34 (6CA7) output valves are only lightly stressed. Our objective here is an operating area that does not exceed any critical values. It is possible to get more output power from the EL34s, but the conservative design of this circuit produces a very calm, unstressed and stable sound.

Here we use a plate voltage of 380 V and a plate current of 60 mA per valve. In triode mode, the output power is 13 W; ultralinear mode produces 33 W and pentode mode produces nearly 40 W. The triode mode is especially good at producing fine sound detail, and it dampens the loudspeakers optimally. See Figures 11.5 and 11.6.

It is interesting to try replacing the EL34 valves with EL34-s valves. The glass envelope of the EL34-s is thicker, and the construction of the anode and screen grid is different. In terms of sound quality, there are distinctly audible differences between the two types. With the EL34-s the bass is softer and less tight, and the higher frequencies are also more 'silky'. The main cause of these differences is the difference in

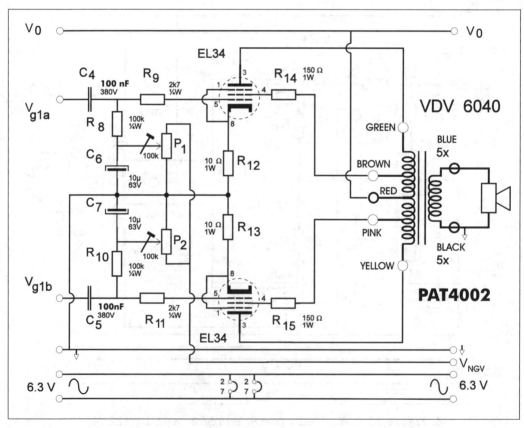

▲ *Figure 11.5* *A 30 watt amplifier with two EL34s.*

◀ Figure 11.6
A very attractive example of the 30 watt balanced amplifier.

the internal resistance of the valves. The EL34-s has a slightly higher internal resistance. It also has a slightly lower power rating. This experiment is a good example of how the type of valve used influences the sound quality. By the way, the EL34-s is a beam power tetrode while the EL34 is a true pentode. Hear the difference!

11.9 | 70 watts using four EL34s with a VDV3070PP (PAT4004)

This amplifier uses four output valves instead of two. We can double the output power and halve the effective internal valve resistance by using valves in parallel. Here again the valves are being operated conservatively; the plate voltage is 380 V and the plate current is 60 mA per valve. Since we are now using parallel valves, the circuit diagram becomes more complex, as shown in Figure 11.7 for ultralinear mode (overleaf). Note that the NGV is separately adjustable for each valve, so capacitors C_4 and C_5 must be duplicated. To avoid overloading the phase splitter, the control grid resistors are changed to 220 kΩ and the values of C_{4a}, C_{5a}, C_{4b} and C_{5b} are reduced to 47 nF.

Warning: the large frequency range of this amplifier means that it can oscillate. Think very carefully about where to place the ground points! A good choice can prevent oscillation. If oscillation still occurs, you can solve the problem by simply increasing the values of R_9, R_{11}, R_{14} and R_{15}.

This amplifier produces 30 watts in triode mode, 70 watts in ultralinear mode and 80 watts in pentode mode. Again, triode mode will produce the best sound quality, while ultralinear mode will be able to handle large power surges. Power supply information is given in Chapter 12.

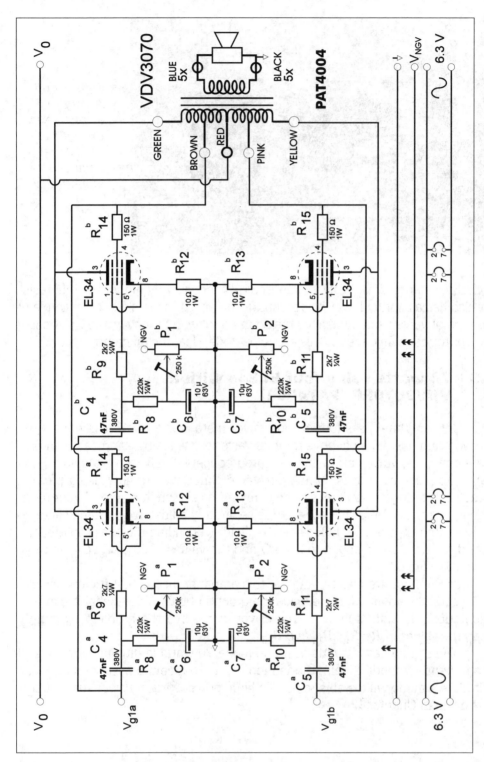

▲ *Figure 11.7 A 70 watt push-pull amplifier with four EL34s.*

11.10 | 100 watts using four EL34s with a VDV2100PP (PAT4006)

This circuit uses the same component values as the previous one. The main difference is that the plate voltage is increased to 450 V and the quiescent current is reduced to 50 mA per valve. The plate current adjustment must carried out very carefully to avoid exceeding the maximum dissipation limit. The higher plate voltage provides a much higher output power. Even though its properties are still 'high end', this amplifier would make an excellent PA or guitar amplifier, due to its high output power.

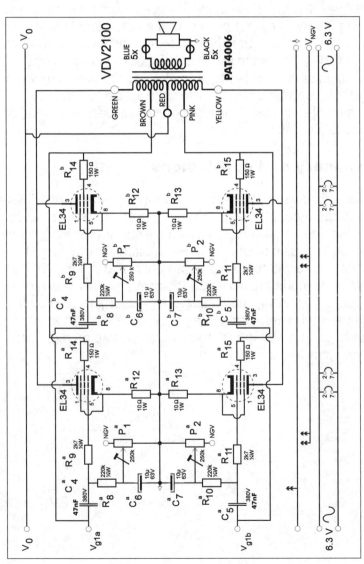

▲ *Figure 11.8 A 100 watt push-pull amplifier with four EL34s.*

11.11 | 80 Watts using eight EL34s in triode mode with a VDV1080PP (PAT4008)

Your preference may lean towards the triode mode setup for the output valves. You may also want to be able to produce plenty of output power. This all means that you will need eight EL34s running at 450 V, with a plate current of 50 mA per valve. The circuit diagram of this amplifier is shown in Figure 11.9. As before, the NGV can be adjusted separately for each valve. The plate currents must be checked to verify that they are 50 mA per valve, as required.

If you compare the performance of this amplifier to that of the previous 100 watt amplifier, you can see that the triode mode has been optimized to a very high degree while maintaining plenty of output power. This spirited amplifier works extremely well with valves having equal transconductance and internal resistance, which means that it is a very good idea to use matched pairs of valves. What will happen if we switch to ultralinear or even pentode mode? Much more output power can be achieved, but the transformer core is not really suitable for these modes. Low frequencies might saturate the core. This transformer has been especially designed for the 80 W triode mode used in this circuit.

11.12 | Summary and conclusions

We have discussed five different output amplifiers with different output powers and operating modes. It is interesting to note the similarities in the circuit designs, which illustrate the idea that valve amplifiers can be designed by following a standard concept. The main reason for these similarities is the use of negative grid voltages to adjust the valves to the optimum operating points. We have also discussed the effect of the output amplifier on the phase splitter, which can require the values of capacitors C_4 and C_5 and resistors R_8 and R_{10} to be modified. We have pointed out the need for careful grounding to prevent oscillations, and noted that increasing the values of the stop resistors can solve this problem as well. Proper grounding also prevents humming.

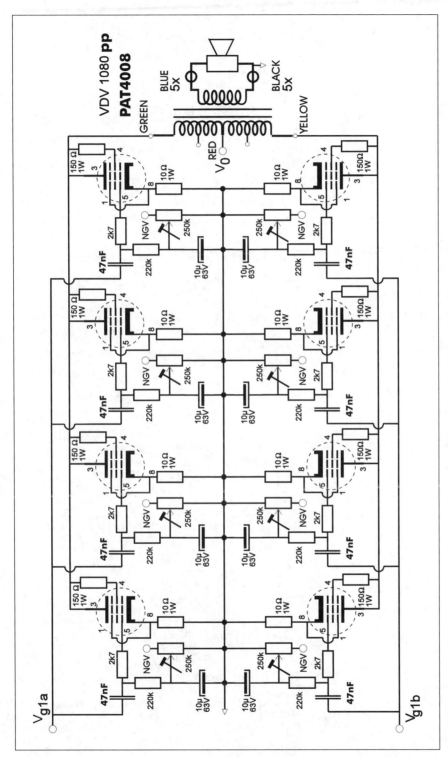

▲ *Figure 11.9 Eight EL34s in a triode-mode amplifier.*

12

Building a Push-Pull Valve Amplifier: the Power Supply

This chapter discusses the power supplies for the various amplifiers described in Chapter 11. A basic, standardized concept is also used for the power supply. We look at various aspects of the power supply, including safety considerations and a standby switch.

12.1 | Safety

In this section, I must demand your total attention.

You must follow all safety rules, at all times, because the mains voltages (230 V or 120 V) is used here, and this is *extremely dangerous*. The filament voltage (6.3 V) is not considered to be particularly dangerous, but the negative grid voltage (−40 V or more) and the plate voltages (over 330 V) are *dangerous*. The plate voltages are especially dangerous. They can be fatal if you do not take suitable precautions.

A few precautions and basic safety rules are:

- Never work on an amplifier while it is still on.
- Always remove the plug from the mains socket before working on an amplifier.
- Discharge the power supply capacitors with a 220 kΩ resistor, and check that they are fully discharged (< 10 V) with a voltmeter, before working on an amplifier.
- Always use the correct types of fuses with the recommended current ratings.
- Be sure that all high voltage conductors are well insulated and kept well away from other metal objects.
- Insulate or cover the contacts of the mains switch and the standby switch.
- Always mount the transformers using the recommended mounting hardware (rubber rings, washers and screws).
- Make sure that no sharp metal objects can touch the power supply transformer.
- Use a lamp or LED circuit to indicate whether the amplifier is switched on.

- Never reach both hands into an amplifier at the same time if there is any possibility that a high voltage is present. If you touch a high voltage component while your other hand 'happens' to be resting on the amplifier chassis, the voltage will discharge through your chest, which means through your heart!

HAVE YOU BEEN WARNED ENOUGH?!

12.2 | The basic power supply circuit

Figure 12.1 depicts the basic circuit of the power supply. All the valve amplifiers use this circuit. The only differences are in the power supply transformers used, the fuse ratings, the voltages and the sizes of the capacitors.

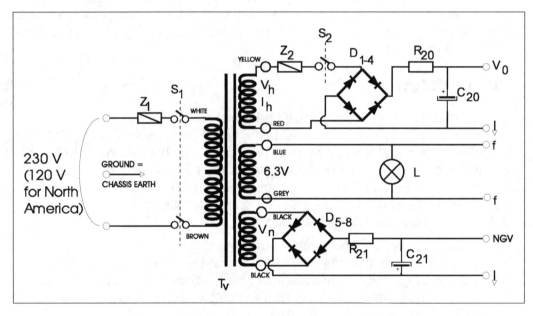

▲ *Figure 12.1* *The standard power supply circuit.*

Even though this circuit is a picture of simplicity, we still need to discuss some of its interesting aspects and certain points that you have to keep in mind.

The mains voltage (230 V or 120 V) is connected at the left. A three-wire cable is used, so that the amplifier chassis can be grounded (via the middle connection). In some cases, the ground lead can cause the amplifier to hum, because other equipment connected to the amplifier is often connected to ground as well. This can cause a ground loop that picks up induction fields, or in which small 50 or 60 Hz difference currents can flow. If this situation should arise, you could disconnect the ground lead, but for safety reasons this is not recommended. A much better and safer solution is to find the cause of the ground loop and cure it.

Fuse Z_1 protects the amplifier and the transformer. The size of Z_1 depends on the transformer used, but there are preferred values that have been established by safety organizations and regulatory agencies. It is a good idea to follow these guidelines.

S_1 is the mains switch, and the unusual feature is that it (dis)connects both mains leads simultaneously. This is to ensure that there is no mains connection at all when the amplifier is switched off. This enhances the safety of the amplifier. Some amplifiers have a small mains switch, which is not really suitable for this task. Small switches do not insulate sufficiently and may not be able to handle the switch-on surge (inrush) current drawn by the transformer. A large switch is recommended, one that can handle heavy currents. Economizing on the mains switch will always cause problems later on.

After the switch, the mains voltage is fed to the power supply transformer. Refer to the documentation that is supplied with the transformer for the proper colour coding.

The secondary side of the transformer consists of three parts: the plate voltage winding, the filament voltage winding and the negative grid voltage winding.

Each amplifier has its own requirements for the plate voltage and current (we deal with specific values later on). Fuse Z_2 protects the plate voltage supply. It will melt if any output valve(s) unexpectedly decides to fail shorted. Therefore, the rated current of Z_2 should not be too high, since otherwise a shorted valve could damage the power supply.

The standby switch S_2 follows Z_2. Its function is so important that we must discuss it in some detail.

12.3 | The standby switch and the on-off switching order

The function of the standby switch is to 'switch off' the amplifier while it is still 'on'. In other words, S_2 should disconnect the plate voltage while the valve filaments continue to glow. This is beneficial, because the valves can stay warm (or can warm up slowly). The plate voltage is only needed if the amplifier has to handle music, and only then do we have to close S_2.

What we need is a standard procedure for switching the amplifier on and off. To switch it on, we should start by closing S_1 while leaving S_2 open. We should then wait a few minutes while the valve cathodes warm up. The circuit diagram shows that the NGV is always connected, so the emission of the output valves will be zero in this situation. Now we can close S_2. The plate voltage will be applied to the amplifier, and the valves will warm up even more due to the anode currents. The valve temperatures will stabilize after a few minutes, as will the sound image.

To switch off the amplifier, we have to follow the same procedure in reverse order. We first open S_2, which disconnects the plate voltage. C_{20} is still charged, so if we leave the filaments on for a while the valves can still function, and they will discharge C_{20}. This is a favourable situation, which also is beneficial if repairs have to be made. In any case, C_{20} will be totally discharged; not even a residual charge will remain. After this has taken place (it takes a few minutes), S_1 can be opened. This is not absolutely necessary, especially if the amplifier will be used again the same day. Actually, why not leave the filaments on all the time?

12.4 | The power supply circuit continued: what do you mean, it hums?

A full-wave bridge rectifier follows the standby switch. It uses 1N4007 diodes, which have excellent maximum current and reverse voltage specifications. The reverse voltage (in the non-conducting direction) can be high enough to burn out a diode with a lower maximum reverse voltage rating. This will not happen with the 1N4007 diodes. Some people prefer soft-recovery diodes, but I leave this sort of optimization up to you.

The next component is resistor R_{20} (10 Ω), which restricts the maximum surge current into capacitor C_{20}. Use a robust 5 watt resistor, and make sure it can readily dissipate its heat.

Next in line is C_{20}. This is an expensive piece of hardware, because it must be able to handle high voltages and must also have plenty of capacitance. There are many possible ways to achieve this. For more information, see Table 12.1.

Now suppose you are at the experimental stage and have not yet installed the valves, but we have tested the power supply. Capacitor C_{20} will be fully charged and will not be able to discharge itself. In this situation, it is advisable to connect a 220 kΩ, 1 W resistor in parallel with C_{20}. This will automatically discharge the capacitor when the mains voltage is disconnected. Discharging C_{20} will take a few minutes, after which you may proceed with your experiments.

Some people are fascinated by sparks and simply short circuit C_{20} with a piece of wire. I am well aware of the pleasure provided by this trick, but I advise you not to do it. Blobs of metal splattered everywhere, burned-out wires and reduced capacitor life are the unpleasant consequences of 'quickly' discharging a capacitor.

The zero-voltage side of the plate voltage supply should be connected to the ground point for the cathode resistors of the output valves. It is not advisable to create several different ground points, distributed over the chassis of the amplifier, because the power supply current will then flow through the chassis. This will always cause an annoying hum. It is much better to use no more than two starred ground points.

One ground point should be used for the output valve cathode resistors, and the plate voltage supply ground should be connected to this ground point (as well as the NGV ground, as shown at the bottom of the diagram). You can also have a second starred ground point for the phase splitter, as described in Chapter 10. If you build you amplifier this way and keep the signal input connector *isolated* from ground, it is very likely that your amplifier will be free from hum.

If the amplifier still hums, it is quite possible that the plate currents of the output valves are not equal. You can correct this by adjusting the NGV trimpots. If the plate currents are equal and the amplifier still hums, a thorough checkout is necessary. If after all this the amplifier still hums, you have probably made a construction mistake. It is absolute rubbish to say that valve amplifiers always hum. The most that you should expect is a small amount of hum when the amplifier is switched on, because the valves need a little time to settle down to their proper operating points. After this, everything should be quiet. Persistent humming is a sign of incorrect biasing, a ground loop or mismatched power valves.

12.5 | The filament supply, NGV supply and indicators

The fat wires carry the 6.3 V needed by the filaments. These wires must be thick, because the filaments need plenty of current. For example, each EL34 (6CA7) demands 1.5 A, an EL84 (6BQ5) wants 0.76 A and the preamplifier and phase splitter valve (ECC81/12AT7 or ECC82/12AU7) needs 0.3 A. Now it's just a question of counting the number of valves in the amplifier and calculating the total current needed — for instance, eight EL34s in triode mode plus one ECC82 means ($8 \times 1.5 + 1 \times 0.3$) = 12.3 A.

The ground point for the filaments is discussed in Chapter 10. It should be located next to the phase splitter. A very good method for distributing the filament voltage through the amplifier is to twist the supply wires together. The magnetic fields produced by these wires will cancel each other out, because they carry an alternating voltage and the current flows in opposite directions in the two wires. If the wires are located far apart, this cancellation is no longer effective.

To let us know that the amplifier is working, we need to install an indicator lamp. A LED with a series resistor is often used for this, connected to the 6.3 V filament supply. However, this is not advisable, because the alternating voltage switches the LED on and off 50 or 60 times a second. This creates pulse disturbances that propagate throughout the entire amplifier and can even ruin the output signal. It is much better to use an ordinary incandescent lamp (6 V or 12 V). A 12 V lamp produces just the right amount of light, and it will have a very long life since it is operated much below its rated voltage.

Finally, we come to the circuit for the NGV supply. Diodes D_5–D_8 rectify the alternating voltage, and R_{21} plus C_{21} smooth and filter the DC voltage. Their values are given in Table 12.1. The grid voltage is negative, so be careful when connecting capacitor C_{21}. Its positive terminal points down in the schematic diagram. The NGV must be grounded to the starred ground point used for the output valve cathodes. This is the only way to avoid hum loops and undesirable ripple voltages.

12.6 │ Power supplies specifications summary

The parameters of the power supplies for all the amplifiers are summarized in Table 12.1. It lists the primary and secondary AC voltages, supply currents, supply voltages after rectification, fuse sizes, supply transformer model numbers and the values of C_{20} and C_{21}.

Note that the power supplies presented here are for *monoponic* amplifiers only, because better sound quality is obtained when a separate power supply is used for each channel. Two complete power supplies (two supply transformers and two times the rest of the circuitry) must be used for a stereo amplifier. Research has proven that this is the best solution.

12.7 │ Summary and conclusions

We have presented an extensive list of safety warnings regarding the high voltages present in valve amplifiers. We have explained what you have to take into account, even when the amplifier is off. We have described a procedure for switching the amplifier on and off and explained why a standby switch is desirable. We have discussed a standard power supply circuit. Table 12.1 lists pertinent information for power supplies that are suitable for the valve amplifiers described in Chapter 11.

Amplifier	10 W	30 W	70 W	100 W	80 W triode	
Transformer	3N604	4N605	6N606	7N707	8N608S	
Primary						
Voltage	230/120	230/120	230/120	230/120	230/120	V
Fuse[1] Z_1	0.4/0.8	0.63/1.2	1/2	1.6/3.2	2.5/5[2]	A
Plate supply secondary						
AC voltage V_h	250	290	290	340	340	V
AC current I_h	200	250	600	700	800	mA
Fuse[1] Z_2	200	250	630	800	800	mA
D_1–D_4: 1N4007 (4 x)						
R_{20}: 10 Ω, 5 W						
C_{20}	2 x 47	4 x 47	4 x 47	4 x 47	8 x 47	µF
	380	450	450	500	500	V
DC voltage V_0	330	380	380	450	450	V
Quiescent current I_0	100	120	240	200	400	mA
Filament supply secondary						
Voltage	6.3	6.3	6.3	6.3	6.3	V
Current	2.2	3.8	6.8	6.8	2 x 6.4	A
NGV secondary						
AC voltage V_n	30	40	40	40	50	V
AC current	100	100	100	100	100	mA
D_5–D_8: 1N4002 (4 x)						
C_{21}	220	220	220	220	220	µF
	63	63	100	100	100	V
R_{21}: 10 kΩ, 1 W or 4 kΩ, 1 W (see Chapter 14)						

1) The primary and secondary fuses are slow-blow types.
2) An additional resistor is needed ahead of the switch for the 80 watt triode amplifier, to provide an extra delay when the power supply is switched on.

▲ **Table 12.1** *Power supply specifications for the amplifiers of Chapter 11.*

13

● ● ● | ● ● ● ● ●

Building a
Push-Pull Amplifier:
Construction Hints

This chapter deals with the practical side of things. I have many years of experience in developing and building valve amplifiers, in the course of which I have made plenty of mistakes and tripped over virtually every imaginable problem. The aim of this chapter is to pass on some of my experience to the do-it-yourselfer.

To start with, it is impossible to quickly 'knock together' a valve amplifier, so don't even think about it! You shouldn't have the idea that you can just play about for an evening and expect everything to work. Valves simply do not behave this way. I am very conscious of the fact that 'ready-made' circuits are described in the preceding chapters. However, a circuit diagram is not the same as a working amplifier. It is all up to *you* to think about what you are about, and carefully construct a good product. Hopefully, the following hints and suggestions will help you on your way to building an amplifier you can be proud of.

13.1 | Why not use a printed circuit board?

It is standard practice nowadays to use printed circuit boards (PCBs) to construct amplifiers. However, in this chapter I assume that the amplifier will be 'hand wired'. (Chapter 14 describes 70 and 100 watt amplifiers that are constructed using a PCB.)

Why do so many DIYers construct amplifiers with hand wiring? First, because designing a good PCB requires a huge time investment. You can't simply leave it up to your computer to make a good PCB; you have to help the computer a lot and tell it what to do. Second, the designer has to think about a lot of things, such as how the various components influence each other. Third, there is the question of whether the PCB base material (glass/epoxy) will have any influence on the amplifier, and if so how to minimize these effects. All these questions can be answered, and the result can be a good PCB design, but it will be a very costly PCB.

Hand-wired construction is a very simple alternative to using a PCB. It also allows for experiments and changes after the amplifier has been built. It does not have to result in a messy-looking product. Proper planning of the layout will produce an attractive result, even with hand-wired construction.

13.2 | Designing a logical layout

In order to arrange the components properly, you can follow a simple rule that will lead you to the optimum electrical and visual form for your amplifier. This rule states, "place the components in the same logical order as they have in the circuit diagram". The following example illustrates this.

Suppose you want to build the 6040 amplifier without feedback. Then you have to deal with the following: a) the input connector, b) the (optional) volume control (see Figure 13.1), c) the phase splitter, d) the output valves, e) the output transformer, f) the loudspeaker output connectors, g) the power supply circuit, h) the power supply transformer and i) the mains cable. Figure 13.2 is an example of how this logical order translates into the logical positioning of the components on the chassis.

What can we see in Figure 13.2? The amplifier has a narrow front, on which the input connector, the volume control and the indicator lamp are located. With this arrangement, the wires from the input connector to the volume control and then to the phase splitter will clearly be short. Everything is close together. Point-to-point, uninsulated wiring can be used, and since the wires are short the wire type is not so critical. Of course, if you want to use silver wire then go right ahead. However, the shorter the wires the less negative influence they will have on the sound quality. This arrangement is thus automatically inexpensive, since esoteric wires usually have esoteric prices.

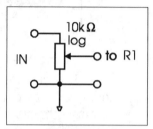

▲ *Figure 13.1*
Volume control circuit.

▼ *Figure 13.2 Logical component placement.*

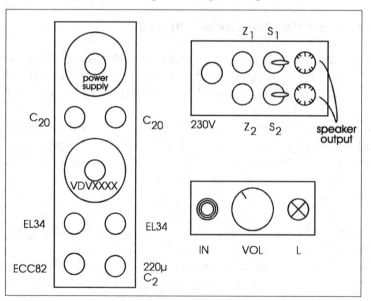

The output valves are placed after the phase splitter, and following them comes the output transformer. Next come the power supply capacitors and then the power supply transformer. The mains connection, the mains switch, the fuses and the loud-speaker connections are all situated on the back panel. The standby switch S_2 may be placed here as well, or next to the output valves. The standby switch could also be put on the front panel, but the wires to the switch would have to be electrically shielded to prevent power supply ripple voltages from affecting the audio circuitry.

The arrangement I have sketched here ensures that the amplified signals cannot be coupled into the sensitive inputs. Also, the distance between the output trans-former and the power transformer is sufficient to prevent their small external mag-netic fields from interfering with each other.

13.3 | Placing the filament wiring

I have already mentioned that the filaments can be powered by a direct voltage to prevent possible disturbances caused by magnetic field effects. There is an easier way to eliminate disturbances from the alternating filament voltage, which is to simply twist the filament supply wires together. Since the current flows in oppo-site directions in the two wires, the external magnetic field caused by the alternating voltage is minimal. It is also a good idea to place the wires in the corners of the chas-sis, and as far away as possible from sensitive parts. You can also place grounded metal shielding around the wires near the input valves. This will minimise the strength of the magnetic field. See Figure 13.3.

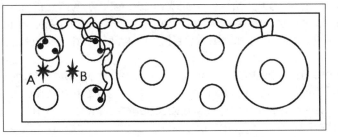

◀ *Figure 13.3*
Twisting and routing the 6.3 V filament supply wires, and the preferred ground point positions A and B.

13.4 | Choosing the ground points

The positioning of the ground points is very important. In the past, ground points were placed all over the metal chassis. It was assumed that the surface area of the metal was so large, and the resistance therefore so small, that the potential differ-ences between the various ground points would be very small. In practice, the situa-tion is totally different.

As an example, I examined an old amplifier and measured the level of the hum voltage. I then carefully reselected the ground points and again measured the hum voltage. The hum voltage of the modified amplifier was 20 dB lower than the original value. In a second experiment, I took a carefully laid out printed circuit board and relocated the ground points in a logical and optimum manner. This caused the hum voltages to drop by 10 dB. These examples clearly show that using many different ground points on the chassis is a bad idea, since it can cause humming. Most chassis are made of steel, and standard EI-core power supply transformers create induction voltages in them. In addition, the potential difference between two separate ground points can be large enough to cause the amplifier to hum. Again, careful selection and positioning of the ground points will solve this problem.

There is another reason why you should be careful about ground points. If you let the ground currents and the supply currents flow freely through the chassis, currents from the power stage of the amplifier may produce a potential difference at the input of the amplifier. This means that you have created some sort of negative or positive feedback via the chassis ground. Since this occurs in a completely uncontrolled manner, you can only wait until the listening test to see how it will affect the 'sound' of the amplifier — it may be completely flat, with no spatial presence at all.

I have already said that all these problems can be prevented by using *no more than two* ground points. The first ground point should be next to the phase splitter (point A in Figure 13.3), and the second one should be next to the output valves (point B). These two points should also be as close together as possible. The power supply ground and the output valve cathodes resistors should all be connected to ground point B. The heavy currents, which come from the output valves, are thus all grounded at point B. Ground point A, by contrast, collects the relatively small currents from the input signals. This arrangement ensures that supply currents and output valves currents do not force their way through to the input. This clearly enhances the sound quality.

In addition, you should ensure that the RCA connector for the input signal is *not* grounded to the chassis itself. This also applies to the loudspeaker output. If grounding is necessary, use separate wires running directly from the connectors to ground point A. I have already remarked on the benefits of well-chosen ground points. In general, we can say that if the amplifier hums, there is probably something wrong with the ground connections.

13.5 | Where should you connect the mains ground?

If a mains ground is used, then the metal chassis is connected to the mains ground. This type of grounding may cause hum, but there are a few ways around this. A sensible solution is to connect the mains ground to point A. Most signal sources, such CD players, have no potential difference between the mains ground and the signal ground. Hum loops can thus be prevented by connecting the amplifier mains ground and the signal ground to a single point (point **A**). This is a very safe method (and I advise you to use this method).

The second method is to put a switch in the mains ground lead. This method is often used in large, complicated systems, such as PA (public address) systems. If hum occurs, the mains ground lead can simply be opened with the switch. This is *not* the best or safest method, but PA systems must often be set up quickly, and the switch can be very handy. (It's better to use symmetric signal cables and balanced signal transformers, but this costs a bit more. Be very careful in such situations; some performers have died because of improper grounding!).

Another alternative is to put a 100 ohm resistor between the mains ground and the signal ground at point **A**. This resistor provides an ground connection, but it prevents large currents from flowing in the ground lead. This is also *not* the safest method. Faults in the power supply transformer or the internal wiring may produce large leakage currents that can burn out the resistor, which means that the mains ground is no longer connected.

A completely different approach is to connect a 100 nF, 630 V capacitor between the mains ground lead and the chassis. The capacitor prevents problems from occurring with high frequency signals, while blocking low frequency currents and voltages. This may be a good method for high frequency decoupling, but it is definitely *not* good with regard to safety. The whole point of a mains ground is to keep the chassis at ground potential at all times. The 100 nF capacitor does not meet this objective.

To summarize this discussion: grounding the chassis is good for safety, but it may cause the amplifier to hum. I nevertheless strongly advise you to provide your amplifier with a mains ground. (Figure 13.4 shows the various grounding methods.)

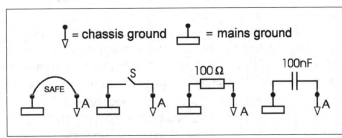

▲ *Figure 13.4*
Alternative mains grounding methods.

If you build the amplifier in compliance with the safety requirements for 'double insulated' equipment, a mains ground may not be necessary. These requirements are: (1) mount the power supply transformer using the supplied rubber rings and washers, (2) ensure that no sharp objects are located next to the power supply transformer, (3) use a two-pole mains switch (S_1) that opens both mains leads, (4) do not use a computer-type mains input filter (since this must be grounded), (5) do not connect any capacitors between the mains leads and the chassis, (6) apply extra insulation to the terminals of the mains switch and all mains connections and (7) fully insulate or enclose the metal chassis so that body contact with metal parts is not possible. (Note that capacitors connected between the mains leads and the chassis are often used to suppress both common-mode and differential-mode interference on the mains lines. Many CD players use them, but in my opinion they are dangerous. If one of these capacitors fails, then the whole chassis will be at mains potential. That can be lethal!)

13.6 | Ventilation and cooling

Valves become very hot, and therefore they need good ventilation. If the valves are mounted in the open, as shown in Figure 13.2, they should be adequately cooled by the heat lost to the freely circulating air. The valves will become much too hot if they are in a closed cabinet, due to the lack of air flow. Whichever way you decide to build the amplifier, you must provide good ventilation. Some commercial amplifiers these days have fans located underneath the (horizontally mounted) valves to provide a supply of cool air. This is a good solution. A simpler and more practical solution is to simply mount the valves vertically, with enough free space around them to ensure adequate air flow.

One heat source that is often overlooked is the valve pins, which become very warm. They conduct heat to the chassis, which in turn may warm up considerably. If the chassis is a closed metal box, then the other internal components will also warm up. Capacitors are particularly sensitive to elevated temperatures. The life span of a capacitor is dramatically reduced at 80° C compared to its life span at 50° C. Operation at elevated temperatures also changes the characteristics of coupling capacitors. On top of this, some resistors also produce a significant amount of heat. All these heat sources force us to cool the chassis. This can be done by drilling ventilation holes (6 mm diameter) around each valve socket and in the bottom plate of the chassis. The amplifier should sit on small feet, to allow for air flow from underneath. All these measures facilitate good ventilation inside the chassis, and our efforts will considerably lengthen the life of the capacitors.

In Figure 13.2, you can see that the output transformer is located between the output valves and the power supply capacitors. This puts the capacitors far enough away from the output valves to keep them from being warmed up by radiated heat from the valves. Of course, the output transformer will be warmed up, which is not what we want. We must therefore provide plenty of free space, especially around the output valves. Don't forget that each output valve dissipates at least 25 W, which is a lot of heat in a small volume.

13.7 | Minimum plate voltage distance

The plate voltage can easily be quite high, so it is a good idea to think about how to prevent *discharges*. A discharge occurs when electricity is conducted through the air. This may produce sparks and crackling noises, together with the smell of ozone. It is a very good idea to maintain a separation of at least one centimetre between the chassis (which is at ground potential) and all components or wires that carry a high voltage. In principle, this should be enough to prevent discharges. Unfortunately, I have seen discharges in amplifiers built according to this rule. These were caused by sharp points on wire ends and/or solder joints. If a high voltage is present on a sharp point in the vicinity of an grounded surface, such as the chassis, the electric field lines will be highly concentrated at the point. This can lead to discharges. For this reason, it is a good idea to round off solder joints on all high voltage parts.

The valve sockets can also produce discharges. This is unlikely for the phase splitter and preamplifier valves, but the output valves are good candidates for producing discharges. This means that you should use only high-quality valve sockets. Plastic sockets are acceptable, but Pertinax sockets are not reliable over the long term, since water vapour and air pollutants penetrate the Pertinax and degrade its insulating properties. This leads to problems, which are visible as black, scorched areas on the socket. Ceramic sockets are well suited for this application, especially if the they are glazed. Unglazed ceramic sockets may be porous, and thus may be less reliable in the long run. In summary, a good choice of valve socket is very important for the life span of the amplifier. If you economize now, you will only pay more at a later date!

13.8 | More about the NGV

The previous chapters have discussed various aspects of the negative grid voltage. We use the NGV to bias each output valve to its optimum working point. To do this, we have to adjust a trimpot (P_1 or P_2) while measuring the voltage across the cathode resistor (10 Ω). The most important aspect of this is the initial procedure. It is possible to make a mistake by starting at the 'wrong end' of the trimpot, which will cause the output valve to overheat due to excessive current. This doesn't have to be fatal for the valve, but there is no guarantee that it will have the same electrical characteristics after being 'cooked' for a while.

One of the most important checks you should make, before operating the amplifier for the first time, is to verify that the NGV is present at the valve sockets. To do this you need a voltmeter (10 MΩ/volt is required due to the values of R_8 and R_{10}). Start by switching off the standby switch (S_2) *before* you switch on the mains switch (S_1) — otherwise you may cook the output valves the first time you switch on the amplifier, which is exactly what you are trying to avoid. Connect one lead of the meter (the plus lead) to ground, and touch the other lead to the G_1 (control grid) pin of each output valve in turn. If you do not read the full NGV on the meter, adjust P_1 or P_2 until the voltage is as negative as possible. If it is not possible to change the measured voltage by adjusting the trimpot, there must be a mistake somewhere in the construction. In this case you must thoroughly check everything, in order to find and remedy the fault before going any further. The EL84 amplifier should have a maximum NGV of −30 V, while the other amplifiers should have a maximum NGV of −50 V or more. After you have successfully set all the trimpots to the maximum negative voltage, you can switch on the high voltage with S_2 without risking blowing up the valves.

The next step is to adjust the trimpot for each valve to obtain the specified voltage across each cathode resistor. You have to do this for each output valve in turn, and the whole process must be repeated a few times. I have already mentioned that the valves need a certain amount of time to settle down, and loud music may shift their working points a little. If you repeat the setup process a few times, they will stabilize at the optimum working point.

You can actually *hear* whether the NGV is set properly for all the valves. If one valve draws more current than another one, the magnetic fields in the two halves of the primary winding will not cancel each other out, and the amplifier will produce hum. In other words, if the amplifier starts humming after a while, this does not mean that it is happy. What it means is that the NGV settings have shifted.

An extra resistor, marked R^{**} in Figure 13.5, is found in quite a few valve amplifiers. This resistor (there is one per trimpot) has the same value as the trimpot, in this case 100 kΩ or 250 kΩ. The purpose of this resistor is to cause only half of the NGV supply voltage to appear across the trimpot. If the trimpot simply carries the full NGV, a small adjustment of the trimpot can cause a large change in the output valve current. The adjustment is thus over-sensitive. When R^{**} is used, the trimpot can adjust the grid voltage from half of the NGV value to its maximum value. This is not a problem, because if we have to use a voltage less than half of the maximum NGV then the output valve is most probably worn out. Resistor R^{**} reduces the sensitivity of the adjustment of the output valve bias. Another good alternative is to use ten-turn trimpots. You can then adjust the NGV accurately and reproducibly.

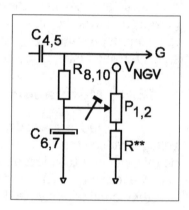

▲ *Figure 13.5*
An extra resistor (R^{**}) makes the NGV setup easier.

13.9 | The 100 Hz (or 120 Hz) square-wave test

As soon as the amplifier is completely built, enclosed in a nice case, and works, you can start with the optimization of the setup. The initial step (after a burn-in period) is to fine tune the bias currents in the power valves. Fine tuning the bias currents is very important, because this prevents the output transformer from becoming saturated by DC currents.

Now comes the next step. It is very important that the AC voltages at the anodes of the power valves have exactly the same value. The transformer is then used optimally, the voltages are optimally balanced and the distortion in the output trans- former is small. However, if the amplification factors of the power valves differ then the AC voltages at their anodes will also differ. In this case the primary winding of the output transformer will no longer be balanced. This results in core saturation at large output powers and low frequencies, and it produces harmonic distortion over the whole frequency range. It is therefore imperative to balance the AC voltages applied to the primary winding, especially in valve amplifiers without overall negative feedback. How can we do this?

There is a very simple test for checking the AC signal balance. You will need an oscilloscope and a square wave generator. If the mains voltage frequency is 50 Hz, then the frequency of the square wave signal must be 100 Hz (twice the mains fre- quency). With a mains frequency of 60 Hz, the square wave signal must be set to 120 Hz.

Connect the square wave signal to the input of the power amplifier. Make sure that the signal level can be varied from 0 V to the maximum input voltage (for exam ple 1 V), at which the amplifier output signal starts to clip. Connect a power resistor (such as 5 Ω, 100 W) to the speaker terminals of the amplifier (do not perform this test with a speaker connected, it might blow up your speaker!). Connect the oscilloscope input to the load resistor. Figure 13.6 shows the test setup.

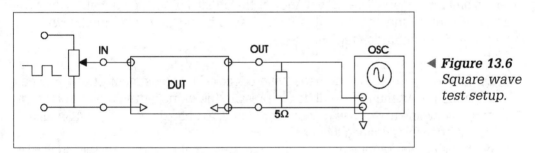

◀ **Figure 13.6**
*Square wave
test setup.*

Switch on the amplifier and let it warm up. Now, slowly increase the input volt- age while observing the square wave on the the oscilloscope. You will probably see a waveform like that shown in Figure 13.7 when the output voltage reaches its max- imum value (just below clipping).

Nasty peaks appear on the square wave, due to transient saturation of the output transformer. This is not what we want. It occurs because the AC anode voltages of the power valves are not equal.

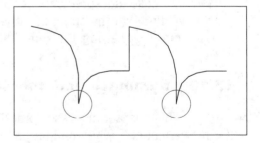

▲ **Figure 13.7**
*Amplifier square wave response
with AC imbalance.*

Now I will show you how to regulate (fine tune) the AC voltages originating from the phase splitter. The schematic diagram in Figure 13.8 hints at how this can done.

You can see in Figure 13.8 that the anode load resistance of the phase splitter can be adjusted between certain limits. The additional resistors around R_6 allow its effective value to be varied between 19.4 kΩ and 27 kΩ. Consequently, the AC output voltage at C_4 can be varied relative to the output voltage at C_5. The anode output signal level can be increased or decreased relative to the cathode output signal level, and this can be used to compensate for differences in the amplification factors of the power valves.

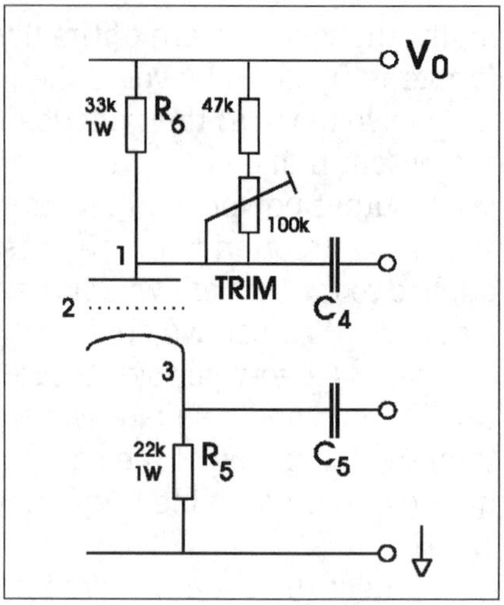

Now let's repeat the square wave test with the modified phase splitter circuit. If we adjust the 100 kΩ trimpot, we will see the sharp peaks disappear, so that the square wave takes on a perfect shape. The AC voltages at the anodes of the power valves are now exactly the same, and the output transformer is being driven optimally, without entering the core saturation region.

Notes:

1: Do this test without overall negative feedback. The adjustment of the voltages will then be optimum. If feedback is present, the amplifier tries to correct itself, and this means that it has to work very hard. You should adjust the AC balance *before* applying negative feedback.

2: If you have the equipment needed to measure total harmonic distortion (THD), and you make measurements at various trimpot settings during this procedure, you will find that the optimum square wave response setting is the same as the minimum THD setting. I'm sure that you now understand the reason for this.

13.10 | Summary and conclusions

This chapter discusses practical solutions to problems that a do-it-yourselfer may encounter when building a valve amplifier. The principles that guide the construction of a valve amplifier are completely different from those that apply to a transistor amplifier. This applies to the initial setup procedure as well as to safety aspects. I have suggested how to arrange the amplifier components for good results, and also the best way to handle the filament wiring. Grounding is often a big problem, and I recommend that you use as few ground points as possible.

▲ *Figure 13.8*
AC balance trimming circuit.

This chapter also address the following issues: (1) Quite a few amplifiers have a mains ground. What are the alternative ways to connect this ground, and how safe are they? (2)Valves must be ventilated for cooling. What has to be taken into account? (3) High voltages can cause discharges. How can discharges be prevented?

We have seen an initial setup procedure, with the emphasis on adjusting the NGV. Finally, we have seen how to make a simple but important adjustment for minimizing the total harmonic distortion.

● ● ● ● ●

Valve Amplifiers using a Printed Circuit Board

This chapter describes the construction of 70 W and 100 W amplifiers based on a meticulously designed printed circuit board (PCB). A PCB drastically simplifies the construction and, thanks to LEP® technology, it need not cause any degradation of audio quality of the finished product. LEP layout minimizes crosstalk and potential problems due to ground currents, while it virtually eliminates signal deformations due to the influence of the epoxy/glass PCB material.

14.1 | General description

Some builders enjoy the challenge of building an amplifier literally from scratch — that is, from the scratches on paper, doodles and scribbles that constitute a circuit diagram. They want to have the final word about the size and shape of the enclosure and the component layout, and they do not shrink away from the effort needed to realize their dream (drafting, drilling and drudgery!). Others, on the other hand, would rather not have to fuss with the layout and thus prefer to have a ready-made PCB. That eliminates a plethora of possible mistakes, and the final result always looks neat.

▲ *Figure 14.1*
An attractive-looking amplifier
does not have to be based on a PCB.

As I have already said, designing a good printed circuit board for a valve amplifier is not a trivial matter. It requires a lot of thought, many calculations and above all, expertise. I was somewhat reluctant to expend all these resources, plus my time, on developing a PCB for valve amplifier projects, but many requests from customers finally convinced me to do so.

The PCB has to meet a long list of requirements. First, the entire amplifier should fit on a single PCB, except for the output transformer and the power transformer. This reduces the 'external' wiring to that necessary to connect the transformers, a mains supply cable and the audio signals. All trimpots should be located on the board, as well as the valves. Bias adjustments should be simple, requiring a minimum of measurements, wire jumpers and what have you.

A well-know property of the epoxy/glass base material is that its dielectric constant – which relates to how it reacts to electric fields – causes a 'lagging' response, which means that the circuit board material exhibits a delayed response to a changing electric field. In 'audio lingo', this means that the PCB material degrades the *resolution* of the auditory image. This effect must somehow be eliminated if we are to produce a PCB for a high-quality amplifier.

In order to achieve this, we used a new track layout technique, called LEP, for the PCB. This technique is based on an explicit analysis of the strength and direction of the electric fields produced in the epoxy/glass substrate by the circuit, combined with an analysis of the currents in the ground planes and ground tracks. With proper track design using the LEP technique, it is possible to eliminate the undesirable effects of the epoxy/glass material and ground currents. Chapter 15 provides more information about LEP design. For now, it is sufficient to say that thanks to the LEP technique, the amplifier PCB (part number BBB70100) combines an aesthetically pleasing layout with amazingly clean sound.

The amplifier that uses this PCB draws on material from several different chapters. The ECC82-based phase inverter (see Figure 14.2) comes from Chapter 10, while the power amplifier design comes from Chapter 11 (see Figure 14.3). The power supply, shown in Figure 14.4, is described in Chapter 12.

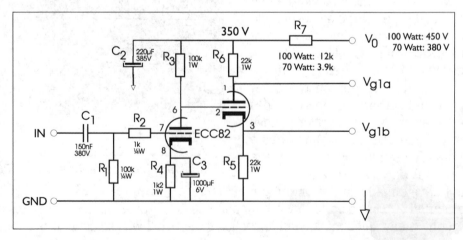

▲ **Figure 14.2** *Preamplifier/phase splitter for the 10/100 W amplifier.*

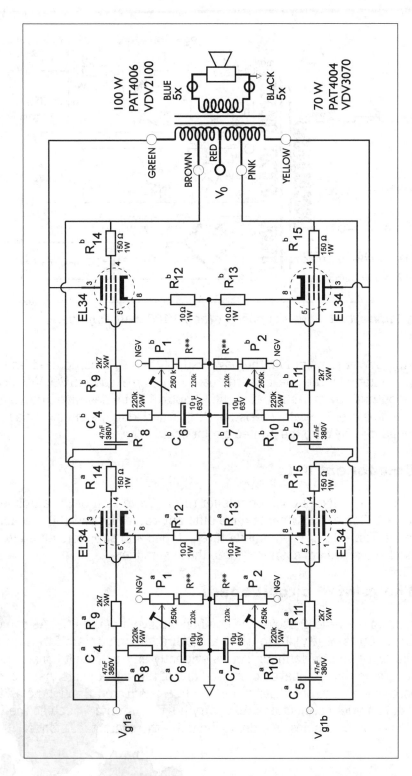

▲ *Figure 14.3* *Power amplifier section of the 70/100 watt PCB-based amplifier.*

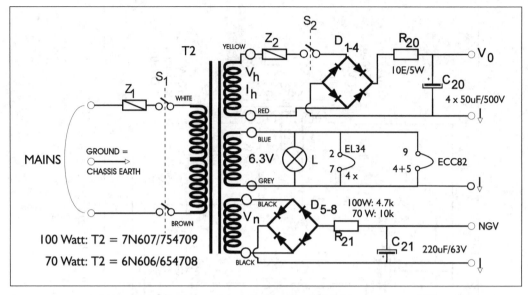

▲ **Figure 14.4** *Power supply for the 70/100 watt amplifier.*

Except for the power transformer, the power supply is also incorporated into the PCB. The supply voltage for the phase splitter has been increased from 280 V to 350 V, yielding higher output power. As noted in the Chapter 13, the negative grid voltage adjustment is made easier if a pair of resistors (R^{**}) is added to the circuit. This modification has found its way onto the printed circuit board.

14.2 | Component lists

The complete list of components for the 70 W version of the amplifier is given in Table 14.1. Some components have different values for the 100 W version; these are listed in Table 14.2. The manufacturers, types and suppliers noted in the components list have proven to sound 'right' in these amplifiers.

14.3 | The printed circuit board

Figure 14.6 (overleaf) shows the component layout of the PCB. As you can see, the construction is pretty straightforward. All components are fitted on the board, except for the two transformers. This is evidently an easily built construction. By the way, make sure that you have not missed any of the solder joints that must be soldered on both sides of the board. Although the PCB has plated-through holes, it is still a good idea to solder connections that carry heavy currents – such as the filament connections – on both sides, in order to minimize the contact resistance.

Resistors:[1]

R_1	100 kΩ	
R_2	1 kΩ	
R_3	100 kΩ	
R_4	1.2 kΩ	
R_5, R_6	22 kΩ	
R_7	3.9 kΩ	
R_8, R_{10}	220 kΩ	(2 pairs)
R_9, R_{11}	2.7 kΩ	(2 pairs)
R_{12}, R_{13}	10 Ω	(2 pairs)
R_{14}, R_{15}	150 Ω	(2 pairs)
R**	220 kΩ	(4 x)
R_{20}	10 Ω 5 W wirewound Philips	
R_{21}	10 kΩ	
P_1, P_2	250 kΩ	trimpot (4 x) 10-mm horizontal Piher

Capacitors:

C_1	100 nF 630 V axial	Siemens
C_2	220 µF 385 V radial, snap-in	Philips
C_3	1000 µF 6 V radial	
C_4, C_5	47 nF 630 V axial (2 x)	Siemens

C_6, C_7	10 µF 63 V radial (2 x)	
C_{20}	47 µF 500 V axial (4 x)	Amplimo
C_{21}	220 µF 63 V axial	

Valves:

B_1	ECC82	(1 x)
B_2	EL34	(4 x)

Semiconductors:

D_1–D_4 1N4007 (4 x)
D_5–D_8 B100C100 bridge module

Transformers:

T_1	VDV3070PP output transformer Amplimo/ Plitron	
T_2	6N606 power transformer Amplimo/Plitron	

Miscellaneous:

Z_1	1 A fuse, slow-blow
Z_2	630 mA fuse, slow-blow
L	9 V/12 V incandescent panel lamp
–	noval socket, silver-plated contacts
–	octal socket, ceramic (4 x)
PCB	BBB70100 Vanderveen PCB Amplimo/Plitron

1) All resistors are 1 W Beyschlag metal film, except as otherwise noted.

▲ **Table 14.1** *Components list for the 70-watt amplifier.*

Resistors:[1]

R_7	12 kΩ
R_{21}	4.7 kΩ

Miscellaneous:

Z1	1.6 A fuse, slow-blow
Z2	800 mA fuse, slow-blow

Transformers:

T1	VDV2100PP output transformer Amplimo/ Plitron
T2	7N607 power transformer Amplimo/ Plitron

1) All resistors are 1 W Beyschlag metal film, except as otherwise noted.

▲ **Table 14.2** *Alternate components list for the 100-watt amplifier.*

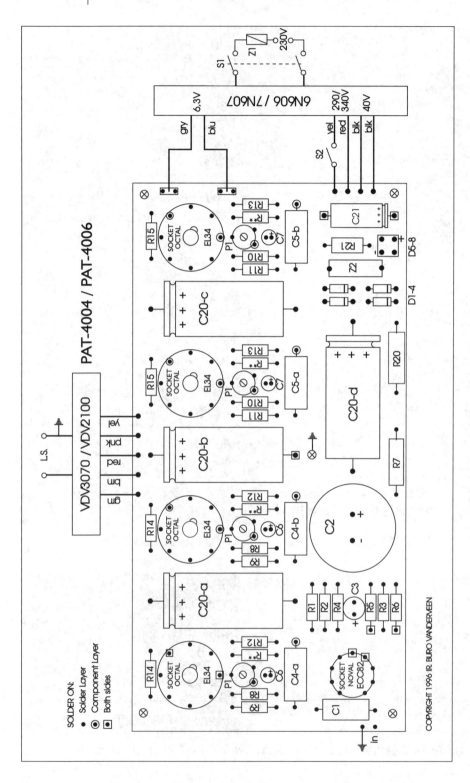

▲ *Figure 14.5* *BBB70100 component layout diagram.*

14.4 | Construction hints

Apart from R_{20}, all resistors are 1 watt, metal film types made by Beyschlag. These resistors yield an excellent sound and provide flawless performance under all circumstances, due to generous 'over-dimensioning'. Those who prefer the somewhat 'rounder' sound of carbon resistors can use them instead, as long as they have the same power rating. The choice of resistor type will not produce any audible difference in the noise characteristics of the amplifiers.

Component numbers are shown by a silk-screened overlay on the component side of the PCB, in order to prevent placement errors. You should fit the octal valve sockets first, because their prongs need some pushing to fit into the holes. Make sure that they are aligned correctly, because it is nearly impossible to remove them once they have been soldered into place! A backslash character (\) is located between the holes for prongs 1 and 8 to mark the proper location of the notch in the socket. Put the octal socket into position and then gently but firmly press it into the PCB. Then solder the prongs to their respective pads (note that prongs 2 and 7 – for the filament leads – must be soldered on the component side, and prong 2 of the leftmost power valve (located next to the ECC82) must be soldered on both sides). Next is the noval socket. You can't go wrong here, since it will fit in only one position. Again, prongs 4 and 5 must be soldered on both sides of the board. These are the prongs for the filament voltage and filament ground, respectively. Note that the ground plane is also used to screen the input capacitor C_1.

Next, all other components can be soldered into place. There is no prescribed order for this, but a good method is to start with the smallest components and mount them close to the PCB (except for R_7 and R_{20}, as noted below). Then proceed with the larger components, such as the non-electrolytic capacitors. Whenever a component has solder pads on both sides of the PCB, it definitely must be soldered on both sides. This applies to capacitors C_{1a}, C_{1b}, C_{2a}, and C_{2b} and resistors R_5 and R_6 (where they are joined at V_{g1-a} and V_{g1-b}, respectively). It also applies to the NGV supply tracks, starting with C_{21} and continuing on to the negative lead of C_{20b} and the leftmost pins of trimpots P_1 and P_2. These pins must also be soldered on both sides. While you're at it, turn both of them fully counterclockwise — that way the grid bias voltages will be set to the maximum negative level when you start setting up the amplifier, so you won't be needing to make a claim against your fire insurance!

Trimpots P_1 and P_2 must be fitted before capacitors C_6 and C_7, because the capacitors slightly overlap the pins of the trimpots. Make sure that C_2 is fitted with the correct polarization; its negative terminal is clearly marked by a dot next to the terminal or a line on the case.

R_7 and R_{20} should not placed directly against the PCB. Mount them slightly above the surface of the board. These resistors get pretty warm; you can avoid unsightly discolourizations by giving them some breathing room.

You can use solder lugs for the 'mechanical' connections — for the audio input connector (at the bottom left), the output transformer (top centre) and the power transformer (right-hand side). The filament voltage connections are best made using sturdy ¼-inch Faston spade connectors, given the thickness of the filament supply leads.

Lamp **L** should also be fitted by means of soldered-on flying leads with spade connectors. A 12 V incandescent panel lamp bulb produces a nice, discrete light with a 6.3 V supply, and it will probably last long enough for you to pass it on to your great-grandchildren. By the way, it is much better to use an incandescent lamp here rather than a LED, because a LED will produce noise pulses at the mains frequency (50 or 60 Hz) unless extensive precautions are taken (as described in Chapter 15). Such pulses can produce an 'untraceable' rattle in the amplifier's output.

You can bolt the PCB to an aluminium plate or chassis after all the components have been fitted. It must be kept at a safe distance from the chassis in order to prevent corona discharge from high voltage points. Mount the board with M3 screws, nuts and washers. Use 10-mm (or ⁷/₁₆-inch) *insulating* ceramic standoffs for the four corners of the board, and a *conductive* standoff of the same height for the mounting hole in the centre of the board (marked with a ground symbol). Galvanic contact between the circuit board ground and the chassis must take place via this central mounting point, and *only* via this point. Use lock washers and a sturdy metal standoff here for a solid, reliable contact. This mounting arrangement combines a safe separation between the circuit board and the chassis with a single, well-defined ground connection.

Figure 14.6 shows what you need to build the amplifier (except for the chassis, mounting hardware, hookup wire ande cables). and Figure 14.7 shows a fully assembled amplifier circuit board.

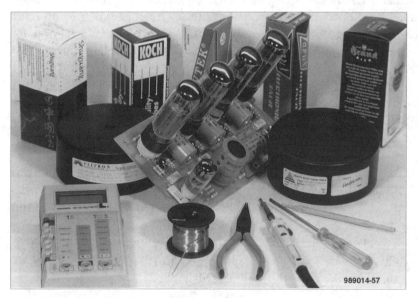

◀ *Figure 14.6*
The parts kit and tools for putting together the 70/100 W amplifier.

989014-57

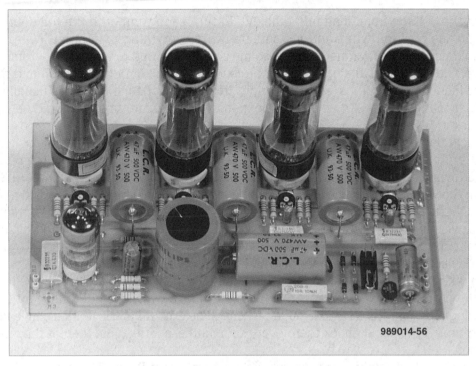

989014-56

▲ **Figure 14.7** *The assembled amplifier circuit board.*

14.5 | **Final checkout and adjustments**

Before going any further, I must again emphasize that certain precautions are mandatory for working safely with valve amplifiers — we are dealing with high voltages! If you are not sure of these precautions, please re-read Section 12.1 before proceeding any further.

Start by plugging all the valves into their sockets (four EL34s and one ECC82). Remove fuse Z_2 to prevent high voltage from reaching the amplifier at this stage. This is equivalent to putting the standby switch S_2 in the open (Standby) position. The time has come to switch on S_1; within a few moments the filaments of all five valves should be visibly glowing.

Now measure the voltage across capacitor C_{21} — it should be about 50 V. This checks the negative grid voltage supply. Make sure that both sets of trimpots P1 and P2 are turned fully counterclockwise — all the way to the left.

After you have checked the voltage at C_{21}, measure the voltage between ground and pin 5 of each EL34 (you can measure from the top of resistor R_9 or R_9 to the bottom of capacitor C_{20b}). You should measure the full negative grid voltage at each of the control grid pins. Turn the associated trimpot clockwise while observing the grid voltage, and verify that it slowly becomes less negative (capacitors C_6 and C_7 prevent the voltage from changing quickly). Return each trimpot to the full counter-clockwise position when you are satisfied that everything is in order. *Note*: you should use a digital voltmeter for these measurements, due to its high input impedance. Old-fashioned analogue multimeters will load the circuit too much and thus give inaccurate readings, since the input impedance of such meters is usually no higher than 20 kΩ/V. Any modern, inexpensive digital multimeter should be adequate.

Now unplug the mains cable, replace fuse Z_2 in its holder, plug in the mains cable and switch on the mains voltage again. Wait a little while, and then switch on the standby switch. Check that voltages are present across R_{12} and R_{13} for all EL34s. With the 70 W amplifier, the operating voltage should be (60 mA x 10 Ω) = 600 mV. If the measured voltage for any valve is less than this, gradually turn the proper trimpot clockwise until the voltmeter reads exactly 600 mV. You have now adjusted the quiescent currents of the power valves.

Play some loud music for a while, and then repeat the last set of measurements. The quiescent currents will probably have drifted somewhat, so readjust the voltages to the correct values. Repeat the adjustment/music cycle several times, until the readings become stable. Once you are finished, these settings will remain stable for a long time. You should check them every six months, and readjust them if they have drifted.

For the 100 W amplifier, set the voltage across resistors R_{12} and R_{13} to 500 mV.

Is there anything else to think about? Well, yes — if the output transformer is located right next to the ECC82, the amplifier may oscillate, due to coupling between the input and output stages. It is OK to mount the transformer on the left side of the PCB, as long as you maintain a separation of a few centimetres between it and the PCB. Also, the amplifier may oscillate if you forget to ground the black lead of the output transformer secondary winding (for the loudspeaker connection).

For the rest, if you faithfully apply the suggestions made in this book when planning and building your amplifier, it should provide you with many years of trouble-free listening pleasure.

15

Practical Aspects of Overall Negative Feedback

In Chapter 6 we examine the effects of negative feedback in an amplifier, using complicated formulas and computer-aided calculations. However, why not simply *use* overall negative feedback, instead of performing these difficult calculations? Are there simple ways to optimize the feedback, and can it be tuned by means of listening tests and simple measurements? This chapter provides some practical solutions to feedback problems. Using a few simple calculations and examples, we examine how feedback affects the amplification, the damping factor, the distortion level and the frequency range. We also look at some of the side effects of feedback.

15.1 | The basic principle of negative feedback

What negative feedback actually does can be explained in very few words. When an amplifier amplifies a signal, it makes mistakes (that is, it distorts the signal). The output signal is not only larger, it also contains components that are not present in the input signal. If we use a resistive divider to attenuate the output signal to roughly the same level as the input signal, and then compare the attenuated signal to the input signal, the two signals will not be the same. The signal that we obtain by subtracting the attenuated output signal from the input signal contains all the distortions, in the form of a difference signal. If we now

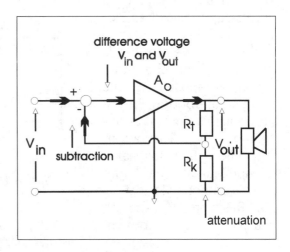

▲ *Figure 15.1*
The basic principle of negative feedback.

pass this signal through the amplifier *with reversed phase*, the amplifier will start to compensate for its own mistakes. The output signal will be cleaner and contain fewer mistakes (less distortion). The accuracy of the result will depend on the accuracy of the difference signal. The more exact the difference signal, the better the output signal. Figure 15.1 illustrates this process.

You can clearly see in Figure 15.1 that the output signal is attenuated by the resistive divider and subtracted from the input signal, and that the resulting difference signal is sent through the amplifier to be processed further. For this reason, some people are against feedback. They say, "The amplifier is not processing the music any more, but its own mistakes instead."

Well, what do *you* think? Later on, I have some comments to make about this idea.

15.2 | Practical implementation of negative feedback

Now we can either delve into complicated and difficult circuitry in order to achieve feedback, or we can simply start right away with the practical aspects. I choose to follow the latter course, so we can start directly with how to achieve feedback using valves. The main element of feedback is the subtraction of the input and output signals. Obviously, we need a circuit that can subtract two signals. With valves, this can be achieved very easily, as shown in Figure 15.2.

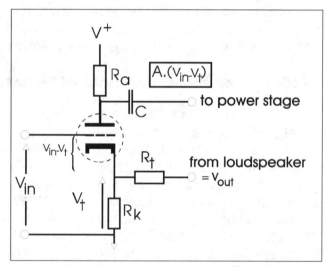

What can we see in this diagram? First, the input signal is applied to the valve's control grid. In our diagram, this signal is represented as V_{in}. The output signal from the loudspeaker is applied to the input valve's cathode via resistor R_{+}. Resistors R_{+} and R_k

▲ *Figure 15.2 A subtraction circuit for feedback.*

ensure that only a portion of the output signal V_{out} reaches the cathode. The amplitude of this signal, designated V_{+}, is given by the following formula:

$$V_{+} = V_{out} \cdot \frac{R_k}{R_k + R_{+}}$$

[15-1]

The valve amplifies the potential difference V_{gk} between the control grid and the cathode. The following formula represents what takes place in the amplifier:

$$V_a = A \cdot V_{gk} = A(V_{in} - V_+)$$ [15-2]

We are subtracting two signals from each other, namely the input signal and part of the output signal. The difference signal (given by Formula 15-2) is then processed further in the amplifier. There is no point in discussing this circuit any further, because we have found what we were looking for. We can now further discuss the principles of feedback.

15.3 | The extra preamplifier

Negative feedback always causes a reduction in the total amplification factor. An important setup condition can be derived from this fact, but we discuss that later.

So far, our amplifier circuit does not have a very large amplification factor. This is because only one half of the ECC82 (12AU7) valve is actually providing any effective amplification. The amplification of the output valves and the reduction of the signal voltage by the output transformer (down transformation) cancel each other out. That leaves an effective amplification factor of approximately 10. If we now apply feedback, the resulting amplification factor is only roughly 2. This is not sufficient, as the following example shows.

Suppose our output power is 30 watts with a load of 5 ohms. This corresponds to an output voltage of 12.25 V. If the amplification factor is 10, our input voltage is 1.2 V. Most preamplifiers and CD players can easily provide this, so we have no problem. However, if the amplification factor is 2, as in our feedback example, the input voltage must be 6.1 V. This is a problem, because most preamplifiers cannot provide such a high voltage. This is why we need an extra preamplifier, as shown in Figure 15.3.

I have chosen an ECC81 (12AT7) for the preamplifier valve. In this circuit, the valve has an effective amplification factor of 14. The maximum amplification factor of the ECC81 is 60, but this drops to around 30 due to the value of R_k. The anode resistance is small (100 kΩ), which reduces the amplification even more. In addition, resistor R_1 of the phase splitter places a relatively large load on the preamplifier. The net result is that the amplification factor drops to a mere 14. Due to an incredible coincidence, this is exactly how much amplification we need — a miracle of modern electronics!

Now we have defined the valve configuration and the supply voltage, and we also know the value of the plate current (1.2 mA). The supply voltage V_1 is tapped off from the phase splitter (see Chapter 10). Since the current for the extra preamplifier stage passes through resistor R_7 (as shown in Figure 10.4), the value of this resistor must be changed. The new value of R_7 can be calculated using the following formula:

$$R_7 = (V_0 - 280) \div (0.0057 + 0.0012) \ [\Omega]$$ [15-3]

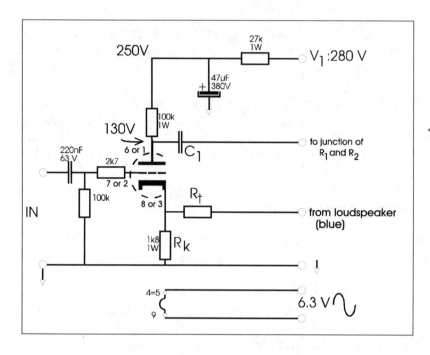

◀ **Figure 15.3**
This extra
preamplifier
is needed
when negative
feedback
is used.

For example, suppose $V_0 = 380$ V and we use the preamplifier in Figure 15.3. The value of R_7 will be $100 \div (0.0057 + 0.0012) = 14{,}493$ Ω. In this case we can use 15 kΩ. The power handling capability of this resistor should be equal to $(0.0069)^2 \times 15{,}000 = 0.71$ W. Use a 1 watt type to provide a bit of safety margin.

I am forced to make another comment here. The input and output signals in the circuits shown in Chapters 5 and 6 have the same phase. When the extra preamplifier stage is used, the phase is shifted by a full 180°, which has the following conse-quences:

a) the absolute phase is not correct,
b) $V_{out} = -1 \cdot$ (amplification factor) $\cdot V_{in}$,
c) which means that the subtraction in Formula 15-2 becomes an addition,
d) which means that negative feedback becomes *positive* feedback, so that
e) the amplifier will now amplify even more,
f) the amount of distortion will increase,
g) the output impedance will increase and
h) the amplifier will probably start to oscillate.

The above list indicates that we have a major problem on our hands. We have to do something about this. Figure 15-4 indicates what has to be done to avoid prob-lems when the extra preamplifier is used. The correct phase relationship can be restored by swapping the primary leads of the output transformer. Pay particular attention to the colour coding of the primary leads.

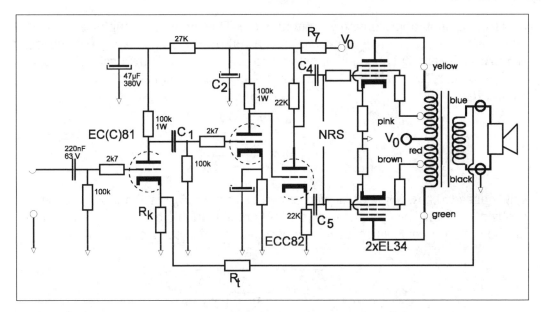

▲ *Figure 15.4*
Correct connection of the output transformer to the output power valves
when feedback is employed with an extra preamplifier stage.
Note the colour coding of the output transformer primary leads.

I can not warn you enough to be especially careful and alert in this situation. It is usually possible to notice when you have created positive feedback instead of negative feedback by incorrectly connecting the transformer leads. Fortunately, there is a very handy method for testing a circuit without using any measuring equipment.

15.4 | Testing for correct feedback connections

You should construct the whole valve amplifier completely and test it without connecting R_t. You can play soft music for this, for example. If everything is in order, connect R_t. This should *reduce* the volume. If the music becomes *louder* when R_t is added, a mistake has been made in the connections to the output transformer primary leads. Consult the relevant diagrams.

15.5 | Dimensioning the amplifier

I will now proceed with dimensioning the amplifier using feedback. To start with, we have to calculate the amplification factor without the use of feedback. A factor of 14 can be assigned to the preamplifier, and the output amplifier (including the phase splitter) will have a factor of approximately 10, for a total amplification factor of 140 (I omit 'approximately' from now on). This amount of amplification is too much. Formula 15-4 shows us how we can use the extra amplification for feedback. Here A_o is the amplification factor without feedback and A_c is the desired amplification factor with feedback. We can adjust the amount of feedback by using resistors R_t and R_k:

$$A_c = \frac{A_0}{1 + A_0 \cdot \dfrac{R_k}{R_t + R_k}} \qquad [15\text{-}4]$$

We already know some of the values in this formula: $A_o = 140$ and $R_k = 1.8$ kΩ. It is obvious that we can produce any desired amplification factor that is less than A_o by choosing a suitable value for R_t. Suppose we would like A_c to be equal to 30:

$$30 = \frac{140}{1 + 140 \cdot \dfrac{1800}{R_t + 1800}} \qquad [15\text{-}5]$$

A little math gives a value of 68,200 Ω (approximately 68 kΩ) for R_t. You should now find it easy to use Formula 15-4 to calculate the value of R_t for whatever value of A_c you need.

15.6 | The side effects of negative feedback

The amplification factor is not the only thing that is changed by negative feedback. The damping factor is also affected. This is easy to explain. In our example, the amplification factor is reduced from 140 to 30, a factor of 4.67. It follows that the damping factor must increase by the same factor, so that if the damping factor is 1.2 without feedback, it will be equal to (1.2·4.67) = 5.6 with feedback.

A second side effect is that the total harmonic distortion is reduced. If for example the harmonic distortion factor at 1 kHz is 0.4% with 10 watts of output power, then with feedback it will decrease 4.67 times, to only 0.09%.

This is a very brief description of the effect of negative feedback on distortion, and as such incomplete. We have not considered how the amplifier's output impedance influences the effective amount of distortion that reaches the loudspeakers. Unfortunately, a full description of this would become too complex. You should regard the above description as indicative only.

The frequency response is also affected by negative feedback. This is discussed further on in this chapter.

15.7 | Feedback terminology

There are several ways in which the amount of feedback is described in various books. Some authors quote amounts in decibels, while others make use of a number of different factors. In some cases it is possible to understand where the quoted values come from, but in other cases they seem to be somehow derived from dark and mysterious formulas. For the sake of clarity, I define feedback here in terms of both factors and decibels, and I present the necessary formulas.

■ | The feedback factor

First, we must determine the open-loop unloaded amplification factor A_o (with no feedback and no loudspeaker connected). Then we must measure the no-load amplification factor with feedback, A_c, again without connecting any loud-speaker to the amplifier.

The feedback factor *NFB* is then given by the formula:

$$NFB = \frac{A_o}{A_c} \qquad [15\text{-}6]$$

In our previous example, the feedback factor was equal to $(140 \div 30) = 4.67$. Remember that this definition requires that no speaker is connected to the amplifier. Otherwise, variations in the damping factor will distort our measurements and invalidate the result.

■ | Feedback in decibels

We have already defined *NFB*. The amount of feedback can be expressed in decibels using the following formula:

$$NFB_{dB} = 20\log(NFB) \qquad [15\text{-}7]$$

The feedback in our example is thus equal to $20\log(4.67) = 13.4$ dB.

■ | Which feedback definition is correct?

The expressions for feedback given so far, in terms of a factor or decibels, are very clear and simple. However, these simple definitions are not always employed. Sometimes the following definition is used: "With actual speakers connected to the amplifier, first measure the amplification without feedback (A_{ol}) and then measure the amplification with feedback (A_{cl}). Then simply calculate the value of the expression $20\log(A_{ol}/A_{cl})$ and you have the amount of feedback in decibels."

This sounds simple, but unfortunately it is in fact rather complex. To illustrate this, I will open my mathematical toolbox and try to properly explain the problem.

Let's assume that the amplification with no load and no feedback is A_o, the output impedance of the amplifier without feedback is Z_{out} (which means that damping factor is $8/Z_{out}$, if the loudspeaker impedance is assumed to be 8 Ω) and the impedance of the speakers is Z_L. Then the effective gain from the input to the loaded output is:

$$A_{ol} = A_o \cdot \frac{Z_L}{Z_{out} + Z_L} \qquad [15\text{-}8]$$

Now we introduce feedback. We can use the term γ to simplify the mathematics somewhat:

$$\gamma = \frac{R_k}{R_k + R_t} \qquad [15\text{-}9]$$

From Formula 15-4, the amplification with feedback (but with no load) is equal to:

$$A_c = \frac{A_o}{1 + \gamma A_o} \qquad [15\text{-}10]$$

As already mentioned, feedback changes the damping factor, so the output impedance with feedback is given by:

$$Z_{out,e} = \frac{Z_{out}}{1 + \gamma A_o} \qquad [15\text{-}11]$$

It follows from this that we have to modify Formula 5-8 by replacing A_o with A_c and Z_{out} with $Z_{out,e}$. The amplification that we measure for a loaded amplifier with feedback is thus:

$$A_{cl} = \frac{A_o}{1 + \gamma A_o} \cdot \frac{Z_L}{\dfrac{Z_{out}}{1 + \gamma A_o} + Z_L} \qquad [15\text{-}12]$$

The amount of feedback in decibels is therefore given by the following formula:

$$NFB_{l,dB} = 20\log\left[\frac{A_o \cdot \dfrac{Z_L}{Z_{out} + Z_L}}{\dfrac{A_o}{1 + \gamma A_o} \cdot \dfrac{Z_L}{\dfrac{Z_{out}}{1 + \gamma A_o} + Z_L}} \right] \qquad [15\text{-}13]$$

This can be simplified mathematically to yield the following formula:

$$NFB_{l,dB} = 20\log\left[\frac{Z_{out} + (1 + \gamma A_o)\cdot Z_L}{Z_{out} + Z_L}\right] \qquad [5\text{-}14]$$

This is unfortunately not a particularly attractive result, because Z_L figures too prominently in the formula. According to this formula, the amount of feedback is strongly dependent on the loudspeaker impedance. This means that if we specify the amount of feedback for the amplifier measured under load, we should also specify the impedance of the loudspeaker used.

On the other hand, we can rewrite Formulas 15-6 and 15-7 from our earlier, simple definition of the amount of feedback as:

$$NFB_{l,dB} = 20\log\left(\frac{A_o}{A_c}\right) = 20\log\left(1 + \gamma A_o\right) \qquad [15\text{-}15]$$

This gives us a formula that depends only on the characteristics of the amplifier; Z_L is not a factor. The choice of how to define the amount of feedback is up to you!

15.8 | The subjective element

Valve amplifier tradition holds that the sound character 'closes up' if there is more than 15 dB of feedback. I decided to test this rule, which is based purely on subjective experience and observation. To my surprise, it seems to be true. If the feedback is greater than 15 dB, the sound quality becomes tighter and colder — not at all like the typical warm sound of a valve amplifier. It is thus not a good idea to go above the 15 dB limit with feedback. Otherwise, you will find that a silly little resistor has changed the pleasant sound of your valve amplifier into something that you wouldn't wish on your dog.

You can test this for yourself. Simply try using several different values of R_+, and you will hear the positive and negative effects of feedback. I am sure that you will confirm my conclusion that more than 15 dB of feedback will make you feel that you have built a bad amplifier.

15.9 | Feedback and the frequency response above 20 kHz

The following discussion deals with the most difficult aspect of feedback, because we are forced to carry out our calculations in the complex domain. In fact, we should construct whole new equivalent circuit models to study the effects of feedback on the frequency response (as we did in Chapter 6). Unfortunately, that is beyond the scope of this chapter, so I will try to explain how feedback affects the frequency response by means of a few practical examples.

To start with, feedback will increase the frequency range. The amount of amplification that we have sacrificed to feedback is effectively used to increase the frequency range of the amplifier. An obvious question is whether we actually need this extra frequency range, since the amplifier can already reach 100 kHz without feedback. I will not pursue this question here. What is important is that feedback can have highly undesirable side effects on the frequency response. It may even cause the amplifier to become unstable. This point deserves more attention.

Without feedback, the amplification decreases at high frequencies, and the phase response starts to change as well. This is already evident from the characteristic curves on the transformer specification sheets. The second graph depicts the phase response the output transformer, which shows that the phase shift increases significantly above 100 kHz. If we also include the phase shift of the valve circuit, we can be sure that there will be a large amount of phase shift between the input and output signals above 100 kHz.

It is obvious that we cannot assume that the phases of the input and output signals are the same above 100 kHz. Unfortunately, phase equality is one of the necessary conditions for feedback based on signal comparison (subtraction). We can even say that above a certain frequency, negative feedback becomes positive feedback, with all that this implies. The negative consequences of positive feedback are:

a) The amplifier will start to oscillate at a very high frequency (it will turn into a medium-wave transmitter).
b) The amplifier will react strongly to inductive and capacitive loudspeaker loads.

The second aspect is not just hypothetical. For example, suppose we use an electrostatic loudspeaker. At high frequencies its impedance is capacitive, and roughly equal to 2 µF. If we connect this speaker to a valve amplifier with feedback without taking any special precautions, large overshoots will occur at high frequencies (usually around 20 kHz). These will produce undesirable oscillations and ringing.

In summary, carelessly applied negative feedback can ruin the high frequency behaviour of the amplifier.

15.10 | Eliminating the effects of feedback on the high frequency response

There are two measures that implemented together, in order to eliminate the problems caused by feedback that are described in the previous section.

Measure 1: limit the frequency range of the preamplifier. To do so, connect a resistor and a capacitor in series across the anode resistor of the primary valve. These are shown as R^* and C^* in Figure 15.5.

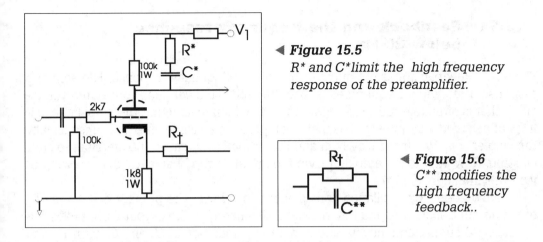

◀ **Figure 15.5**
R* and C* limit the high frequency response of the preamplifier.

◀ **Figure 15.6**
C** modifies the high frequency feedback..

The additional components cause the amplification to start to drop off fairly early, starting at 5 kHz, This first-order rolloff, with a slope of 6 dB/octave, allows us to use feedback without creating instability problems. Calculating the values of R^* and C^* is fairly complex, so it is better to determine them experimentally. Start with approximately 2 kΩ and 390 pF.

Measure 2: connect a capacitor across R_+ to make the high frequency feedback different from the low frequency feedback. This capacitor, which typically has a value between 27 pF and 390 pF, is shown as C^{**} in Figure 15.6.

How can you verify that you have chosen optimum values for R^*, C^* and C^{**}? One good technique is to use a 1 kHz square wave test signal connected to the input of the amplifier. The amplifier output should be connected to a 5 Ω, 50 W dummy load. Monitor the output signal with an oscilloscope. With overall negative feedback and without any correction, the amplifier will show overshoots on the edges of the square wave, and will probably oscillate as well. Now add R^* and C^*. With properly selected component values, the amplifier will not oscillate (this is controlled by R^*) and there should be practically no overshoots on the waveform (this is controlled by C^*).

Now replace the dummy load with a standard electrodynamic loudspeaker. The amplifier may oscillate with a loudspeaker load, since the load is not purely resistive. The oscillation can be corrected by the proper choice of C^{**}. This will take some experimentation, and the value may depend on the particular loudspeaker used, since every loudspeaker has its own non-constant complex impedance. This suggests that the amount of compensation is loudspeaker-dependent. However, I have learned from experience that it is always possible to find an optimum compensation that will work fine with all types of loudspeakers.

Once again, calculating the optimum values of R^*, C^* and C^{**} can be very complex. Chapter 6 gives a general indication of how to do this. In practice, an experimental approach is often faster, certainly in comparison to working through the complete complex-domain calculations.

15.11 | Feedback and the frequency response below 20 Hz

Feedback does not affect only the high frequency response. The amplifier response at very low frequencies is also affected. This can lead to an unfortunate effect that is often referred to as *motor boating*, which means that the amplifier oscillates at a very low frequency. This may even produce a visible effect, because usually the woofer cone will move slowly in and out. It may even cause the amplifier to start clipping. Now, why is our amplifier trying to imitate a tug boat, and how can we prevent this from happening?

The low frequency oscillation comes about as follows. The primary inductance L_p of the output transformer and the internal resistance r_p of the output valve produce a lower −3 dB cutoff frequency. In addition, the combination of C_4 and C_5 with R_8 and R_{10} produces a second −3 dB cutoff frequency. Finally, C_1 and R_1 in the extra preamplifier (that we have to use to provide enough amplification to allow feedback to be used) create yet a third cutoff frequency.

The combination of these cutoff frequencies may shift the phase at very low frequencies so much that the phase difference between the input and output signals reaches 180 degrees. If this happens, the negative feedback turns into positive feedback, and the amplifier will oscillate at a very low frequency.

There are two ways to alleviate this problem.

Method 1: *increase* the capacitance of C_1 to at least ten times the recommended value of 150 nF. This moves one of the cutoff frequencies down to 2 Hz, so that the 180 degree phase shift occurs at much lower frequencies where the amplification is so small that oscillation will not occur.

Method 2: *reduce* the capacitance of C_1 to no more than one tenth of the recommended value of 150 nF. This reduces the amplification at low frequencies to such a degree that oscillation will not occur. The negative feedback will ensure that the frequency response of the amplifier remains flat above 20 Hz.

You may ask, what about an 'exact' solution to this problem? This is very difficult, because the cutoff frequency due to the transformer inductance and the internal resistance of the output valves varies with the strength of the output signal, since the value of L_p depends on the signal level. This means that it is best to prevent the amplifier from imitating a motor boat by changing only C_1, and nothing else.

These solutions for motor boating can only be used if it occurs due to the use of feedback. In addition, the optimum value of C_1 depends on the amount of feedback used.

An amplifier can also motor boat when feedback is not used. What causes this? In this case, the problem is caused by an unstable power supply together with an insufficient amount of capacitance for C_{20}. The large value of C_{20} in the designs described in this book is intended to eliminate this possibility.

When everything is taken into account, applying feedback is no easy task. The aim of this chapter is to highlight this issue and to help you understand the problems you can expect. Extensive mathematical models (as illustrated in Chapter 6) are needed for a theoretically 'correct' approach to using feedback, but you can achieve a certain amount through simple experimentation if you know where the problems lie. I have described the most important ones in this chapter.

15.12 | Summary and conclusions

This chapter discusses how feedback functions. I have presented definitions and formulas for calculating the amount of feedback used. Feedback reduces the amount of amplification, which means that an additional preamplifier is needed. Feedback reduces distortion and increases the damping factor. More than 15 dB of overall feedback causes the sound image to 'close up'. The effect of feedback on the frequency response is a complex and difficult area. I have shown how two compensation measure can be used to correct the high frequency response when feedback is used. Low frequency oscillation due to feedback can be prevented by increasing or decreasing the value of C_1 by a factor of ten.

16

The UL40-S
Stereo Valve Amplifier

Marketing research has shown that there is a demand for a DIY amplifier kit that is based on the design concepts in this book. This kit should be complete, including all components plus the enclosure; it should also be easy to assemble and present few mechanical hassles, which means that it should include a finished cabinet. Hand wiring should be kept to a minimum, which means that everything should preferably fit on a single printed circuit board. Understandably, a step-by-step construction guide also ranks high on the wish list. All these wishes are fulfilled in the UL40-S kit, which contains everything necessary to produce a working and nifty-looking amplifier. This chapter discusses the ideas behind the design, showing the remarkable properties of this DIY amplifier.

16.1 | Outline of the UL40-S

This amplifier has many features that set it apart from most other DIY amplifier projects. The output power, at more than 30 watts, should be sufficient for most applications. The frequency response is exceptionally broad for a valve amplifier, and this is achieved without overall negative feedback. The design is based using a minimum number of high quality components. This has two distinct advantages. First, the fewer components in an amplifier, the easier it is to build. Second, a small number of components also minimizes the damage to the music signal — every junction that the signal passes, and every nonlinearity that it encounters, is a potential source of distortion. The design supports several configurations for the output valves, which may be operated in the triode, ultralinear or pentode mode. This allows the builder to experiment with the damping factor, the frequency response and the output power, so that the final result will truly be 'custom'. The kit includes an Alps volume control potentiometer and five-position input selector switch with gold-plated RCA/Cinch jacks, so that the amplifier can accommodate commonly-used signal sources such as CD, tuner and tape. The cabinet is made of black plastic with gold labeling. A plastic cabinet is used instead of a metal cabinet in order to avoid eddy currents and ground loops, thereby keeping a boatload of potential interference out of the finished amplifier. The amplifier is built on two PCBs, consisting of a main board plus a small board for the input connectors and selector switch. The internal wiring is thus kept to a minimum. The power supply is built in, and the necessary mains and standby switches and fuses are all present. LED indicators clearly show the status of the amplifier. The concepts presented in the previous chapters are all incorporated into this kit.

16.2 | The philosophy behind the UL40-S

This is literally a straightforward design. It is intended to provide no-frills amplification of the signal from a CD player to the level needed to drive the loud-speakers. As can be seen from Figure 16.1, there is an input selector but no further preamplification. The input sensitivity of the amplifier is 630 mV for full output power, which is more than adequate for any modern signal source. The circuit is as basic as it gets — three valves per channel, that's it. This is not a sign of Dutch thrift, but rather an attempt to maintain the fidelity of the signal. It is evident that every component tends to more or less degrade the signal, so less is more! As already stated, this amplifier represents the shortest imaginable path between the signal source and the loudspeakers. This means that every part of the design is crucial, and every component must be of impeccable quality. This is reflected in the components chosen, as will become clear. Following the convention in this book, the amplifier uses three toroidal transformers, consisting of a 6N536 for the power supply and two VDV6040PP output transformers. Figure 16.2 (overleaf) shows the circuit diagram of the power supply, and Figure 16.3 shows the component layout of the main circuit board.

16.3 | Feedback: yes or no?

The UL40-S does not use overall negative feedback. Since the input and output signals are never compared to each other, there is no way the amplifier can correct any errors that it makes. They must therefore be prevented from occurring, which is not an easy task. Further on, I explain how I managed to keep the distortion wonderfully low.

If you carefully examine the circuit diagram, you will see that the network around valve B_{1b} forms a local negative feedback loop. This is required to generate an antiphase signal at the junction of R_{16} and C_3. I can almost hear you thinking, "Aha — feedback!" That's true, but thank goodness it is only local, rather than external negative feedback from the output to the input.

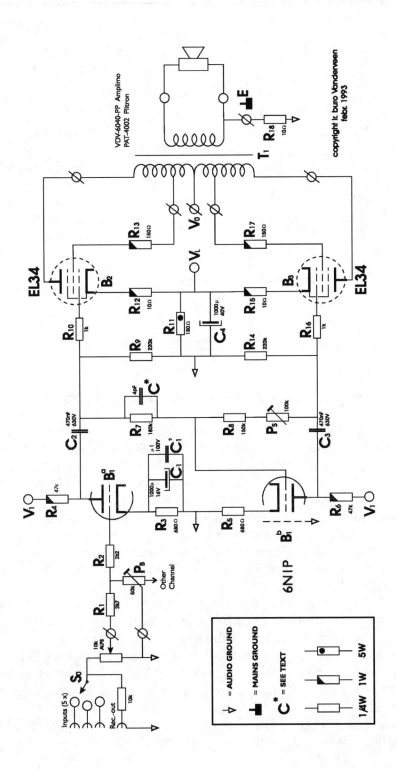

▲ *Figure 16.1* *The audio circuit of the UL40-S (one channel).*

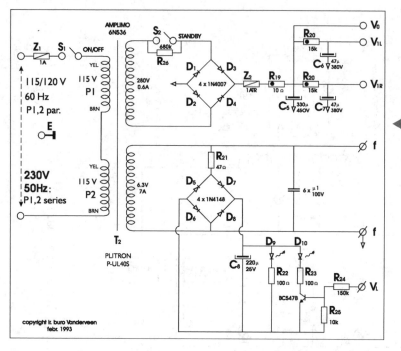

◀ **Figure 16.2**
Schematic
diagram of the
power supply
for both channels
of the ULS-40
amplifier

16.4 | Output power and class A or AB₁ operation

The output transformer in this balanced amplifier is driven by a matched pair of power valves. The valves are biased by resistor R_{11} in parallel with the electrolytic capacitor C_4 (1000 µF), which is a so-called 'auto-bias' configuration. This approach is rather different from the negative grid voltage used in most other designs in this book.

Since the bias voltage for both valves is generated by a single resistor, the valves must be matched to keep them balanced. If we use unmatched valves, their quiescent currents will differ, which will cause hum. The balance can be checked by comparing the voltages across R_{12} and R_{15}; they should be close to 0.70 V, and more importantly, they should be identical!

With a supply voltage of 380 volts, the UL40-S can deliver 33 watts per channel as a pentode amplifier, and close to 30 watts in the ultralinear configuration. The output power drops to 15 watts per channel when the triode configuration is used.

Approximately 25 V will build up over the common cathode resistor R_{11}, corresponding to a quiescent current of 69 mA per valve. Each EL34 dissipates $(380 - 25) \times 0.069 = 24.7$ watts. This is just under the maximum allowed anode dissipation of 25 watts, so we are safe.

It is a simple exercise to calculate the maximum output power level for which the power valves still operate in class A. The maximum power efficiency of a triode

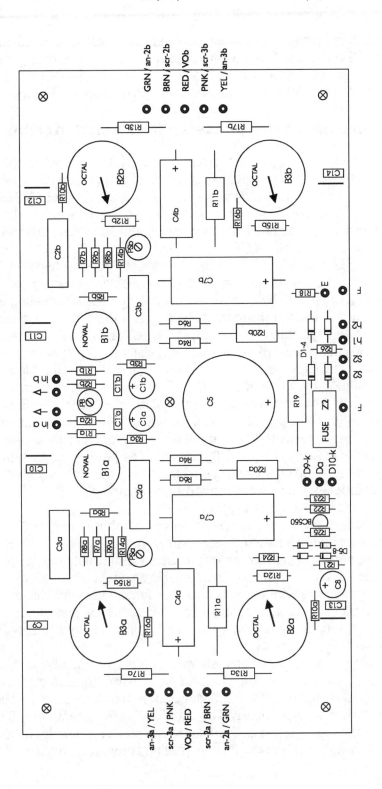

▲ **Figure 16.3** *The circuit board component layout of the UL40-S (one channel).*

amplifier is 25%, corresponding to 12.5 watts. The pentode setting more than doubles this amount, so 25 watts is still well within class A for the pentode configuration, and right on the edge for ultralinear. Driving the amplifier above these levels causes it to shift from class A to class AB_1, and consequently to produce more output power.

16.5 | More about the phase splitter and distortion

As already noted, stringent requirements must be placed on the intrinsic distortion characteristics of the amplifier, since there is no feedback to reduce any distortion that may occur. A highly linear valve, such as the E88CC or 6922 (Sovtek) or the preferred type, the 6N1P (Svetlana), is therefore a good choice for the driver stage. The anode voltage will be somewhere between 90 and 100 V. The distortion is still under 1% when the anodes of the 6N1P are driven to 80 V_{pp} (28 V_{eff}). This is acceptable, since the output valves will be driven beyond their limits at this level. The contribution of the driver section to the overall distortion is therefore negligible.

There is another reason why I chose the 6N1P. The output impedance of each valve section is about 4 kΩ in this circuit. This output impedance is connected in series with the input capacitance of the output valves, forming a first-order low pass network. The grid capacitance of the output valves is low in the pentode configuration – a couple of picofarads – but it becomes quite substantial in the triode configuration (around 50 pF), due to the Miller effect. The latter value, combined with the output impedance of the driver, results in a bandwidth of 800 kHz. This is much larger than the bandwidth of the output transformer, which is just what I wanted.

But – hoho! – there's a caveat! The antiphase signal for valve B_3 is generated by valve B_{1b} via feedback across R_7 and R_8 with P_S. The parallel combination of the grid-to-anode capacitance of B_{1b} and the resistance of the latter two components produces a significantly smaller bandwidth of about 180 kHz, which is still respectable. Still, the bandwidth of B_{1a} is much larger.

This means that there is a certain asymmetry at high frequencies. This can be compensated by adding capacitor C^* (approximately 4 pF) in parallel to R_7. This is not necessary for normal audio use, but connoisseurs with access to a signal generator and an oscilloscope can add this refinement. No commercially available capacitor meets all my requirements with respect to the maximum operating voltage, frequency response and internal absorption, so I recommend that you make your own! This is not as hard as it sounds — just twist together two insulated wires approximately 10 cm long, and there you have it.

To adjust this capacitor, proceed as follows. Load the loudspeaker output with a 5 Ω power resistor, and drive the amplifier with a sine wave signal to produce an output level of 8 V_{pp}. Now increase the frequency to over 100 kHz. You should see some asymmetry on the oscilloscope display. The upper half of the sine wave will be either larger or smaller than the lower half. You can restore perfect symmetry by increasing or decreasing the length of the twisted wires (adding or removing twists).

16.6 | AC balance and the 100 Hz square wave test

The symmetry of the phase splitter is important over the entire frequency range of the amplifier. Both power valves need grids signals with equal amplitudes and opposite phase, to avoid distortion due to an asymmetric output signal. This balance is achieved by adjusting the gain of B_{1b} using trimpot P_S. If you do not have access to measuring equipment, then set this trimpot to its midrange position. This will give the best results within the tolerance of the components used.

If you have the necessary equipment, you can add more icing to the cake. With a distortion analyzer, you can minimize the THD by adjusting P_S. A quick and dirty adjustment can be made by applying a 100 Hz square wave to the input with a 5 Ω resistor load, as in Section 16.5. Slowly increase input level while observing the output waveform. When P_S is correctly adjusted, the rising and falling edges of the square wave will both be straight, without overshoots or dips. See also Chapter 11.

16.7 | Logistic Earth Patterns: LEP®

As noted in Chapter 13, suspending the components in 'mid air' results in a good-sounding amplifier, while using a printed circuit board often negatively affects the sound quality. What about the PCB for the UL40-S — will it ruin everything? Not necessarily, as long as a lot of care and attention are given to its layout and construction. A new layout technique, called Logistic Earth Pattern technology (LEP for short), has been used in the design of this board.

What does LEP do? In simple terms, ground currents from previous or subsequent stages of an amplifier can degrade the performance of a particular stage. For example, if the relatively large currents from the power valves are allowed to affect the small input currents via the ground conductors, a certain amount of uncontrolled positive or negative feedback will occur. The LEP technique employs special ground layouts and techniques to avoid such disturbances. This involves the proper placement and interconnection of the ground tracks. Designing a layout in this way requires a lot of time and concentration, since every ground current must be individually calculated and checked, including its influence on adjacent parts of the circuit via the dielectric properties of the board material. Using the LEP technique to design a PCB is therefore expensive.

The LEP technique has been used extensively in the design of the PCB for the UL40-S amplifier. When the design of the board was finished, we performed a long and costly series of comparison tests. The amplifier was first built in the 'classical' fashion, with point-to-point wiring and 'airborne' components. Then we had two LEP PCBs manufactured, one using glass-epoxy base material and the other using Teflon®. After extensive listening tests, I concluded that there were practically no demonstrable differences in the results for the three construction methods. A valve amplifier can thus safely be built on a PCB, as long as the board is carefully designed.

16.8 | High frequency filament circuits

An interesting feature of the circuit is the high-frequency decoupling of the filament circuit. This is achieved by connecting a 100 nF capacitor across the filament pins of each valve, as well as by coiling the filament winding leads of the power transformer to form a small inductor.

Why is decoupling necessary? The PCB tracks for the filament supply form a large double loop that is located at the edge of the board. To ensure that each valve has the same filament voltage, the voltage drop along these tracks must be minimized. As the filament currents add up to a hefty 6 ampères, this is no unnecessary luxury. The solution is to connect the filament supply leads to both sides of the loop. However, this means that the filament currents flow in the same direction in the parallel tracks, which results in a large net loop inductance. The loop will thus unavoidably radiate electromagnetic signals, not only at the mains frequency (50 or 60 Hz), but also at the frequencies of all the HF noise signals present on the mains circuit. The magnetic field of the mains-frequency radiation is perpendicular to the PCB, so it does not present a problem. Radiation from high-frequency signals, however, can create havoc in the amplifier, due to the short wavelengths of these signals.

High-frequency decoupling is used to keep the filament loop from radiating, by shorting out the high frequency signals. This may be only a small detail, but believe me, it is the combined effect of many small details that makes the difference between a mediocre amplifier and a top-quality product.

16.9 | The standby switch and the status LEDs

The standby switch S_2 is used to disconnect the high voltage from the amplifier circuit and thus place the amplifier in the standby state. There is a small resistance (R_{26}) connected across the switch. There are two reasons for using this resistor. The first reason is that it maintains a low voltage across the electrolytic capacitors, so they stay polarized. This will substantially lengthen their life span. The second reason is that with this resistor, the amplifier *still works* in the standby state and can deliver a very small amount of power to the loudspeakers (less than a milliwatt). This is enough to let you hear whether the input is open, or if an input signal is present. This is particularly handy in the latter case, since you might otherwise have a literally earth-shaking experience when you switch from standby to the operating mode!

The status indicator LEDs are fed from the filament supply. Although they are not intended to be used as rectifiers, LEDs switch surprisingly fast. They will thus generate strong pulse disturbances when driven by an AC voltage. In order to prevent this, the supply voltage for the LEDs is rectified and then filtered by the combination of R_{21}, R_{22}, R_{23} and capacitor C_8. This prevents any nasty high frequency signals from being injected into the filament circuit.

The Standby LED lights up when the right-channel EL34 cathode voltage exceeds +16 V. This indicates the presence of anode current. It's always pleasant to see this lamp light up after a 'cold' amplifier is switched on with S_1 and S_2. The Standby LED comes on slowly, and at the same time music starts to come from the loudspeakers. This is a sign that the valves have warmed up enough to start drawing current.

By the way, it is recommended to always switch on S_2 a little while after S_1. This gives the valves time to warm up, so that they are ready to work when the high voltage is applied. This also keeps the high voltage from reaching its full no-load value, and this is good for the life span of the electrolytic capacitors as well as the valves.

16.10 | The specifications

Table 16.1 summarizes the main specifications of your handiwork.

UL40-S Specifications			
Description:	Stereo valve amplifier, complete DIY kit		
Valves:	2 x Svetlana 6N1P		
	4 x EL34 (standard kit)		
	4 x KT66 (option 1 kit)		
	4 x 6550WA (option 2 kit)		
Output valve operating modes:	triode	ultralinear	pentode
Output power:	2 x 12	2 x 29	2 x 33 W
a_2 (see text):	1.8	1.97	2.22
$f_{-3\,dB\text{-low}}$[1]:	8	8	8 Hz
$f_{-3\,dB\text{-high}}$[1]:	100	80	68 kHz
Damping factor (5 Ω load):	3	1.5	0.2
Input sensitivity[2]:	670 mV		
Input impedance:	10 kΩ		
	$P_{out} = 0.1$ W	$P_{out} = 1$ W	$P_{out} = 10$ W
THD[3]:	0.04%	0.06%	0.3%
IMD[4]:	0.06%	0.1%	0.4%
Stability:	Unconditional for any complex load impedance		
Hum:	−93 dB(A_{rms}) referred to 29 W, 5 Ω load		

1) Measured with EL34 valves at 8 V_{pp}, 5 Ω load.
2) Ultralinear mode, 29 W, 5 Ω load.
3) 1 kHz, EL34 valves, ultralinear mode.
4) 11+ 12 kHz, EL34 valves, ultralinear mode.

▲ **Table 16.1** Specifications of the UL40-S in various configurations.

The specifications of the UL40-S are pretty straightforward, apart from the parameter a_2. This needs some explanation. The high frequency behaviour of the amplifier can be entirely described by the combination of a first order and a second order filter, which has the following overall transfer function:

$$H(f) = \frac{1}{1 + a_2(\dfrac{jf}{f_o}) + (\dfrac{jf}{f_0})^2} \cdot \frac{1}{1 + (\dfrac{jf}{f_1})} \qquad [16\text{-}1]$$

Here f is the frequency, j is the square root of -1 and f_1 is the previously-mentioned corner frequency of the 6N1P (800 kHz).

The frequency f_0 and the parameter a_2 are both determined by the output transformer, the internal resistance of the power valves and the loudspeaker impedance (note that a_2 equals $1/Q$, where Q is the quality factor of the second-order filter of the output transformer). See Chapter 5 for a thorough discussion of Formula 16-1.

Analyzing the transfer function for the triode configuration yields a filter characteristic with small differential phase distortion. It is lightly underdamped, but stable enough to prevent overshoots with square wave signals. The ultralinear configuration is right on the money; critically damped with exemplary flat phase response, while the pentode circuit is slightly overdamped. This results in a small decrease in bandwidth for the pentode configuration. However, the differential phase distortion and the square wave response are still excellent.

All the above is grist for the mill for designers that like to work with mathematical models. The nice thing about the toroidal-core transformers is that these models are fully valid, and they accurately predict the high-frequency behavior of the amplifier. Again, see Chapter 5 for a full discussion of the theoretical basis and mathematical manipulation of theses models.

16.11 | Output power and impedance

The output transformer has only one secondary section, without taps, matched to a load impedance of 5 Ω. I chose not to make the transformer unnecessarily complicated, since any 'extras' would inevitably be reflected in its price. Besides, as it is the output power bandwidth is constant within 0.5 dB for load impedances between 3 Ω and 8 Ω, which is a generous range.

A more important reason to refrain from using multiple secondary taps is that the high-frequency performance of the transformer strongly benefits from uniform stacking of the consecutive winding layers. Branching wires for secondary taps would inevitably disturb this delicate relationship, thereby degrading the quality of the transformer.

Yet another reason is that loudspeaker impedance is never constant to begin with. It generally ranges between 4 and 8 ohms, typically with a couple of sharp peaks located at the crossover frequencies of the filters used. In order to achieve a good match, it is best to choose a secondary impedance that is close to the *minimum* impedance of the loudspeakers. Calculations and measurements have both proven that 5 ohms is a good choice.

16.12 | Alternative choices for the power valves

The specifications in the previous section show that a wide variety of power valves can be employed in the output section. The standard EL34 is a good choice; it is a true pentode, manufactured by Philips, Tesla, Sovtek and Svetlana (with gold control grid wires), among others. Many American valves, such as the EL34S (6CA7) beam-power pentode, the 6550 and the KT66, can be used as well, and even the old favourite 6L6 'musician's' valve will fit. Some valves may require the value of the common cathode resistor to be changed. Table 16.2 shows the results of some measurements made with various types of valves. I have omitted the results of the measurements for pentode mode, since the pentode damping factor is uncomfortably low, resulting in massive colouration — nice for instrument amplifiers, but not really 'hi-fi'.

Valve	Mode	R_{11} (Ω)	P_{max} (W)	DF	V_{out}/V_{in}	f_{-3dB} (kHz)
EL34	Triode	220	13.8	3.3	10.5	100
Tesla,	UL	220	28.5	1.6	17.0	86
Svetlana						
EL34	Triode	220	13.0	3.3	10.5	100
Sovtek	UL	220	28.0	1.5	17.0	84
KT66	Triode	220	8.5	3.1	7.8	97
GEC	UL	220	21.8	1.4	12.1	81
6550C	Triode	220	13.1	4.6	8.0	106
Svetlana	UL	220	25.8	1.7	12.4	90
6550WA	Triode	220	13.2	4.5	7.8	104
Sovtek	UL	330	25.6	1.6	12.5	81
6L6-GC	Triode	—	—	—	—	—
Philips	UL	220	20.3	1.2	12.9	80

▲ **Table 16.2** *UL40-S performance with various types of valves.*

The results in Table 16.2 show that all valves perform nicely, although both the damping factor and the amplification vary. The overall gain (V_{out}/V_{in}) is clearly different for the triode and ultralinear modes. This is understandable, since a triode has more 'internal' feedback and thus lower amplification. What we cannot read from this table is the effect of the choice of valve and configuration on the subjective 'sound' of the amplifier, which I discuss in the following section.

16.13 | How does it sound?

Although I am accustomed to bursting into paeans of praise when reviewing the products of others (see my earlier articles in 'Home Studio', for example), it is a different thing when the design is my own. I therefore restrict myself to general characteristics, leaving the final evaluation to you (the builder).

My listening tests were mainly done using the following 'chain':

- loudspeakers: Quad ESL63, Meyst-Corbier M3 and B&W 803 Series 2;
- speaker cables: Ocos, and Van den Hul's 'Revelation';
- low-level signal interlinks: STC 4/80, as well as Van den Hul's 'The First' and 'The Second';
- CD players: STC Project 19 MK2 and Wadia X-32;
- phonograph: VPI; Mørch arm and Adcom cartridge, together with a Vanderveen MD/MC preamplifier (E88CC-01 triode) with MC/MM transformer coupling.

The UL40-S performs without even a hint of strain. Even long listening sessions do not produce any listener fatigue or irritation; the sound is never tiresome, but consistently smooth and tranquil. The bass response is somewhat emphasized with the dynamic loudspeakers used for testing. This is understandable, given the rather low damping factor of the UL40-S. With the ESL63 speakers, however, this slight emphasis changes into outright colouration, which is not good! These loudspeakers are designed for a damping factor of 10 or higher; nothing less will do. You should thus use the UL40-S with dynamic loudspeakers and not with electrostatic loudspeakers.

By the way, this low-end emphasis is by no means always present, as tests with other loudspeakers and reports from other builders have shown. Some report a bass response with 'body', some describe the base as 'throbbing', and yet others find the bass response somewhat meager. Why is this? The low damping factor of the amplifier affects the response of the loudspeaker. Electric damping (Q_e) is nearly absent, and this can alter the balance of the loudspeaker, causing the bass to be louder or softer. Nearly all listeners found that low frequencies are reproduced with better than average detail. Compared to transistor amplifiers with their typically high damping factors, the UL40-S is always judged to produce a 'mild' rendering of bass tones. This is understandable, and in total agreement with theory. Personal taste will dictate whether you prefer this 'valve' sound to the 'tight' bass reproduction of a transistor amplifier.

The spatial image is wide and extends far to the rear, with lots of 'air' around the instruments — a clear indication of the absence of overall negative feedback. The amplifier responds lightning-fast to transients, and it returns to the rest state just as fast. This highlights the 'silences' in the music, which substantially enhances the perception of spatial detail. The damping naturally plays a role here as well. A high damping factor tends to compress the stereo image, and the spatial distribution of the instruments or voices then depends very much on the quality of the amplifier. The image of the UL40-S image is not 'larger than life', but the individual instruments are fluidly distributed over the auditory stage, with smooth transitions from one to the next without loss of detail. This is close to the way we hear a large ensemble in reality. These effects can be clearly heard with Roger Waters' CD *Amused to Death*, which utilizes Q-sound to produce an exceptionally large stereo image that extends far beyond the loudspeakers. (The version that I use is the specially mastered Columbia CD CK53196, in the golden edition with Super Bit Mapping.) If this CD is played through a high quality transistor chain, the auditory image is about 180 degrees wide. When the UL40-S is used instead, the image shrinks to about 150 degrees, but individual voices can be distinguished much more easily, with better ambience and more warmth and very little 'clutter' — very much as though real, live people were talking right in front of the listener. As the designer of this amplifier, I am again and again impressed by the naturalness of its reproduction. Whether others will like it equally well is something that I can not dictate — you have to find out for yourself. In this design I aimed for a 'real' and natural sound, and fortunately, I think that I succeeded when I listen to the final result. You may find this a rather subjective view, which it is, but I feel entitled to take such a view.

As far as detail is concerned, the triode mode performs better than the ultralinear mode, and the pentode mode is (relatively speaking) beyond redemption — I cannot recommend it, and it is included only because it is easy to implement and can be used for interesting experiments.

Hum should be inaudible under normal listening conditions with well-matched valves, as supplied in the kit. You may hear a slight hum if you put your ear right up against the speaker; the level will depend on the exactness of the valve matching and the age of the valves.

The high frequency reproduction is absolutely calm, with a total absence of stridency or 'smearing' in time. The triode configuration, again, comes out on top.

Distortion is inaudible at normal levels, and still very mild if the amplifier is driven into overloading. The spatial image is remarkably calm and stable once the amplifier has been properly set up and burned in.

The differences associated with using various types of valves are substantial. If we compare EL34s from Svetlana, Sovtek and Tesla, for instance, the Tesla valves sound broad and well balanced, while the slim Sovtek valves produce a somewhat thinner bass but show more detail at high frequencies. This has nothing to do with their external profiles; it is due to differences in their internal construction. The Svetlana valves have been chosen for the standard kit because they deliver the best musical balance between high and low frequencies and show the most detail from the loudest to the softest levels, without any distortion and with full, rich tonal structures.

The sound of the 6550WA is very 'slick'. This valve sounds as though it is driven nowhere near its limits, and its transparency is peerless. You hardly have the impression that there is even an amplifier present.

However, the king of them all is the KT66. All tests with this valve were done using original General Electric Company valves, manufactured in 1956. Listeners describe the triode performance of this valve as 'a class above the EL34'. The amplifier gains an immense refinement and tranquillity of image, with substantial gains in spatial definition. This valve is the best possible choice for the UL40-S, as far as I am concerned. However, the Svetlana EL34 is a close second.

16.14 | Output power, gain, and ... what's with the volume control?

As the performance in the triode mode is so clearly superior, we have to deal with its relatively small output power and low amplification. Will these be enough? With a few calculations, I can show that all will be well if a CD player is used as the input source.

Let us suppose that we have loudspeakers with an efficiency of 90 dB/W-m — this figure (or better) is the recommended value for the UL40-S. Should the efficiency be lower, such as around 86 dB/W-m, then the amplifier will be pushed to its limits to deliver a reasonable output level. When we feed 10 watts into a loudspeaker with the recommended efficiency, the resulting sound pressure level (SPL) is $(90 + 10\log(10))$ = 100 dB. Each channel will produce this level at one metre distance, since this is a stereo amplifier, but we hardly ever sit that close to the loudspeakers. Three metres (ten feet) is a more realistic value. Reflections in the listening space also contribute to the sound pressure level.

I have come up with the following rule of thumb: if we calculate the sound pressure level from one channel at one metre distance, the SPL from both loudspeakers at three metres in a normal room will be nearly the same. I will thus use a 100 dB SPL for the rest of my calculations.

The effective voltage across a 5 ohm load resistance that dissipates 10 watts is equal to $\sqrt{(10 \cdot 5)} = 7.07\ V_{eff}$. The amplification factor of the UL40-S is around 10 in the triode configuration, so the required input voltage is $(7.07 \div 10) = 0.707\ V_{eff}$. This input voltage will produce the desired output level (100 dB SPL).

Now let us move over to the CD player. Its absolute maximum output voltage is $2\ V_{eff}$. This is a hard limit, often referred to as the '0 dB' level of the CD player. As some headroom is necessary, the average signal level is often set to −12 dB. This corresponds to $0.5\ V_{eff}$ (remember that −6 dB corresponds to half of the output voltage, and a half times a half is a quarter).

Now for the final calculation: $0.5\,V_{eff}$ into the UL40-S with the volume control 'wide open' yields $(100 + 20\log(0.5 \div 0.707)) = (100 - 3) = 97$ dB SPL. That is a lot of bang. Most audio reviewers — including yours truly — listen to music at an average level of 80 dB, and consider that to be more than adequate. Their families agree with them (and so do their neighbours!).

In conclusion, an UL40-S in triode mode, when driven by the relatively high output levels of a CD player and connected to efficient loudspeakers, should produce adequate sound pressure. This will not be the case if less efficient loudspeakers are used — some of these monsters require output powers of hundreds of watts, and that is way too much for the miller. You have been warned.

The phrase 'with the volume control wide open' in our little calculation also suggests another property of the UL40-S. The input stages of most commercial preamplifiers are over-dimensioned, so that the nominal output power is reached when the volume control is only partly opened, with the pointer at (for example) ten o'clock. Only a quarter of the volume control's range is actually used! This is not the case with the UL40-S. For normal programs, the knob will be somewhere in the middle, and all the way to the right if you want to play soft passages at a loud level. This is clearly different from what most of us are used to, conditioned as we are by sales psychology. A purchaser is likely to think that an amplifier that produces an ear-blasting sound level with the volume control only partly open is more 'muscular' and has more power reserve than one whose volume control has to be turned up all the way to reach the same level (even if the first amplifier is on the edge of clipping!). The average person thus associates the setting of the volume control with how much power the amplifier can deliver. Nothing could be further from the truth!

The volume control of the UL40-S certainly takes some getting used to, but I had solid reasons to design it the way I did. To begin with, the less the signal is amplified, the less potential there is for distortion. It is therefore a good idea to amplify not a single decibel more than strictly necessary — high amplification leads to more noise, the potential for clipping in the driver stages, and innumerable other problems. Secondly, the mid-point of the Alps potentiometer used here corresponds to an attenuation of 20 dB, due to its logarithmic characteristic. Given the modest sensitivity of the UL40-S, it is inevitable that control has to be opened up more than with a more sensitive amplifier. Finally, the two parallel sections of a stereo volume control never track perfectly, and the relative tracking error is the greatest when they are only slightly opened (maximum attenuation), so it is better to avoid this region. The tracking balance (and incidentally, the noise characteristics) of the Alps volume control are the best from around midrange to fully open. This is exactly where I designed this amplifier to be operated.

In summary: although it may take some getting used to, the chosen setup of the volume control gives the best results. Those of you that need a psychological antidote can always affix a dial scale numbered from zero to eleven; fans of 'Spinal Tap' know how effective a solution this is....

For anyone who works a lot with low-level sources, such as older-model tape decks and tuners (typical output levels around 250 mV), there is a small extension kit to boost the input sensitivity of the amplifier. This kit (model UL40-SVV) is a preamplifier with a gain of 4, which is enough to drive the amplifier to its nominal output power level.

16.15 | Summary and conclusions

The UL40-S is a complete kit, with extensive step-by-step building instructions. The optional UL40-SVV preamplifier is equally complete and also well documented. Both are available from the sources listed in the Appendix.

All the information in the previous chapters has been applied to produce this mature design. The builder has a lot of freedom to modify the amplifier, without incurring high additional costs. A full range of operating modes can be realized, from triode to pentode. Various types of power valves can be employed as well.

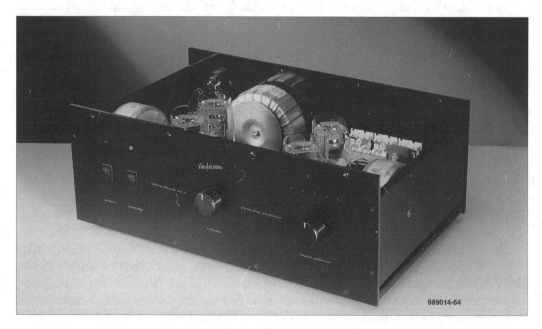

▲ *Figure 16.4 The UL40-S is an attractive, easily-built, high-quality amplifier.*

We have seen the relationship between the output power and the sound pressure level. The UL40-S is a good match for CD player output levels. High-efficiency loudspeakers pair up nicely with this amplifier, but low-efficiency types are not recommended. I have explained why the volume control is set up as it is, and noted that a supplementary preamplifier kit is available for dealing with low-level input signals.

17

A Guitar Amplifier with a Toroidal Output Transformer

This chapter presents one of my earliest designs based on a toroidal output transformer, first published in 1985. This is a 30 watt guitar amplifier, with four EL84s in the output stage and an ECC81 in a simple phase splitter configuration. Although it was clearly designed as an instrument amplifier, it has found a lot of application in high-end audio installations.

17.1 | The circuit diagram of the VDV40

I had a typical guitar amplifier in mind when I went about designing the VDV40. The characteristics of such an amplifier are: (1) little feedback, and therefore a low damping factor, to provide the typical colouration, (2) multiple output taps to accommodate all possible types of loudspeakers, (3) about 30 to 40 watts of output power and (4) high input sensitivity for the necessary 'drive'. It was intended to be a DIY design, which meant that it should be easy to build, with a printed circuit board and minimal adjustments. Given the application, the frequency bandwidth was generous at around 30 kHz.

After the publication of this design, something unexpected happened: typical 'hifi' reviewers started to comment on it – 'what a wonderfully warm and mild-sounding amplifier' – and I received numerous reactions from people who were tickled pink to include the VDV40 in their stereo installations. That was not my intention! Nevertheless, these reactions have convinced me to include this vintage Vanderveen design in the present book.

Figures 17.1 and 17.2 show the circuit diagrams of the amplifier and its power supply. Both fit on a single, slender PCB.

The preamplifier consists of a ECC81 triode with a decoupled cathode resistor $(C_1 \parallel R_3)$. Thanks to the decoupling, its amplification is rather high at around 40. Feedback is injected via resistor R_4, in the lower part of the cathode string.

The second halve of the ECC81 is a simple and reliable phase splitter. All it needs is two equal-valued resistors (R_5 and R_6) at the anode and cathode.

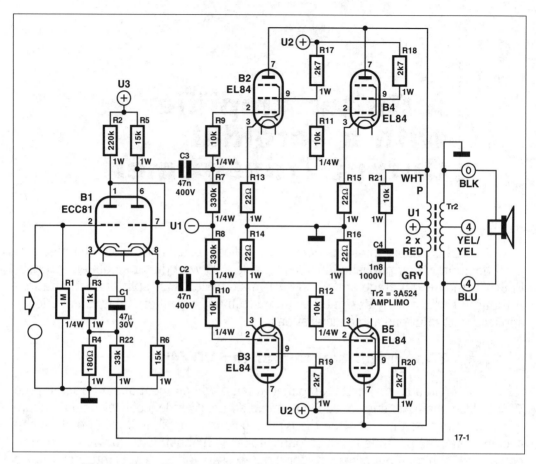

▲ **Figure 17.1** *Circuit diagram of the audio section of the VDV40.*

There are only two capacitors in the entire audio path: C_2 and C_3. They carry the output signals from the phase splitter to the power valves. The four EL84s are arranged as two pairs, all biased from a single negative supply. This configuration does not allow for individual biasing, so the valves must be closely matched. The negative voltage power supply consists of a B40C800 rectifier, a filter capacitor (C_9) and a 20 V Zener diode (Z_1). The output voltage can be adjusted with trimpot R_{29}. The bias supply line is shorted for AC signals by C_{10}, to keep music signals from leaking through.

The screen grids receive their supply voltage through 2.2 KΩ, 1 W resistors, because guitar amplifiers are heavily overloaded most of the time, and this produces hefty screen currents. If these currents were not limited by resistors, the screens would turn into vapour in no time at all. Although the resistors reduce the damping factor of the amplifier somewhat, lowering their values would substantially shorten the life spans of the hapless valves.

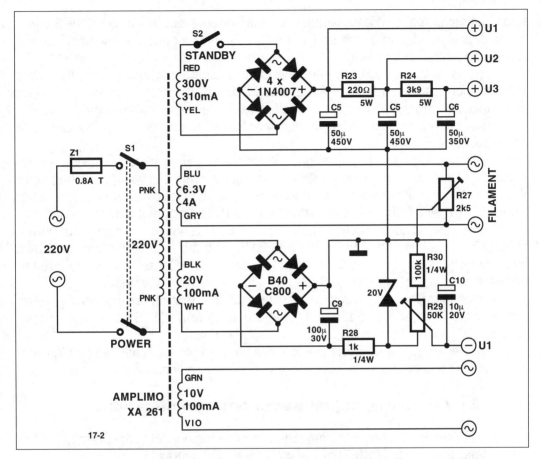

▲ *Figure 17.2* Circuit diagram of the power supply for the VDV40.

The anodes are connected in pairs to the primary of the output transformer. This is a model 3A524, a transformer specially designed for guitar amplifiers. The cathodes are individually coupled to ground via 22 Ω resistors. These have two functions: first, they allow the quiescent current of each valve to be measured — for example, 20 milliampères will produce 0.44 volts, which can be easily measured. Second, they smooth out small mismatches between valve pairs. If the valves are well matched, they can be left out or reduced to around 1 Ω, which will slightly increase the damping factor.

Originally I included a small network, consisting of R_{21} and C_4, across the primary of the output transformer to damp overshoots in the square wave response. This is a useful addition for high-end applications, but not for instrument amplification, since the wealth of high frequency components in a distorted guitar signal will thermally overload R_{21} unless a 10 watt (!) type is used. More importantly, when I reconsidered this amplifier for inclusion in this book, I also considered using a newer output transformer, such as the VDV6040, which does not benefit from this network in the first place. Consequently, components R_{21} and C_4 have been omitted on the updated version of the printed circuit board.

The signal from the secondary of the output transformer is fed back via R_{22} to the injection point at the cathode of the preamplifier. As already mentioned, the amount of feedback is small, just enough to provide a slight damping at the output. Thanks to the centre tap on the secondary winding, 4 or 8 ohm loudspeakers can be used with this amplifier.

The supply voltage is high – about 450 Volts – allowing plenty of headroom for those impulsive guitar signals. An EL84 would not survive this voltage for long, were it not for the large screen resistors that keep it out of harms way. A simple rectifier bridge (4 × 1N4007) and filter capacitor are used. The original amplifier used two 50 µF/450 V capacitors for C_5, which I later replaced with two capacitors with a slightly higher maximum voltage (50 µF/500 V). The high voltage is switched by a standby switch (S_2). This must be a sturdy chap, and well insulated too, due to the substantial charging currents for C_5 and C_6 and the high voltage used.

The standard filament voltage (6.3 V) is coupled to ground via trimpot R_{27} — an old-fashioned but effective method for eliminating hum. The last vestige of hum should vanish once this trimpot has been properly adjusted.

The power supply transformer (XA261) has an extra winding that can provide 10 V at 100 mA for something 'extra', such as an effects unit or whatever you want.

17.2 | Assembly, adjustments and specifications

Figures 17.3 and 17.4 show the component side and copper track layout of the original single-sided PCB. They are pretty self-explanatory.

However, this board has been substantially reworked and modernized by the application of LEP® technology. The new double-sided board, measuring 20.4 × 8.0 cm, is protected by a thick tin plating and features an improved layout, with clear markings for component numbers and values. The part number for this circuit board is VDV40. Refer to suppliers listed in the Appendix for more information.

Figure 17.5 (overleaf) shows how easily this amplifier can be mounted inside a 19" rack-mount chassis (2 standard units high), with the two transformers on either side of the PCB and the valves placed horizontally. Large ventilation holes at both top and bottom are essential, of course.

Once the amplifier has been assembled, the time has come to power it up for the first time. Do not place the power valves in their sockets yet, and leave S_2 in the standby position. Switch on the mains voltage, and turn trimpot R_{29} full on. Check that the voltage at pin 2 of each EL84 socket is −20 V. Now you can plug in the valves, and then switch on the high voltage. Measure the voltages across R_{13}, R_{14}, R_{15} and R_{16}. Adjust R_{29} so that these read 0.44 V, which corresponds to a quiescent current of 20 milliampères. This is the recommended value for guitar applications.

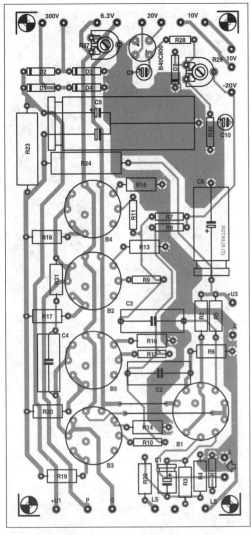

▲ *Figure 17.3*
Component layout of the
original VDV40 circuit board
(75% of true size).

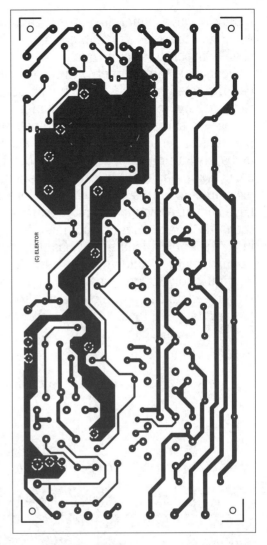

▲ *Figure 17.4*
Copper side track layout of the
original VDV40 circuit board
(75% of true size).

The anode dissipation is now 9 watts per valve. This should keep the power valves safe and sound for a long time. For hi-fi use, the quiescent current can be increased to 30 mA. At this level, the dissipation rises to the maximum allowed level of 12 watts, and the internal resistance and distortion are reduced to a minimum — all the things you would expect with a high fidelity amplifier. I recommend the Sovtek

EL84WA valve, which is a sturdy military version of the EL84. It combines a long life span with splendid sound quality.

I conclude this chapter with the specifications listed in Table 17.1. This presents the measured performance results for this simple, yet solid amplifier. The original output transformer (3A524) provides a frequency bandwidth of 'only' 33 kHz; this can be easily extended to 80 kHz, as subsequent experiments with a VDV6040 transformer have shown. Although it is more expensive, the latter transformer is recommended for high-end applications, and it has the additional benefit of allowing the ultralinear configuration to be used. For this, the screen resistors must be connected to the primary-winding taps. Further information can be found in Chapter 11.

▲ **Figure 17.5**
The VDV40 fitted in a 19" rack-mount chassis.

▼ **Table 17.1** *VDV40 specifications.*

VDV40 valve amplifier specifications	
Valves:	ECC81, 4 x EL84
Continuous output power:	30 W (THD < 1 %, 1 kHz)
Peak output power:	40 W (30 ms pulse)
Frequency range (−3 dB):	15 Hz - 33 kHz (with 3A524 transformer)
Frequency range (−3 dB):	15 Hz - 80 kHz (with VDV6040 transformer, ultralinear mode)
Output impedance:	4 Ω and 8 Ω (with 3A524 transformer)
Input impedance:	1 MΩ
Input sensitivity:	300 mV$_{eff}$ (ref. 30 W in 8 Ω)
Noise and hum:	−93 dB with matched power valves (ref. 30 W in 8 Ω)

18

The VDV100 Power Amplifier

This amplifier, originally designed in 1987, utilizes a quartet of EL34s. A wide frequency response and a high damping factor are achieved by means of unusual coupling with the output transformer, combined with local feedback. Both the phase splitter and the driver stage are more complex than in previous circuits. I present the original version of the amplifier first, followed by some modifications made in later years.

18.1 | The basic circuit

Figures 18.1 and 18.2 (overleaf) shows the circuit diagram of this design. The actual amplifier is on the left, with the power supply to the right. The four EL34 power valves are arranged as two pairs – B_3 with B_4 and B_5 with B_6 – while a single ECC81 is used at the input in a fairly standard preamplifier and phase-splitter configuration. As the latter circuit is used frequently in this book, I will not discuss it in any more detail.

The interesting part comes right after the ECC81: the two halves of valve B_2, an ECC82. At first glance these look like ordinary triode amplification stages – one for each phase – but the circuits around the cathodes are unusually complicated. The two networks R_{25}–$R_{27} \parallel C_7$–C_9 and R_{28}–$R_{30} \parallel C_{10}$–C_{12} couple the signals at the primary of the output transformer to the cathodes of the driver stage, providing local feedback. This is the central point around which the entire design gravitates, as I show below.

The power supply is fairly standard and does not contain any exotic parts. Each power valve is biased individually. The negative grid voltages are adjusted by trimpots P_1, P_2, P_3 and P_4. Originally, I did not fit the amplifier with a standby switch, but just switched the mains voltage to the primary. In retrospect, this is not such a good idea. I therefore advise you to fit a sturdy switch to open the upper lead of the high-voltage secondary winding; this will substantially lengthen the life of both the valves and the electrolytic capacitors.

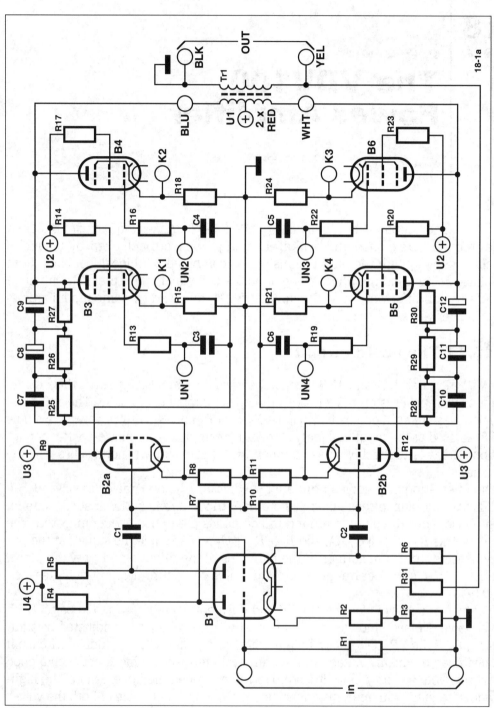

▲ **Figure 18.1** *Circuit diagram of the VDV100 power amplifier. Component values are listed in Table 18.1.*

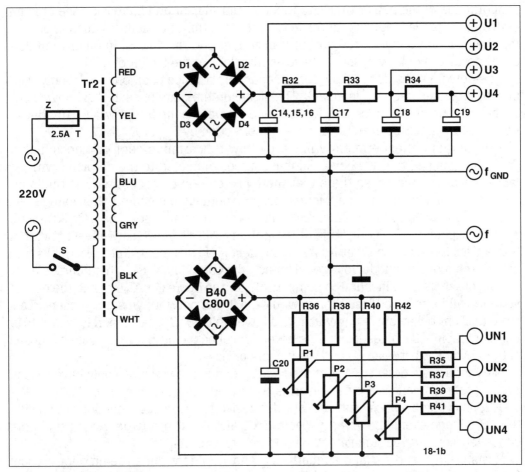

▲ *Figure 18.2* *The power supply circuit for the VDV100 amplifier.*

18.2 | **Why use local feedback?**

I encountered a peculiar phenomenon while developing this amplifier. Originally, I did not utilize local feedback, and the amplifier sounded fine when driving dynamic loudspeakers. However, pronounced colouration occurred when Quad ESL63 speakers were connected, and measurements soon revealed why. These loudspeakers require high damping, but the amplifier's damping factor turned out to be around 2. This explained everything.

To increase the damping, the effective internal resistance of the valves must be lowered. This has the additional benefit of broadening the frequency response. There are several ways to reduce the effective internal resistance, including changing the configuration of the power valves to triode or ultra-linear and increasing the amount of overall negative feedback. In this case I chose a third possibility, which is changing the coupling between the output transformer and the valves. In order to understand how this works, you should have another look at the circuit diagram.

The power valves do not function independently, since each one is strongly coupled to its driver stage via feedback. The signal on the plate of each EL34 flows back to the cathode of the preceding ECC82 triode via a decoupling network. Any deviation in this signal causes an instantaneous correction by B_{2a} or B_{2b}.

A little thought experiment will clarify how this arrangement produces higher damping. Imagine that we have a signal source connected to the amplifier with no loudspeaker connected, so there that there is a certain output voltage at the loudspeaker terminals. As soon as a loudspeaker is actually connected, this voltage will decrease due to Z_{out}, the internal resistance of the amplifier (see Chapters 3 through 5 for an explanation). The voltage at the primary will decrease as well — remember that a transformer does what its name suggests! Now the extra network kicks into action; the reduced anode voltage will reach the cathodes of B_2, which immediately churns out more amplification to compensate for the decrease. As a result, the output voltage will be reduced less than it would be if this network was not present. This more resilient behaviour is equivalent to a lower value of Z_{out}, and therefore results in higher damping. Local feedback thus lowers the effective output resistance by means of tight coupling between B_2 and the power valves.

Now for a more detailed look at the local feedback networks. We only have to look at the upper network, since the lower network works in the same way. Resistors R_{26} and R_{27} have high values; they are 'bleeder' resistors whose sole function is to divide the AC voltage evenly between capacitors C_8 and C_9. These large-value capacitors effectively conduct AC signals to the important resistor R_{25}.

Resistors R_{25} and R_8 (and similarly R_{28} and R_{11}) determine the amount of local feedback. The lower the value of $R_{25}:R_8$, the stronger the local feedback and the lower the effective output resistance of the power valve. The damping factor can thus be varied widely – within reasonable limits – by adjusting the value of R_{25} and R_{28}. This means that the output valves, output transformer, frequency range and damping factor can all be tuned to each other by choosing a suitable value for R_{25} and R_{28}.

In this design, both local and overall (external) feedback are utilized. The former is much stronger than the latter, so the total amplification is largely defined by the local feedback. The role of R_{31} – which determines the amount of overall negative feedback – is minimal. This is a good thing, given the bad effects on auditory image and timbre that usually result from strong overall negative feedback. The value of R_{25} and R_{28} is based on both subjective criteria (how the amplifier sounds) and objective requirements (electrostatic speakers, such as the ESL63, require a large damping factor). Additional considerations are discussed below, where modifications to this circuit are described. In any case, this design provides a simple and elegant way to combine local and overall feedback.

Resistors[1]		Capacitors		
R_1, R_7, R_{10}, R_{36}, R_{38}, R_{40}, R_{42}	100 kΩ	C_1, C_2	150 nF	400 V
R_2	820 Ω	C_3, C_4, C_5, C_6	330 nF	400 V
R_3	180 Ω	C_7, C_{10}	82 pF	1000 V !
R_4	220 kΩ	C_8, C_9, C_{11}, C_{12}	10 μF	450 V
R_5, R_6	15 kΩ, 1 W	C_{14}, C_{15}, C_{16}, C_{17}	50 μF	500 V
R_8, R_{11}	1 kΩ	C_{18}, C_{19}	47 μF	400 V
R_9, R_{12}	47 kΩ, 2 W	C_{20}	100 μF	63 V
R_{13}, R_{16}, R_{19}, R_{22}	10 kΩ			
R_{14}, R_{17}, R_{20}, R_{23}	150 Ω, 1 W	**Diodes**		
R_{15}, R_{18}, R_{21}, R_{24}	10 Ω, 1 W	D_1–D_4	1N4007	
R_{25}, R_{28}	27 kΩ, 2 W	D_5	B80C100 bridge	
R_{26}, R_{27}, R_{29}, R_{30}	2.2 MΩ			
R_{31}, R_{34}	10 kΩ, 1 W	**Valves**		
R_{32}	100 Ω, 5 W	B_1	ECC81	
R_{33}	4.7 kΩ, 2 W	B_2	ECC82	
R_{35}, R_{37}, R_{39}, R_{41}	220 kΩ	B_3–B_6	EL34	
P_1–P_4	100 kΩ trimpot 10 mm horizontal Piher	**Transformers** Tr_1 XC462 output transformer (original) Tr_2 7B649 mains transformer		

1) All resistors are 0.25 W, except as otherwise noted.

▲ *Table 18.1* Component values for the VDV100 amplifier.

18.3 │ Construction and specifications

A printed circuit board, available from the sources listed in the Appendix, has been developed for the amplifier. This double-sided board has plated-through holes and measures 22.9 by 12.7 cm. Most components are fitted on the lower side of the PCB to keep them cool, while the valves are fitted on the upper side. The entire circuit – amplifier and power supply – fits on the board, except for the two transformers. These are connected along the narrow sides of the board, thus minimizing external wiring. The component layout is shown in Figures 18.3 and 18.4, while Figures 18.5 and 18.6 show how the amplifier can be housed.

You should give some thought to safety before you switch on this power amplifier for the first time, since the valve supply voltages are quite high. By all means review the various parts of this book that deal with safety, in particular Section 12.1. One point that can easily be overlooked is that you should take care to mount the printed

◀ **Figure 18.3**
The 'valve side'
of the circuit
board. Note
that the bias
adjust trimpots
are readily
accessible.

989014-60

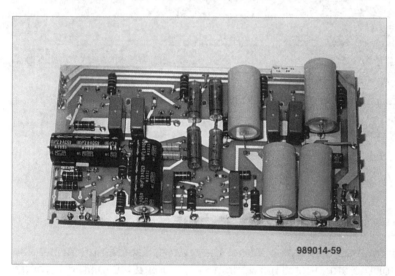

◀ **Figure 18.4**
The component
side of the circuit
board. Capacitors
C_8, C_9, C_{11} & C_{12}
are in the centre,
with the parallel
resistors soldered
directly on top.

989014-59

circuit board some distance away from the metal of the case, to prevent discharges. The minimum allowable separation is 1 cm.

The quiescent currents of the four power valves must be set to 45 mA each, using trimpots P_1, P_2, P_3 and P_4. This corresponds to a voltage drop of 450 mV across R_{15}, R_{18}, R_{21} and R_{24}, respectively. The adjustment procedure is described in Chapters 11 and 13. Be sure to verify that the negative grid voltage is present at each output valve before you flip on the standby switch!

Now on to the specifications, which are listed in Table 17.2. This amplifier is rated at 100 watts, but test versions delivered quite a bit more: 121 watts of continuous RMS power, and an impressive 156 watts of short-term transient output power, show

◀ **Figure 18.5**
The transformers can be located at either end of the circuit board. The power supply end is shown here. This arrangement makes for an oblong chassis; each transformer has its own compartment.

◀ **Figure 18.6**
The transformers can be located in a separate compartment behind the circuit board. This makes a distinguished-looking amplifier. (Design by J. de Zwart.)

that this amplifier is a true powerhouse! The combination of the toroidal output transformer and local feedback yields a frequency response range of 5 Hz to 125 kHz (and that is only the beginning — read on to see what happens when a modern output transformer is used). The power bandwidth is 30 Hz to 80 kHz. At the low end the core saturates, while the high end is limited by the valves themselves. Churning out 50 watts at 80 kHz makes them literally turn red in the face: the plates and screen grids will show a dull red glow when driven to this level. The specifications thus state '5 s maximum at 80 kHz'– you have been warned! The remaining specifications and characteristic curves are self-explanatory (see Figures 18.7 through 18.10).

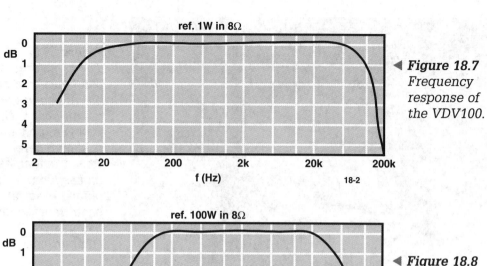

Figure 18.7
Frequency
response of
the VDV100.

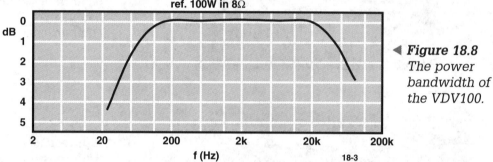

Figure 18.8
The power
bandwidth of
the VDV100.

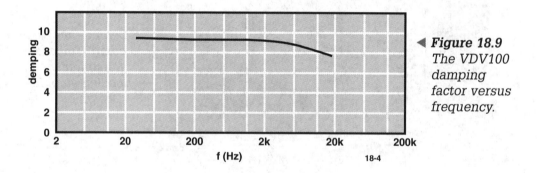

Figure 18.9
The VDV100
damping
factor versus
frequency.

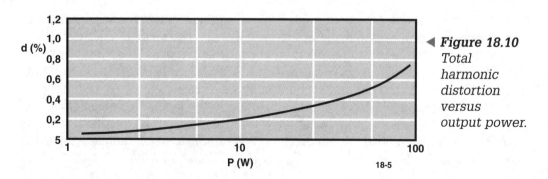

Figure 18.10
Total
harmonic
distortion
versus
output power.

VDV100 Specifications (standard configuration)	
Description:	100 W Monobloc valve amplifier
Valves:	1 x ECC81 1 x ECC82 4 x EL34
Frequency range:	5 Hz to 125 kHz (–3 dB, ref. 1W, 8 Ω load)
Continuous output power:	121 W (1 kHz, 8 Ω load)
Burst power:	156 W (1 ms on, 64 ms off, 8 Ω load)
Power bandwidth:	30 Hz to 80 kHz (–3 dB, ref. 100 W) 5 s maximum at 80 kHz!
Total harmonic distortion:	0.78% (1kHz, 100 W, 8 Ω load)
Slew rate:	14.2 V/μs (50 W, 80 kHz sine wave)
Operating mode:	Class A up to 16 W, 8 Ω load Class AB, 16 W to 100 W, 8 Ω load
Damping factor:	8.7 (see Figure 18.10)
Input sensitivity:	0 dBm (0.775 Vrms) (ref. 100 W, 8 Ω load)
Input impedance:	100 kΩ, DC coupled
Loudspeaker impedance:	8 Ω
Hum and noise:	–87 dBa(rms) (ref. 100 W, 8 Ω load)
Stability:	will tolerate 80 V_{pp} at 1 kHz with no load

▲ *Table 18.2* *Measured specifications of the VDV100 amplifier.*

18.4 ┃ Modifications

■ ┃ Modification 1: UL configuration with older-model transformers

The VDV100 can be built with the XC462 balanced output transformer, as shown in the schematic diagram, but the 5B535 (another first-generation toroidal Vanderveen design) can also be used. The primary of the 5B535 has ultralinear taps that can be connected to the screen grids. Various circuits in previous chapters use this configuration, so you can refer to them for information on wiring and so on. In this case the screen grids are not connected to U_2, but to the UL taps of the transformer, which results in twofold local feedback: first via B_2, and second inside the power valves themselves via the ultralinear coupling. Opinions are divided about the audible effects of this configuration, with comments ranging from 'less warmth in the bass' to 'tighter; better definition'. This is understandable, if you consider the effect of this modification. The twofold feedback increases the damping, so the woofer excursions are better controlled. The 5B535 and the XC462 have the same high-frequency behaviour, so we must look for other means to improve the latter aspect.

■ Modification 2: Pentode configuration with a VDV2100PP

The older generation of transformers (i.e. XC462 and 5B535) can be replaced by their successor, the VDV2100PP. This is a compatible transformer with a better core and a significantly improved winding structure. As a result, the frequency response is much wider, compared to the XC462 and 5B535. The replacement is easy, since the colour codes of the transformers are identical except for the primary, where the blue and white wires of the XC462/5B535 correspond to the green and yellow wires of the VDV2100PP.

The new configuration is a pure pentode; all feedback networks must therefore be eliminated. This means removing R_{31} (the external feedback resistor) and the two local feedback networks $R_{25}-R_{27} \| C_7-C_9$ and $R_{28}-R_{30} \| C_{10}-C_{12}$.

The bandwidth of this amplifier extends to 65 kHz, which is not all that spectacular. This is due to the combination of the of limitations of the preamplifier and drivers and the abominably high internal resistance of the power stage, and is not the fault of new transformer. The effective impedance at the secondary measures 109 ohms! This corresponds to an impedance of 44 kΩ for the power valves. As there are four valves, arranged as two parallel pairs connected in series through the primary, the total resistance of the chain equals the resistance of a single valve. A value of 44 kΩ may appear abnormally high to those familiar with what is specified in the valve data books (17 kΩ). However, the specified value applies for $V_{ak} = 250$ V and $I_a = 100$ mA, while the EL34s are operated in this circuit at a higher voltage and lower current, with $V_{ak} = 450$ V and $I_a = 45$ mA. The characteristics of the EL34 are much more horizontal under these conditions, which is reflected in a higher internal resistance. Although the leakage inductance and internal capacitance of the output transformer are both small, they combine with the limitations of B_1 and B_2 to produce a network whose −3 dB bandwidth is around 70 kHz.

Given all of the above, it is easy to predict that this amplifier will sound both dark and intensely coloured. The loudspeakers are not damped at all, resulting in a strong dropoff at high frequencies. This is no good for hi-fi applications, and there is not much that can be done about it. However, the dark tone colour may be useful for guitar amplifiers.

■ Modification 3: Ultralinear configuration with a VDV2100PP

Let us move on to the ultralinear configuration. Here the screen grid resistors R_{14} and R_{17} are connected to the brown leads of the VDV2100PP, while R_{20} and R_{23} are connected to the violet leads. The feedback networks are still out! The output impedance drops to 10.4 Ω, ten times lower than with the pentode configuration — a clear consequence of using internal feedback. The damping factor is still low, at $(8 \div 10.4) = 0.8$ for an 8 Ω loudspeaker, but this may be sufficient for some applications. The square-wave response looks perfect, with good flanks and clean transitions to flat plateaus. Nevertheless, the bass response will be too 'round' in most cases, so let's move on to the next modification.

■ Modification 4: Pentode configuration with local feedback and a VDV2100PP

In this configuration the screen resistors (R_{14}, R_{17}, R_{20} and R_{23}) are disconnected from the UL taps and reconnected to U_2, so that the pentode reigns again. Next, the two local feedback networks R_{25}–R_{27} ‖ C_8–C_9 and R_{28}–R_{30} ‖ C_{11}–C_{12} are reconnected (excluding C_7 and C_{10}). The latter two capacitors would restrict the bandwidth; they can be left out as long as we do not apply overall external feedback with R_{31}. Due to the hefty amount of feedback in this circuit, the output impedance plummets to a measured value of 3.43 Ω, corresponding to a primary r_i of 1371 Ω — triode impedance combined with pentode output power, not bad! The damping factor is increased to $(8 \div 3.43) = 2.3$.

This is however not all. As the source impedance of the stage driving the output transformer decreases, the cutoff frequency of the second-order network formed by the transformer's leakage inductance and internal capacitance shifts to a higher value. Valve B_2 has a low-pass characteristics well, and its cutoff frequency is also raised by local feedback. The combined result is a −3 dB bandwidth of more than 100 kHz.

The limits of the VDV2100PP have not yet been reached; the bandwidth of this transformer extends to 250 kHz. The limitations of both B_1 and B_2 restrict the overall response. The bandwidths of these valves were sufficient for the original design of 1987.

The increased damping factor and wide bandwidth of this modification allow brilliant reproduction over the full frequency range, from *de profundis* bass to bat-frequency trebles. The power bandwidth has also increased. The original design allowed short power bursts at 80 kHz, but this configuration allows 109 watts of *continuous* power at this frequency, a clear sign of its superior speed and stability at high frequencies. The low end has improved as well; the original 50 watts at 30 Hz has risen to 90 watts. The 'old' amplifier with the 'new' transformer thus performs significantly better than the original configuration. The input sensitivity has also increased somewhat, to around 390 mV$_{\text{eff}}$ for 100 watts into 5 ohms, about twice the sensitivity of the original design. The square-wave response is clean as a whistle, no overshoots or anything – the amplifier is unconditionally stable with capacitive loads.

■ | **Modification 5: Complete negative feedback**

As a final experiment, the external feedback resistor R_{31} is reconnected. Capacitors C_7 and C_{10} must also be included, to keep the constellation stable. The good news is that the frequency response extends to 125 KHz, and the damping factor rises to 11.2. The square-wave response shows a slight overshoot; the amplifier has become more sensitive to capacitive loads. The input sensitivity, at 775 mV$_{\text{eff}}$, is close to its original value. This all looks good on paper, but ... the amplifier sounds bland, and much less lively and open than before.

18.5 | Conclusion

Using the VDV2100PP transformer has substantially enriched what was essentially an old design. The amplifier has become both faster and more stable, especially when operated close to its power limits. Modification 4 has proved to be the best, both on the measuring bench and in listening tests. It provides increased depth of image and freshness of timbre, both substantial gains.

Were the original transformers no good then? Yes, they were good, but they had to be more heavily corrected than the VDV2100PP by means of additional components — C_7, C_{10} and R_{31}. Overall negative feedback can be eliminated with the new transformer, while retaining a sizeable damping factor and a broad frequency response, resulting in a much more detailed and wider auditory image.

The VDV100 still has room to grow, making it an ideal target for further modifications. It is robust enough to be used for evaluating new types of components. In this respect, it is a pretty universal design that encourages new improvements.

19

●●● ●●●●●

Experiments with the Specialist Series of Output Transformers

The Specialist toroidal output transformers present several challenging possibilities to the designer. They allow unusual circuits to be realized, such as the Super-Pentode and Super-Triode configurations, and support a myriad of feedback arrangements. Cathode feedback and various screen couplings can all be used, alone or combined. The various arrangements described in Chapter 8 can all be implemented using the amplifier described in this chapter.

19.1 | A valve amplifier for the Specialist cathode feedback transformers

In the course of developing the Specialist series of output transformers (see References 1, 2 and 3), a number of experiments were made to test the underlying theory. This chapter describes the main beast of burden for these experiments, a general-purpose valve amplifier that supports various types of coupling to the output transformer. Chapter 8 deals with the theoretical aspects of these transformers, and Figure 8.16 shows a number of 'shorthand' circuit diagrams, in which the entire amplifier is represented by a pair of power valves. To refresh your memory – and spare you the effort of thumbing all the way back to Chapter 8 – you can see these diagrams again in Figure 19.1 (overleaf).

Many persons have found these diagrams somewhat sketchy, and they have requested a more detailed description of an amplifier that can be used with the Specialist transformers. I have chosen to base my story on the amplifier that was used for the experiments of Chapter 8, as I have come to know this circuit fairly well. Other circuits are possible too, of course. The audio part of this amplifier – without the output transformer – is depicted in Figure 19.2 (overleaf).

This circuit is an adaptation of the VDV100, slightly altered to accommodate the various arrangements that are possible with the Specialist transformers. An ECC81 triode combines the functions of preamplifier and phase splitter. The cathode resistor R_2 of valve B_{1a} is not decoupled, so it provides a possible injection point for external

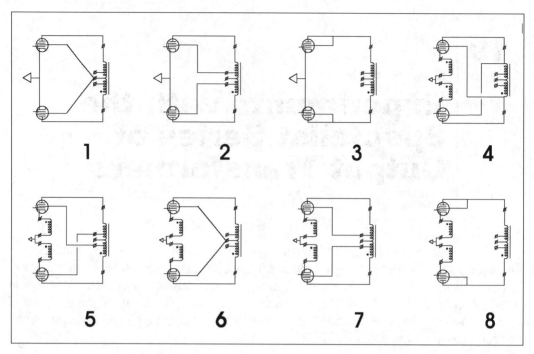

▲ *Figure 19.1* *Outline of the experiments with the VDV-2100-CFB/H transformer.*

feedback. The phase splitter can be balanced using the combination of resistors R_4 and R_5 with trimpot P_1. This allows the output voltages at the anode and cathode of B_{1b} to be exactly matched, in order to achieve minimum harmonic distortion. Refer to the description of the 100 Hz square wave test in Section 13.9 to see how to adjust the phase splitter.

The following stage provides extra amplification, which is necessary for driving the output valves. The cathode resistor of valve B_2 (an ECC82) is decoupled. This is different from the VDV100 amplifier in Chapter 18, since the local feedback technique employed in the VDV100 does not allow this. Next come the two trimpots P_2 and P_3, which provide separate negative grid voltages to the power valves. As noted on the diagram, the quiescent current of each power valve must be set to 45 mA. I explain how to measure the current further on. You can use the adjustment procedure described in previous chapters.

The power valves in Figure 19.2 terminate in thin air — except for the control grid, none of the electrodes is connected to anything. The anode, cathode and screen grid can be connected to the output transformer in various manners, as you will see.

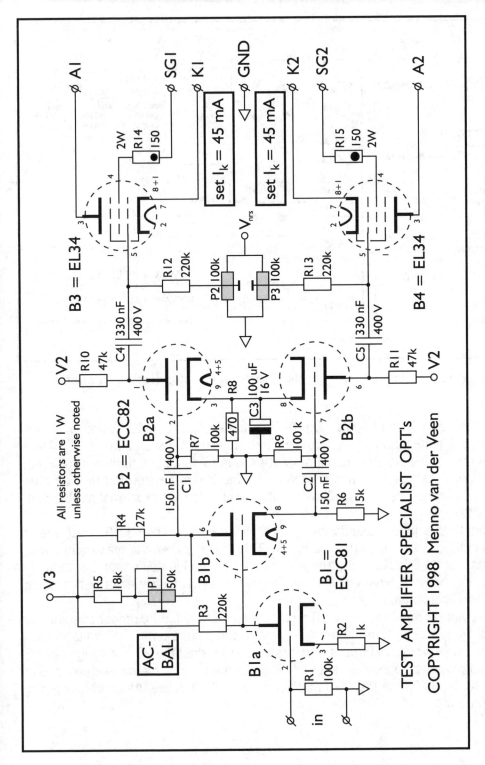

▲ *Figure 19.2 Circuit diagram of the test amplifier for specialist transformers.*

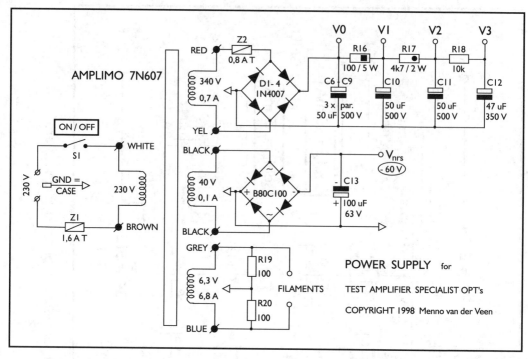

▲ **Figure 19.3** *Power supply for the Specialist transformers test amplifier.*

The power supply depicted in Figure 19.3 is a straightforward design, which is more than adequate for powering two amplifiers in a stereo installation.

This amplifier has some unusual properties, due to its 'convertible' nature. First, the input sensitivity is high, lying between 50 and 200 mV according to the transformer configuration used. This allows relatively high levels of external feedback to be used if desired.

Second, the frequency bandwidth is not all that wide. The –3 dB point lies at 80 kHz (with no overall negative feedback). This is lower than the maximum bandwidth that can be achieved with the transformer, but still wide enough for comfortable listening. After all, what we're interested in here is not measurements, but rather how the amplifier sounds.

Good ground connections – two at most! – are essential for the proper operation of this amplifier. Special attention must be paid to the insulation of high voltage connections; a safe separation from the chassis must be maintained. Twisting the filament supply wires is recommended, as well as all the usual precautions described in Chapter 13. If you follow these suggestions, you will increase the reliability of the final product.

19.2 | Coupling to the output transformer

Figure 19.4 shows the connection diagram of the cathode feedback (CFB) output transformer. All CFB transformers have the same wiring scheme. The experiments described in this chapter were made with the VDV-2100-CFB/H transformer, but the 2100-CFB and 4070-CFB can be used in the same fashion, as described in Section 19.3.

Figure 9.4 shows not only inductors, but also two resistors. R_{21} and R_{22} are used for measuring the quiescent currents of the output valves. When the valve currents are set to the correct value of 45 mA, there will be 0.45 V across each of R_{21} and R_{22}.

The VDV-2100-CFB/H is blessed with more leads than usual, but fortunately they are sensibly bundled. The right-hand part of Figure 19.4 shows the lead arrangement, as seen from the wiring side.

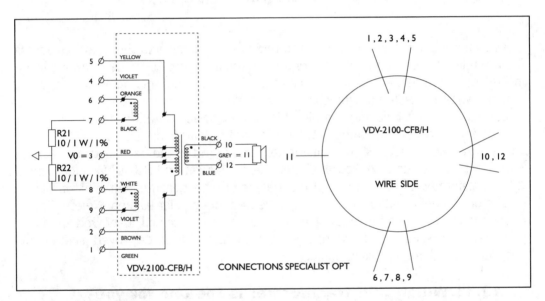

▲ **Figure 19.4** *Connection diagram of the VDV-2100-CFB/H transformer.*

The secondary winding has a centre tap (lead 11). If this is connected to ground, the loudspeaker output is nicely symmetrical. It is not strictly necessary to ground lead 11, but a 'floating' output is not recommended. You should connect one secondary lead to ground, either lead 11 or (for example) lead 12.

Regardless of the chosen configuration, the red primary centre tap (lead 3) is always connected to the positive supply voltage, as can be read from the diagram. Table 19.1 (overleaf) describes how the power valves B_3 and B_4 must be connected to the output transformer to realize the configurations shown in Chapter 8. The left-

Circuit:	1	2	3	4	5	6	7	8
A1	5	5	5	—	5	5	5	5
SG1	V_1	4	5	—	2	V_1	4	5
K1	7	7	7	—	6	6	6	6
K2	8	8	8	—	9	9	9	9
SG2	V_1	2	1	—	4	V_1	2	1
A2	1	1	1	—	1	1	1	1

▲ **Table 19.1**
*Transformer and valve connections for the
circuits shown in Figure 19.1 (see text).*

most column lists the electrodes of the two power valves, and the numbers across
the top refer to the eight amplifier configurations in Figure 19.1. The numbers listed
in the column underneath each amplifier configuration number show which transformer lead is connected to which valve electrode.

Let's take circuit 1 as an example; this is the classic pentode configuration. The
connections are, in order: anode A_1 to transformer lead 5, screen grid SG_1 to high
voltage V_1, and cathode K_1 to transformer lead 7 (and to the measurement resistor
R_{21}). Next comes anode A_2 to transformer lead 1, screen grid SG_2 to V_1 and cathode
K_2 to transformer lead 8, which is also connected to the measurement resistor R_{22}.

The other configurations can be implemented in a similar fashion. Notice that no
connections are shown for circuit 4. When this setup was tested, it showed an imbalance between positive and negative feedback, which quickly destroyed a set of output valves. So, don't try this at home!

19.3 | Which CFB transformer is the one for you?

As already mentioned, all three Specialist CFB transformers can be used in
this amplifier. Transformer VDV-4070-CFB has a primary impedance of 4000 Ω and
can handle 70 watts of output power. Types VDV-2100-CFB and VDV-2100-CFB/H
can both handle 100 watts and have a primary impedance of 2000 Ω; the second type
has a slightly smaller power bandwidth at the low end of the spectrum.

Calculations and measurements both show that EL34 valves deliver maximum
output power when driving a primary impedance of 3200 Ω. The choice of transformer now mainly depends on the loudspeaker impedance to be connected to the
secondary. Let's look at two sample calculations.

The VDV-4070-CFB combine a 4000 Ω primary impedance with a 5 Ω secondary impedance; the impedance transformation ratio is (4000÷5) = 800. If we connect a loudspeaker with an impedance of 4 Ω, the primary impedance will be (800·4) = 3200 Ω. The VDV-4070-CFB and a 4 Ω loudspeaker are thus an excellent match!

Should we decide for the VDV-2100-CFB or VDV-2100-CFB/H, the impedance transformation ratio is (2000÷5) = 400. In order to achieve the optimum primary impedance of 3200 Ω, these transformers need to be terminated with 8 Ω.

Therefore, the choice of output transformer depends on the secondary impedance that you want to use. References 1, 2 and 3, listed in Section 19.5, describe how to use the VDV-2100-CFB/H in combination with an 8 Ω loudspeaker.

There is another factor to be taken into account. The 2100-CFB can handle the most power (100 watts at 20 Hz), while the 4070-CFB can handle 70 watts at the same frequency. The smaller model 2100-CFB/H can handle 50 watts at 23 Hz, reaching full power (100 watts) at 33 Hz. So your choice also depends on how serious you are about generating loud, deep bass and infrasonics!

In parting, I would like to point out that this circuit does not exploit the full power capacity of the transformer. It employs two EL34s, but there is nothing to stop you from building an amplifier using four valves instead, with individual quiescent current settings (similar to the VDV100). In that case, resistors R_{21} and R_{22} must be replaced by wire bridges, and four 10 Ω resistors must be added, one between the cathode of each valve and the connection point K_1 or K_2 as appropriate. Also, two more trimpots will be needed, to set the bias voltages of the two extra valves. Such an amplifier will deliver a whopping 140 watts with circuit 5, if the primary impedance is 1600 Ω. The VDV-2100-CFB would naturally be the best choice for this amplifier, as long as it is loaded by a 4 Ω loudspeaker. This setup will deliver full power from 24 Hz upwards, with the −3 dB power bandwidth extending down to 17 Hz.

In summary, the required output power, the loudspeaker impedance and the low-frequency full power bandwidth, taken together, together determine the choice of the output transformer.

19.4 │ Summary and conclusions

The main subject of this chapter is the Specialist series of cathode feedback output transformers. A general purpose amplifier that can be used to perform the experiments described in Chapter 8 is discussed, and the factors that affect the choice of transformer are explained. This amplifier can be further optimized, since the bandwidth of the transformers is greater than the 80 kHz upper −3 dB rolloff point of the amplifier circuit. The necessary calculations and tinkering are left as a challenge to the reader.

19.5 | References

1) Menno van der Veen, *Lab Report: Specialist Range Toroidal Output Transformers*, Plitron Manufacturing Inc, Toronto. 416-667-9914; Internet: www.plitron.com.
2) Menno van der Veen, *Specialist Ringkern Uitgangstransformatoren: De Super-Pentode-Schakeling ®©*, Amplimo BV. 31-74-376-3765; Internet: www.amplimo.nl.
3) Menno van der Veen, *Modelling Power Tubes and their Interaction with Output Transformers*, 104th AES Convention, May 1998, Amsterdam. Preprint 4643.

20

● ● ● ● ● ●

The VDV-6AS7
(The Maurits)

It is a rare thing that an amplifier receives a personal name, rather than just a product code. This amplifier wears one with pride, for reasons given below. The 6AS7 valve is normally used as a series regulation triode for power supplies — not exactly your first choice for an audio application. What will it sound like? After all, it is a real triode, not a pentode mimicking a triode. Will it be hard to drive or to bias? This chapter tells all.

20.1 | How it came to be

Most audio designs coming from the VDV labs are commissioned, or come to be in response to market trends. This is not the case here — this was an in-depth tinkering enterprise, just for fun. After digging through my cupboards, I had some tubes, a couple of transformers and a forlorn chassis lying on my desk. Designing and building – just soldering the components in, no PCB or anything – took a week. Then came a long process of fine tuning, in which the final result slowly took shape. During this period, a former colleague fell ill, and I told him about the development during visiting hours. Not only did this take his mind off his disease, but his growing eagerness to hear the actual product gave him a good reason for a speedy convalescence, and he did get well. Therefore this amplifier bears his name.

20.2 | The audio circuit

Figure 20.1 shows the circuit diagram of the amplifier. This is only the left channel. The stereo amplifier utilizes three dual triodes for the drivers, plus one 6AS7 power valve per channel, for a total of five valves. The 6AS7 is a large, sturdy valve, somewhat similar to a 300B. At first glance, the amplifier seems to be single-ended, but a closer look reveals the double structure inside the bulb of the 6AS7, so it is a balanced amplifier after all. I estimate the output power to be about 7 watts per channel, so efficient loudspeakers are recommended — at least 90 dB/W-m.

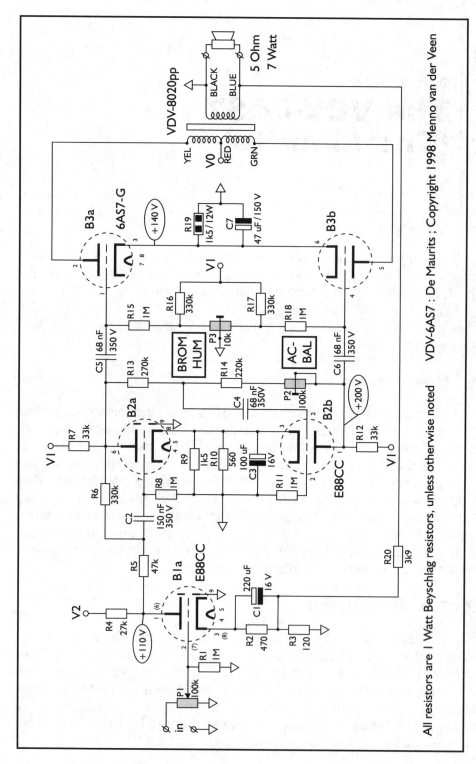

▲ *Figure 20.1 Circuit diagram of the 6AS7 amplifier audio section (one channel)*

All resistors are 1 Watt Beyschlag resistors, unless otherwise noted   VDV-6AS7 : De Maurits ; Copyright 1998 Menno van der Veen

For the drivers and the phase splitter, I chose an E88CC. This valve is a 'steep' dual triode with low internal resistance, allowing a high output voltage swing — all highly desirable in this design. The first stage uses a single valve whose two triodes serve as preamplifiers for both channels; B_{1a} for the left and B_{1b} for the right. This is a standard triode stage, in which the cathode resistor is decoupled by C_1. It features both high amplification and low internal resistance. The values of C_1 and C_2 are strongly related. The junction of the low-valued resistor R_3 and the R_2–C_1 pair serves as an injection point for negative feedback via R_{20}. Note that R_3 is not decoupled.

The network around the phase splitter is relatively complex. Capacitor C_2 injects the amplified signal into the grid of valve B_{2a}, the cathode of which is decoupled by C_3. After amplification, the signal passes via R_{13} and C_4 to the grid of valve B_{2b}. Resistors R_{13} and R_{14} plus trimpot P_2 serve to compare the signal at the anode of B_{2b} to the signal at the anode of B_{2a}. The phase splitter can be exactly balanced by adjusting P_2. When it is properly adjusted, both halves of the 6AS7 receive identical signals – in antiphase, of course – thus minimizing harmonic distortion.

P_2 is labeled 'AC-BAL', which is pretty self-explanatory. The adjustment is best done using a distortion analyzer. Apply a 1 kHz sine wave to the input, and set the output power to 5 watts in a 5 Ω load. Then adjust P_2 to produce minimum distortion at the output. The 100 Hz square wave test may serve as an alternative method; see Chapter 16.

There is yet more going on in the phase splitter. Grid currents will flow in the power valves when they are driven above a certain voltage, creating an extra load on the driver. If the phase splitter has a high output impedance, this will cause its output signals to 'collapse', and any resulting asymmetry in the drive signals will produce some pretty coarse distortion.

If we leave R_5 and R_6 out of the circuit, the output impedance of B_{2a} will be about 4 kΩ, whereas the impedance of B_{2b} will be only 200 Ω. Trouble lies straight ahead with such a discrepancy (more than an order of magnitude), since the positive signal is bound to collapse much sooner than the negative one, leaving B_{2b} in the dominant position.

There are two easy ways to lower the output impedance of the upper triode. The first way is depicted in the diagram. Feedback is introduced in valve B_{2a} by means of resistors R_5 and R_6, lowering the output impedance to about 800 Ω. There is still a difference between the two halves, but it dramatically reduced, so the phase splitter should function flawlessly under normal circumstances.

The second solution, which is not shown, is to add a cathode follower after B_{2a}. This takes another half of a dual triode, so a stereo amplifier will need an entire extra E88CC. Each triode fits in as follows: the grid is connected to the junction of the anode of B_{2a} and R_7, the anode is connected directly to the supply voltage V_1, and the cathode is connected to the junction of C_5 and R_{13}, which branches off to an extra 33 kΩ resistor connected to ground. Resistors R_5 and R_6 are both removed, of course, with the former being replaced by a direct connection – a wire jumper –

between C_2 and the anode of B_{1a}. Finally, R_{22} in the power supply must be changed to 1 kΩ, 2 W. This modification results in higher input sensitivity, which may be useful for the amplification of low-level signals, such as those from older tuners and tape recorders. The circuit shown in Figure 20.1 is designed to work with signals of around 2 V_{eff}, as produced by present-day CD players. Have a look at Chapter 16 for a discussion of the relationship between the volume control and the input sensitivity.

Now on to the power valve section. A circuit with a common cathode resistor emerged as the favourite during listening tests. Capacitor C_7 decouples the AC voltage on R_{19}, which dissipates 12 to 14 Watts — a hefty component. When I tested several 6AS7 valves, it became clear that none of their triode halves are exactly the same. Therefore, there will always be differences in the quiescent currents, resulting in hum. In order to compensate for this, I added the network around trimpot P_3. A fraction of the supply voltage is fed into the grids of the power doublet via R_{15} and R_{18}. Turning P_3 to either side of its center position simultaneously *increases* one grid voltage and *decreases* the other one. In this way, the quiescent currents of the two triode sections can be made identical, thereby eliminating hum. The adjustment is simple — with no input signal, hold your ear close to the loudspeaker while turning P_3. At a certain point the hum level will decrease, and in most cases it will become inaudible. Reader, beware! Trimpot P_3 must be of **impeccable** quality. If it should ever break down, the full power supply voltage will blast onto the grids of the 6AS7, causing instantaneous destruction of the valve. So do not save pennies on an inferior trimpot — trimpot-wise, valve-foolish, you might say.

In operation, the effective voltage on the cathode resistor R_{19} is about 140 V. This voltage causes a current of $(140 \div 1500) = 93.3$ mA to flow through the resistor. This current is divided evenly between the two halves of the valve, so the quiescent current of each triode is 47 mA. With a supply voltage of 385 volts, there is a voltage drop of 245 volts across the valve. This is close to the edge, since the maximum allowed value of V_{ak} is 250 volts for a 6AS7. The power dissipated by the valve is $(245 \cdot 0.047) = 11.4$ watts, while the maximum allowable anode dissipation for the 6AS7 is 13 watts — a pretty wide margin.

Next let's estimate the power efficiency. From the last paragraph, we find that the total valve dissipation is $(2 \cdot 11.4) = 22.8$ watts, while the output power is 7 watts, yielding an efficiency of 31%. This somewhat unflattering value is unfortunately intrinsic to the circuit.

The grid-to-anode amplification factor of the 6AS7 is effectively 1.3 in this configuration. Given the characteristics of the output transformer, which has a primary impedance of 8 kΩ, 7 watts corresponds to a primary voltage of 335 V_{pp}. Each triode bears half of this voltage, or 167 volts. The phase splitter must deliver $(167 \div 1.3) = 129$ V, due to the amplification factor of 1.3. But do not start cheering yet, because this is only *half* of the total peak-to-peak voltage; the total output voltage of the phase splitter must be $(2 \cdot 129) = 258$ V_{pp}. This brings us to the bottleneck in the circuit: the present arrangement simply cannot generate this output voltage across its load, due to the grid currents in the power triodes. If we had chosen the alternative circuit with the extra cathode follower, then B_{2a} could deliver a higher output voltage and the output power would even rise above 10 watts. However, in order to preserve the simplicity of the design and the specific sound that it produces, I have chosen to let quality prevail over quantity. The phase splitter is the limiting factor in this amplifier, and not the power valves; they are never driven to their maximum power.

And now I will literally close the loop — with an external feedback resistor. Apparently, as listening tests demonstrated, this circuit benefits from a small amount of negative feedback via R_{20}. Just a little bit seems to give the finishing touch; it yields more detail, without 'collapsing' the overall auditory image — unlike what happens if the resistance of R_{20} is lowered too much. You are free to alter the value of R_{20}, or to leave it out entirely — your ears will tell you what to do.

20.3 | Some power supply details

There are some interesting 'extras' in the power supply schematic, which is shown in Figure 20.2 (overleaf), and they deserve some explanation.

Starting at the mains side, we see the fuse Z_1 and the mains switch — DPST, just to be safe. The mains ground must be connected to the metal chassis — nothing unusual here. The 6N536 toroidal power transformer has two primary and two secondary sections. The primary windings can be connected in parallel or in series, depending on the mains voltage available. The fuse value and series connection shown in the diagram are suitable for a nominal mains voltage of 230 V. The leads of the two secondary sections – the high voltage and filament windings, respectively – are coloured red/yellow and blue/grey.

All filaments are connected in parallel, and are fed with 6.3 volts. Resistors R_{25} and R_{26} eliminate hum by connecting the filament winding to ground; they act as a 'centre tap'. In the unlikely case that hum is still noticeable – the design is not particularly 'buzzy' – they can be replaced by a single 1 kΩ trimpot, with its wiper connected to ground. If the filament wiring is kept close to the chassis and far away from the sensitive parts of the circuit (B_1 and B_2), shielding should not be necessary; just twisting the wires will suffice. See the construction hints in Chapter 13.

Now comes the interesting part, the high-voltage supply. It looks pretty run of the mill – rectifier, filter capacitors and series resistors R_{23} and R_{24}, plus the fuse Z_2 and the standby switch – but what about resistors R_{21} and R_{22} and capacitors C_8 and C_9? A power transformer has a wide bandwidth, and it will pass a gamut of signals in addition the desired 50 or 60 Hz mains voltage. Spurious signals enter through two separate pathways. The predominate one is capacitive coupling between the primary and the secondary, which produces common-mode noise. This can be prevented by static shielding inside the transformer, or by the network consisting of R_{21}, R_{22}, C_8 and C_9. The second type of interference, differential noise, is coupled in via the all-too-wide frequency response of the power transformer. This type of noise appears

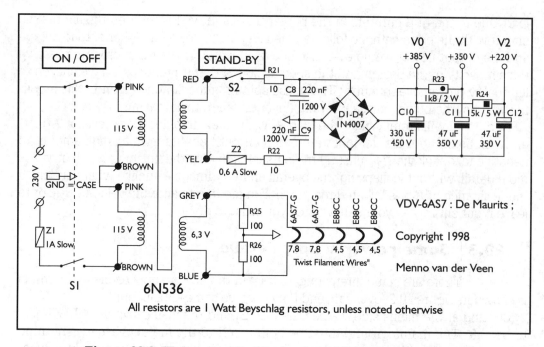

▲ Figure 20.2 *The power supply for the 6AS7 'Maurits' amplifier.*

between the red and yellow leads of the secondary. The filter network will deal with this as well. The transformer can be blamed for a lot, but not everything; there is a third noise source in the form of the rectifier bridge D_1–D_4. Since these diodes act as fast switches, they generate sharp transients during zero crossings. These are damped by C_8, C_9 and C_{10}.

In summary, our modest little circuit acts as a highly effective interference suppressor. Chapter 16 shows a preliminary version of this network, as used in the UL40-S, consisting of a single 10 Ω, 5 W resistor. Here a further refinement has been added in the form of C_8 and C_9.

It is well known that a vacuum diode used as a rectifier, such as the GZ34, sounds smoother than its solid state counterpart. There are two reasons for this: first, the relatively high internal resistance of the valve has an effect similar to that of resistors R_{21} and R_{22}. Second, the gentle switching of a vacuum diode is not prone to generating transients. The network consisting of R_{21}, R_{22}, C_8 and C_9 does its very best to mimic the behaviour of a vacuum rectifier. The mild sound of this amplifier demonstrates how well they do their job.

20.4 | Subjective properties

As already mentioned, this amplifier was conceived in less than a week. Listening to the first version was not exactly an overwhelming experience; let it suffice to say that the amplifier worked, and nothing more. In the months thereafter, I made improvements one by one, until the excellent final version came to be. What did I do to get there?

First, the addition of R_5 and R_6 proved to be essential. Without these resistors, reproduction becomes messy at high output levels. Their presence virtually eliminates distortion, which drops to way below the 0.7% of a plain-vanilla sine wave generator, so the effect of adjusting P_2 becomes clearly noticeable.

The hum elimination network around P_3 was the second vital addition to the basic circuit. It suppresses hum effectively, and more important, meticulous balancing of the power triodes drastically improves the behaviour of the output transformer. Not only does silence reign, but the sound becomes effortless.

A further essential step was the introduction of the filter network for the rectifier (R_{21}, R_{22}, C_8 and C_9). This burnished off the last sharp edges of the auditory image.

After all this, I tweaked the various driver valves. It is of paramount importance to have the right valve in the right place. Sovtek's 6922 performs well as a phase splitter, while the Svetlana 6N1P produces superb preamplification. Paying attention to the choice of driver valves is rewarded with better reproduction of details and more 'atmosphere'. This can be nicely illustrated with the CD *Amused to Death* by Roger Waters (which I played so often for testing that it should probably be renamed 'Played to Death'). Track 13 features children at play on the left side of the sound stage. With a properly selected set of valves, not only is the sound image of the children more distinct, but it is abundantly clear that the recording level was turned down near the end of this short passage. You can hear both the voices and the 'inaudible' ambience fading out. Being able to hear this is quite an experience! This is in-depth listening at its finest, hearing details you are normally not even aware of.

Next on the list are the coupling capacitors (C_2, C_5 and C_6). I used general-purpose types at first, but soon replaced them with yellow HQ capacitors from Philips. These capacitors are probably not available any more, and that is a shame, for they unmistakably added lots of small detail. I recommend that you try any type that tickles your fancy, but do stick to the recommended values of 150 nF and 68 nF, and nothing else. Different values could momentarily upset the 6AS7 triodes during power up, which might cause them to melt down. They are somewhat prone to this, but should be fine with the circuit exactly as it is given.

The final parameter that I 'massaged' to the full was the amount of feedback. The auditory image can be pushed in every direction by varying the amount of negative feedback, from moribund through lively to positively sparkling. I found 3k9 for R_{20} to be optimum, but you can experiment and decide for yourself.

There's only one question left: how does a genuine triode balanced amplifier compare to an ultralinear/pentode or pentode/triode amplifier? Well, it's different, to be sure. The differences are similar to the differences between the various modes of the 'convertible' amplifiers. Real triodes excel at presenting a clean and direct sound image, with lots of atmosphere and engagement. This amplifier masters all of this, but so does the UL40-S with KT66s in triode mode. It is difficult to say whether real triodes are always superior to pentodes operated as triodes. Some claim this to be true, and I acknowledge their opinions. In any case, this 6AS7 amplifier is capable of producing an astoundingly vivid auditory image, which totally overshadows any arguments about the relative merits of triodes and pentodes.

By the way, if you are looking for measurements and other technical mumbo-jumbo in this chapter, you have come to the wrong place! Obviously, tons of measurements were made during this project, but I do not want to bore you with the details. The emphasis here is on experimentation and modification – just having the guts to try something different – listening, and above all, enjoyment. Good luck with your own version!

Appendix

A.1 | Bibliography

1) Rickard Berglund, 'Quick, Simple Output Transformer Tests',
    Glass Audio, Vol. 7/1, pp. 24 & 49.

2) Jens Blauert, *Spatial Hearing*. MIT Press, ISBN 0-262-02190-0.

3) John Borwick, *Loudspeaker & Headphone Handbook*.
    Butterworth, ISBN 0-408-01387-7.

4) N.H. Crowhurst, 'Realistic Audio Engineering Philosophy', *Audio*, Oct. 1959.

5) Don & Carolin Davis, *Sound System Engineering*.
    Howard Sams & Co, ISBN 0-672-21857-7.

6) Martin Colloms, 'Audio Research Reference Series',
    Hi-Fi News and Record Review, Febr. 1994, pp. 30-33

7) Ir. J. Deketh, *Grondslagen van de Radiobuizentechniek*. Philips Eindhoven, 1943.

8) Ir. R. Drucker & Ir. J. R. G. Isbrucker, *Leerboek der Elektrotechniek, Deel VII:
    De Radiotechniek*. Nijgh & Van Ditmar NV, Rotterdam.

9) Prof. dr. Malcolm Hawksford,' The Essex Echo',
    Hi-Fi News and Record Review, Aug. 1985, pp 27–33.

10) Ir. S.J. Hellings, *Het ontwerpen van versterkers*. de Muiderkring.

11) Jean Hiraga, *Initiation aux Amplis a Tubes*.
    Diffuse par Eyrolles, 61, bld Saint Germain, 75240 Paris Cedex 05.

12) August Hund, *High-Frequency Measurements*. McGraw-Hill.

13) *IPO, NIU, ASA, Auditory Demonstrations*. Philips CD 1126061.

14) Matthijs van Laar, 'De A-30 Hybride eindversterker',
    Audio & Techniek 10/35, pp 29–34.

15) R. zur Linde, *Audio- en Gitaarschakelingen met buizen, voor een zo goed als nieuw geluid.* Elektuur, ISBN 90-70160-78-1.

16) ——, *Audio en HiFi-buizen, gegevens - karakteristieken - schema's.* Elektuur, ISBN 90-5381-076-5.

17) ——, *Build your Own Audio Valve Amplifiers.* Elektor, ISBN 0-905705-39-4.

18) ——, *Buizenversterkers, Toepassing voor HiFi en Gitaar.* Elektuur, ISBN 90-5381-011-0.

19) ——, *Röhrenverstärker für Gitarren und HiFi.* ISBN 3-921608-41-4.

20) W. Marshall Leach,Jr, 'The Differential Time-Delay Distortion and Differential Phase-Shift Distortion as Measures of Phase Linearity', JAES 37/9, Sept.1989, pp 709-715.

21) Morgan Jones, *Valve Amplifiers.* ISBN 0-7506-2337-3.

22) De Muiderkring, *Tube & Transistor Handbook, Volume 1.* Nov. 1964.

23) N. Partridge, 'Distortion in Transformer Cores', *Wireless World,* June 22 & 29, July 6 & 13, 1939.

24) Edouard Pastor, 'L'Audiophile', *Special Tubes,* 1987.

25) B. Perkins, 'A little input on audio-output transformers', *Audio Note* 2.1 + update, Calgery, Alberta, Canada T2T 4X3.

26) *Electron Tubes,* Philips Pocketboek, 1969.

27) R.B. Randall, *Frequency Analysis.* Bruel & Kjaer, ISBN 87-87355-07-8.

28) Roederstein, *Voorraadcatalogus.* [resistor data].

29) Harvey Rosenberg, *Understanding Tube Electronics.* 1984, New York Audio Laboratories, Inc, 33 North Riverside Avenue, Croton-on-Hudson, NY 10520.

30) John D. Ryder, Ph.D, *Engineering Electronics.* McGraw-Hill, 1957.

31) R.F. Scott,' Circuit Features of High-Fidelity Power Amplifiers', *Radio Electronics*, Aug. 1955, pp 44–46.

32) Siemens, *Metallisierte Kunststoff Condensatoren,* Datenbuch 1989/90.

33) A.J. Sietsma, *Radiotechniek deel 1.* Uitgeverij H. Stam, 1959.

34) ——, *Radiotechniek deel 2.* Uitgeverij H. Stam, 1959.

35) G. Schwamkrug & R. Romer, *Luidsprekers: Fabels en Feiten,* Elektuur, ISBN 90-70160-46-3.

36) P.G. Sulzer, 'Survey of Audio-Frequency Power-Amplifier Circuits', *Audio Engineering*, May 1951.

37) Gerald F. J. Tyne, *Saga of the Vacuum Tube.* ISBN 0-672-21470-9.

38) Ir. Menno van der Veen, 'Buizenversterker van 40 W',
    Radio Bulletin 9/85, pp 329–333.

39) ——, 'Hi-Tech met Buizenbak, 100 W buizenversterker',
    Radio Bulletin 10/87, pp 22–27.

40) ——, 'Kabels zijn meetbaar en berekenbaar, deel 1', *HomeStudio* 7/6, pp 32–39.

41) ——, 'Kabels zijn meetbaar en berekenbaar, deel 2', *HomeStudio* 7/10, pp 20–24.

42) ——, 'Kabels zijn meetbaar en berekenbaar, deel 3', *HomeStudio* 10/4, pp 49–50.

43) ——, 'Tegenkoppeling van de werkelijkheidsweergave, Deel 1: vóór
    tegenkoppeling', *Radio Bulletin Elektronica*, November 1993, pp 23–25.

44) ——, 'Tegenkoppeling van de werkelijkheidsweergave, Deel 2: tegen
    tegenkoppeling', *Radio Bulletin Elektronica*, December 1993, pp 8–12.

45) ——, ' Tegenkoppeling van de werkelijkheidsweergave, Deel 3: Het meten van
    deze weergave', *Radio Bulletin Elektronica*, February 1994, pp 26–30.

46) ——, 'Vanderveen UL40-S, High-End klasse-A buizenversterker',
    Radio Bulletin Elektronica, December 1994, pp 6–11.

47) ——, 'Ringkerntransformatoren voor Audio?',
    Radio Bulletin Elektronica, February 1995, pp 28–33.

48) ——, 'Compilatie Vanderveen buizenontwerpen',
    Radio Bulletin Electronica, July/August 1996.

49) ——,' Theory and Practice of Wide Bandwidth Toroidal Output Transformers',
    97th AES Convention, November 10–13 1994, San Francisco. Preprint 3887 (G-2)

50) ——, 'Measuring output transformer performance',
    Glass Audio, Vol.9/5, pp 20–34.

51) ——, *Lab Report Specialist Range Toroidal Output Transformers*.
    Plitron Manufacturing Inc, Toronto. (www.plitron.com).

52) ——, *Specialist Ringkern Uitgangstransformatoren,
    De Super Pentode Schakeling* ®©. Amplimo. (www.amplimo.nl).

53) ——, 'Modelling Power Tubes and their Interaction with Output Transformers',
    104th AES Convention, 1998, Amsterdam. (preprint)

54) Dr. H. de Waard, *Electronica*, 1966 edition, Chapter 1. W. de Haan.

55) Gerald Weber, *A desktop reference of hip vintage guitar amps*.
    ISBN 0-7935-6368-2.

56) Max Wutz, *Theorie und Praxis der Vakuumtechnik*.
    Friedr. Vieweg & Sohn, Braunschweig.

A.2 | Where to obtain Vanderveen parts and services

Ir. buro Vanderveen

Audio electronics R&D, consultation and publications.

address: Vordensebeek 34
8033 DE Zwolle
The Netherlands

fax: 1 (0)38 453 3178
e-mail: mennovdv@noord.bart.nl

Amplimo bv

Sales and distribution for the Benelux countries
*Toroidal transformers, amplifier modules, valves,
valve amplifier kits, printed circuit boards and
special components for Vanderveen amplifiers.*

address: Vossenbrinkweg 1
7491 DA Delden
The Netherlands

phone: 31 (0)74 376 3765
fax: 31 (0)74 376 3132
e-mail: amplimo@amplimo.com
www: amplimo.nl

Plitron Manufacturing Inc

Manufacturing, sales and worldwide distribution
*Toroidal transformers, amplifier modules, printed
circuit boards and kits.*

address: #8 601 Magnetic Drive
Toronto, Ontario
Canada M3J 3J2

phone: 1 416 667 9914
fax: 1 416 667 8928
e-mail: sales@plitron.com
techinfo@plitron.com
www: plitron.com